PRENTICE HALL
LITERATURE

PENGUIN EDITION

Reader's Notebook

Grade Ten

PEARSON

Prentice
Hall

Upper Saddle River, New Jersey
Boston, Massachusetts

ISBN 0-13-165106-4

4 5 6 7 8 9 10   10 09 08 07

ACKNOWLEDGMENTS

Grateful acknowledgment is made to the following for copyrighted material:

Alexandra Broyard
"Books of the Times" by Anatole Broyard from *New York Times, November 9, 1983.* Copyright © 1983 by Anatole Broyard. Used by permission of Alexandra Broyard.

Anchor Books/Doubleday
"The Sun Parlor" from *The Richer, The Poorer* by Dorothy West, copyright © 1995 by Dorothy West. Used by permission of Doubleday, a division of Random House, Inc. All rights reserved.

Geoffrey Bownas and Anthony Thwaite
"When I went to visit" by Ki no Tsurayuki translated by Bownas & Thwaite from *The Penguin Book Of Japanese Verse.* Penguin Books 1964, Revised edition 1998. Translation copyright © Geoffrey Bownas and Anthony Thwaie, 1964, 1998.

City of Durham, NC – Human Resources Dept.
"Summer Employment Application" by Staff from *City Of Durham, NC – Human Resources Department.* Reprinted by permission.

Christo and Jeanne-Claude
"Christo and Jeanne-Claude: The Gates Project for Central Park, New York" by Christo Vladimirov Javacheff & Jeanne-Claude Denat de Guillebon from *www.christojeanneclaude.net.* "Special Exhibitions: Christo and Jeanne-Claude: The Gates, Central Park, New York" by Christo Vladimirov Javacheff & Jeanne-Claude Denat de Guillebon from *www.metmuseum.org.* Copyright © 2000–2004 The Metropolitan Museum of Art. Reprinted by permission.

Don Congdon Associates, Inc.
"Contents of the Dead Man's Pockets" by Jack Finney from *Collier's, 1950.* Copyright © 1956 by Crowell Collier Publishing, renewed 1984 by Jack Finney.

Dianne L. Durante
"Forgotten Delights" by Dianne L. Durante from *www.forgottendelights.com.* Copyright © 2004 Dianne L. Durante, (www.forgottendelights.com). Reprinted by permission. All rights reserved.

Dutton, a division of Penguin Group (USA) Inc.
From *Touch the Top of the World* by Erik Weihenmayer. Copyright © 2002 by Erik Weihenmayer. Used by permission of Dutton, a division of Penguin Group (USA) Inc.

Cornelius Eady
"The Poetic Interpretation of the Twist" and "The Empty Dance Shoes" by Cornelius Eady from *Victims Of The Latest Dance Craze: Poems By Cornelius Eady.* Copyright © 1985 by Cornelius Eady. All rights reserved.

Farrar, Straus and Giroux LLC
"The Fish" from the COMPLETE POEMS 1927–1979 by Elizabeth Bishop. Copyright © 1979, 1983 by Alice Helen Methfessel.

G.P. Putnam's Sons
"Arthur Becomes King" Part I, Chapter XXII from *The Once and Future King* by T.H. White. Copyright © 1938, 1939, 1940, © 1958 by T. H. White, renewed. Used by permission of G.P. Putnam's Sons, a division of Penguin Group (USA) Inc.

Sanford J. Greenburger Associates
"The Threads of Time" by C.J. Cherryh from *The Collected Short Fiction of C.J. Cherryh.* First Printing, February 2004. DAW Books, distributed by the Penguin Group (USA). Reprinted by permission. All rights reserved.

(Acknowledgments continue on page V57)

Contents

UNIT 2 Short Stories

UNIT 3 Types of Nonfiction

UNIT 4 Poetry

UNIT 6 Themes in Literature

INTERACTING WITH THE TEXT

As you read your hardcover student edition of *Prentice Hall Literature* use the ***Reader's Notebook*** to guide you in learning and practicing the skills presented. In addition, many selections in your student edition are presented here in an interactive format. The notes and instruction will guide you in applying reading and literary skills and in thinking about the selection. The examples on these pages show you how to use the notes as a companion when you read.

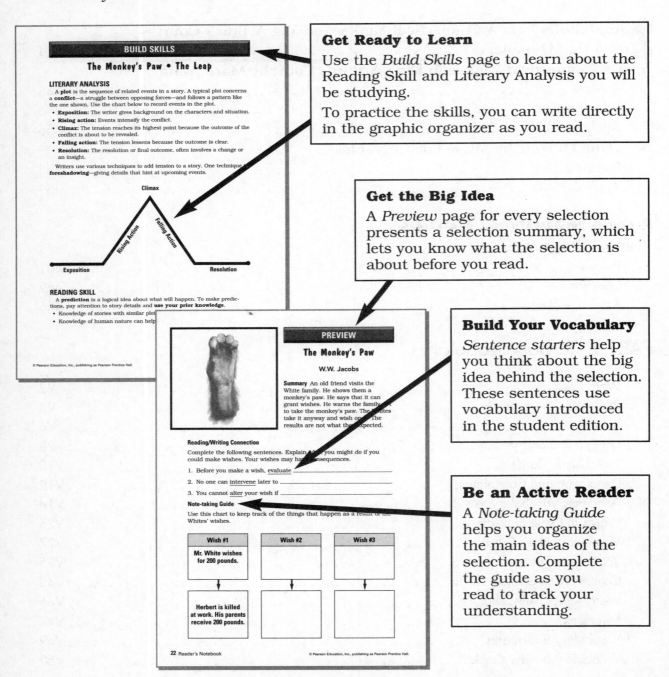

Get Ready to Learn

Use the *Build Skills* page to learn about the Reading Skill and Literary Analysis you will be studying.

To practice the skills, you can write directly in the graphic organizer as you read.

Get the Big Idea

A *Preview* page for every selection presents a selection summary, which lets you know what the selection is about before you read.

Build Your Vocabulary

Sentence starters help you think about the big idea behind the selection. These sentences use vocabulary introduced in the student edition.

Be an Active Reader

A *Note-taking Guide* helps you organize the main ideas of the selection. Complete the guide as you read to track your understanding.

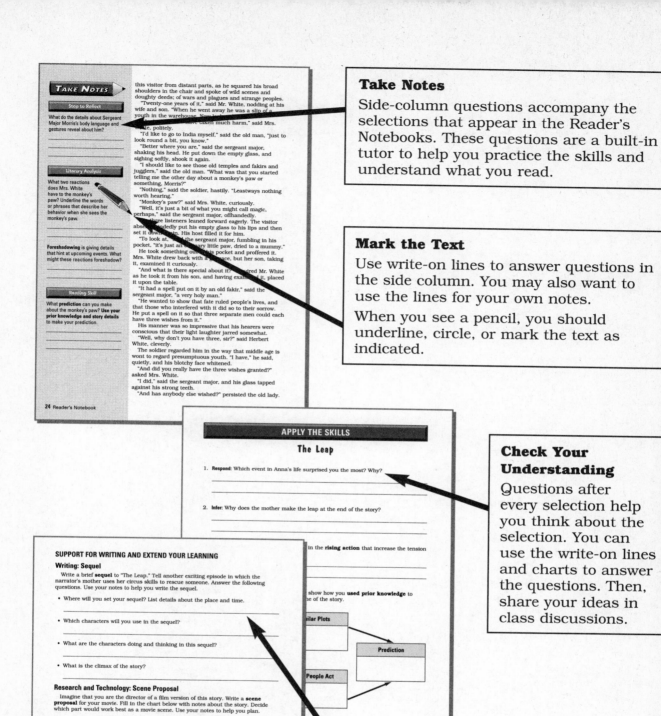

Take Notes

Side-column questions accompany the selections that appear in the Reader's Notebooks. These questions are a built-in tutor to help you practice the skills and understand what you read.

Mark the Text

Use write-on lines to answer questions in the side column. You may also want to use the lines for your own notes.

When you see a pencil, you should underline, circle, or mark the text as indicated.

Check Your Understanding

Questions after every selection help you think about the selection. You can use the write-on lines and charts to answer the questions. Then, share your ideas in class discussions.

Go Beyond the Selection

This page provides step-by-step guidance for completing the Writing and Extend Your Learning activities presented in your student edition.

PART 1

SELECTIONS AND SKILLS SUPPORT

The pages in your *Reader's Notebook* go with the pages in the hardcover student edition. The pages in the *Reader's Notebook* allow you to participate in class instruction and take notes on the concepts and selections.

BEFORE YOU READ

Build Skills Follow along in your *Reader's Notebook* as your teacher introduces the **Reading Skill** and **Literary Analysis** instruction. The graphic organizer is provided on this page so that you can take notes right in your *Reader's Notebook*.

Preview Use this page for the selection your teacher assigns.

- The **Summary** gives you an outline of the selection.
- Use the **Reading-Writing Connection** to understand the big idea of the selection and to join in the class discussion about the ideas.
- Use the **Note-taking Guide** while you read the story. This will help you organize and remember information you will need to answer questions about the story later.

WHILE YOU READ

Selection Text and Sidenotes You can read the full text of one selection in each pair in your *Reader's Notebook.*

- You can write in the *Reader's Notebook.* Underline important details to help you find them later.
- Use the **Take Notes** column to jot down your reactions, ideas, and answers to questions about the text. If your assigned selection is not the one that is included in the *Reader's Notebook,* use sticky notes to make your own **Take Notes** section in the side column as you read the selection in the hardcover student edition.

AFTER YOU READ

Apply the Skills Use this page to answer questions about the selection right in your *Reader's Notebook.* For example, you can complete the graphic organizer that is in the hardcover student edition right on the page in your *Reader's Notebook.*

Support for Writing and Extend Your Learning Use this page to help you jot down notes and ideas as you prepare to do one or more of the projects assigned with the selection.

Other Features in the *Reader's Notebook* You will also find note-taking opportunities for these features:

- Exploring the Genre
- Support for the Model Selection
- Support for Reading Informational Materials

Magdalena Looking

Fiction is narrative prose writing that tells a story from a writer's imagination. Fiction has these basic parts:

- **Setting** is the time and place of the story.
- **Plot** is a series of related events in a story. The plot has a **conflict**, or problem, that the characters face. The conflict sets off a series of events and then rises to a **climax**. The climax is the point at which the action is most intense. After the climax comes the **resolution**, which is how the story ends.
- **Characters** are the individuals who take part in the story.
- **Dialogue** is what is being said between and among the characters. Sometimes the characters speak in an *idiom* or *dialect*. This is a way of speaking that is particular to a group or region. *Idiomatic expressions* are phrases that mean something different from the combined meaning of individual words. For example, "raining cats and dogs" is an idiomatic expression that means "it is raining very hard."
- **Point of view** is the viewpoint of the character who tells the story. A story told by a character involved in the action is in **first-person point of view**. A story told by someone outside the story is in **third-person point of view**.
- **Theme** is the message the writer wants to tell you about life or human nature. A **universal theme** applies to people everywhere.

Types of Fiction		
Type	**Definition**	**Example**
Short story	brief work of fiction	"The Monkey's Paw"
Novel	long work of fiction	*Girl in Hyacinth Blue*
Novella	work of fiction that is shorter than a novel but longer than a short story	*The Old Man and the Sea* by Ernest Hemingway

Artful Research

Nonfiction is writing that gives information about a subject. A nonfiction writer may write about his or her opinion about a subject. The writer's opinion may be stated directly or it may be suggested through his or her tone and perspective.

- **Tone** is the writer's attitude toward the subject. It is expressed with his or her choice of words and details.

- **Perspective** is the writer's point of view, including his or her opinions.

There are many different reasons why someone writes nonfiction. These include the following:

- **To persuade:** Newspaper and magazine editorials, speeches, and reviews are written to convince readers that they should do or believe something.

- **To inform:** Newspaper and magazine articles, news reports, and instructions give information to readers about a subject.

- **To entertain:** Newspaper and magazine columns and many biographies and autobiographies interest and amuse readers.

Magdalena Looking

Susan Vreeland

Summary Magdalena is 14 years old and lives in the Netherlands in the middle of the 1600s. Her father is a painter. Magdalena would also like to paint. She does not ask her father to teach her because she is afraid that he will refuse. She is also afraid that she will spend her life doomed to household duties.

Note-taking Guide

Use this series-of-events chain to record what happens to Magdalena in the story.

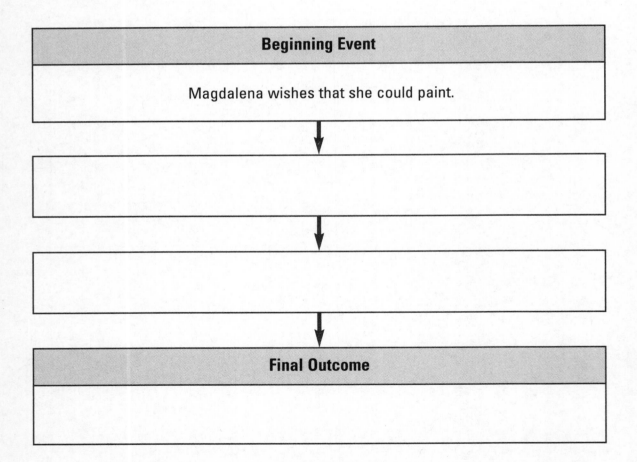

Beginning Event
Magdalena wishes that she could paint.

Final Outcome

Magdalena Looking

Susan Vreeland

Late one afternoon when Magdalena finished the clothes washing and her mother let her go out, she ran from their house by the Nieuwe Kerk across the market square, past van Buyten's bakery, over two cobbled bridges across the canals, past the blacksmith's all the way to Kethelstraat and the town wall where she climbed up and up the ochre stone steps, each one as high as her knee, to her favorite spot in all of Delft,[1] the round sentry post. From that great height, oh, what she could see. If only she could paint it. In one direction Schiedam Gate and beyond it the twin towers of Rotterdam Gate, and ships with odd-shaped sails the color of brown eggshells coming up the great Schie River from the sea, and in another direction strips of potato fields with wooden plows casting shadows over the soil like long fingers, and orchards, rows of rounded green as ordered as Mother wished their eleven young lives to be, and the smoke of the potteries and brickeries, and beyond that, she didn't know. She didn't know.

She stood there looking, looking, and behind her she heard the creak and thrum of the south windmill turning like her heart in the sea wind, and she breathed the brine[2] that had washed here from other shores. Below her the Schie lay like a pale yellow ribbon along the town wall. The longer she looked, the more it seemed to borrow its color from the sky. In the wind, the boats along the Schie docks with their fasteners clanking and their hollow bellies nudging one another made a kind of low rattling music she loved. It wasn't just today. She loved the sentry post in every kind of weather. To see rain pocking the gray sea and shimmering the stone bridge, to feel its cold strings of water on her face and hands, filled her to bursting.

She moved to a notch in the wall and just then a gust of wind lifted her skirts. The men on the bridge waiting with their bundles to go to sea shouted something in words she did not understand. She'd never tell Mother. Mother did not want her going there. The sentry post was full of guards smoking tobacco, Mother had said. There was some dark thing in her voice, as though she thought Magdalena should be afraid, but Magdalena did not know how to feel that then, or there.

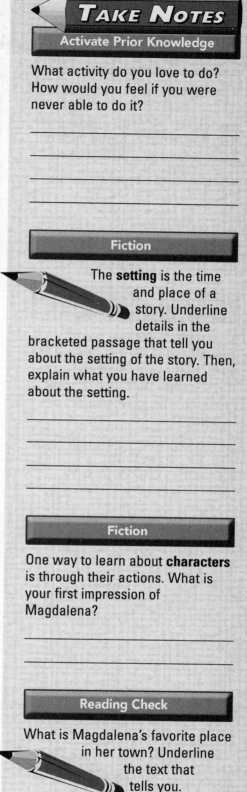

TAKE NOTES

Activate Prior Knowledge

What activity do you love to do? How would you feel if you were never able to do it?

_____

_____

_____

Fiction

The **setting** is the time and place of a story. Underline details in the bracketed passage that tell you about the setting of the story. Then, explain what you have learned about the setting.

_____

_____

_____

Fiction

One way to learn about **characters** is through their actions. What is your first impression of Magdalena?

_____

_____

Reading Check

What is Magdalena's favorite place in her town? Underline the text that tells you.

---

1. **Nieuwe Kerk** (NOO e kark) . . . **van Buyten's** (fahn BY tens) . . . **Kethelstraat** (KAH tel straht) . . . **Delft**; *Nieuwe Kerk* means "New Church"; Kethelstraat is a street in the city; Delft is a manufacturing city on the Schie River in the Netherlands.
2. **brine** (bryn) saltwater.

TAKE NOTES

In **first-person point of view**, a character involved in the action tells the story. In **third-person point of view**, someone outside the story tells the story. Which point of view does Vreeland use? How do you know?

_____

_____

_____

A **character's** thoughts often reveal important details about her and the situation she is in. Read the bracketed passage. What does this passage reveal about Magdalena and her family?

_____

_____

_____

_____

What is one thing Magdalena wishes her father would do? Underline the text that tells you.

Up there, high up above the town, she had longings no one in the family knew. No one would ever know them, she thought, unless perhaps a soul would read her face or she herself would have soul enough to speak of them. Wishes had the power to knock the breath out of her. Some were large and throbbing and persistent, some mere pinpricks of golden light, short-lived as fireflies but keenly felt. She wished for her chores to be done so she'd have time to race to the town wall every day before supper, or to the Oude Kerk[3] to lift the fallen leaves from her brother's grave. She wished her baby sisters wouldn't cry so, and the boys wouldn't quarrel and wrestle underfoot or run shouting through the house. Father wished that too, she knew. She wished there were not so many bowls to wash, thirteen each meal. She wished her hair shone flaxen in the sunlight of the market square like little Geertruida's.[4] She wished she could travel in a carriage across borders to all the lands drawn on her father's map.

She wished the grocer wouldn't treat her so gruffly when he saw her hand open out to offer four guilders,[5] all that her mother gave her to pay the grocery bill that was mounting into the hundreds, as far as she could tell. She wished he wouldn't shout; it sent his garlic breath straight into her nostrils. The baker, Hendrick van Buyten, was kinder. Two times so far he let Father pay with a painting so they could start over. Sometimes he gave her a still-warm bun to eat while walking home. And sometimes he put a curl of honey on it. She wished the grocer was like him.

She wished Father would take the iceboat to the Schie more often. He'd bought a fine one with a tall ivory sail. "Eighty guilders," Mother grumbled. "Better a winter's worth of bread and meat." On winter Sundays if the weather was clear, and if he was between paintings, it whisked them skimming across the white glass of the canal. She'd never known such speed. The sharp cold air blew life and hope and excitement into her ears and open mouth.

She remembered wishing, one particular morning when Father mixed lead white with the smallest dot of lead-tin yellow[6] for the goose quill in a painting of Mother writing a letter, that she might someday have someone to write to, that she could write at the end of a letter full of love and news, "As ever, your loving Magdalena Elisabeth."

He painted Mother often, and Maria he painted once, draped her head in a golden mantle and her shoulders in

---

3. **Oude Kerk** (OW de kark) "Old Church."
4. **Geertruida's** (kher TRY das)
5. **guilders** (GIL duhrz) The guilder is the basic unit of Dutch currency.
6. **lead white . . . lead-tin yellow** references to pigments made from lead and tin and mixed with oil to produce paints of various colors.

---

a white satin shawl. She was older, fifteen, though only by eleven months. It might be fun to dress up like Maria did, and wear pearl earrings and have Father position her just so, but the only part she really wished for was that he would look and look and pay attention.

More than all those wishes, she had one pulsing wish that outshone all the others. She wished to paint. Yes, me, she thought, leaning out over the stone wall. I want to paint. This and everything. The world from that vantage point stretched so grandly. Up there, beauty was more than color and shapes, but openness, light, the air itself, and because of that, it seemed untouchable. If only the act of wishing would make her able. Father only smiled queerly when she told him she wanted to paint, just as if she'd said she wanted to sail the seas, which, of course, she also wished, in order to paint what she would see. When she said so, that she wished to paint, Mother thrust into her hands the basket of mending to do.

Often from the edge of the room, she'd watch him work. Because he was always asking for quiet, with the little ones running through the room laughing or shouting, she didn't ask him many questions. He rarely answered anyway. Still, she studied how much linseed oil he used to thin the ultramarine,[7] and watched him apply it over a glassy layer of reddish brown. By magic, it made the dress he painted warmer than the blue on the palette. He would not let her go with him to the attic where he ground lead-tin yellow to powder, but he did send her to the apothecary[8] for the small bricks of it, and for linseed oil. Always there was money for that, but she didn't know what to answer when the apothecary demanded the guilders for her brother's potions still owed after he died.

If only she could have colors of her own, and brushes. She wouldn't just paint pictures of women inside cramped little rooms. She'd paint them out in marketplaces, bending in the potato fields, talking in doorways in the sunlight, in boats on the Schie, or praying in the Oude Kerk. Or she'd paint people skating, fathers teaching their children on the frozen Schie.

Fathers teaching their children. The thought stopped her.

Looking from the sentry tower at a cloud darkening the river, she knew, just as she knew she'd always have washing and mending to do, that it would not be so. She'd worn herself out with wishing, and turned to go. She had to be home to help with supper.

---

7. **linseed oil . . . ultramarine** Linseed oil, made from the seed of the flax plant, can be used as the base for oil paint. Ultramarine is a rich blue.

8. **apothecary** (uh PAHTH uh ker ee) historical term for a pharmacist; a dealer in medicines and various other preparations and chemicals.

TAKE NOTES

Fiction

A **conflict** is a problem that characters face. Read the first bracketed paragraph. What do you think Magdalena's conflict is?

_____

_____

Stop to Reflect

Why do you think Magdalena's parents do not encourage her to paint?

_____

_____

_____

_____

_____

Fiction

Read the second bracketed paragraph. Underline the ways Magdalena would paint women. What does this tell you about the **character** Magdalena?

_____

_____

Reading Check

Why does the apothecary demand guilders from Magdalena? Circle the text that tells you.

Fiction

Dialogue is conversation between or among characters. What does Magdalena's dialogue in the bracketed paragraph show about her? Why is it important that Magdalena said these words aloud?

_____

_____

_____

Stop to Reflect

Read the underlined sentences. Given this underlined passage, how might Magdalena and her father's relationship change?

_____

_____

_____

Reading Check

What does Magdalena have to do to have her father paint her? Circle the text that tells you.

On a spring day that began in no special way, except that she had climbed the town wall the afternoon before, and all over Delft lime trees lining the canals had burst into chartreuse[9] leaves, and light shone through them and made them yellower except where one leaf crossed over another and so was darker—on that spring-certain day, out of some unknown, unborn place came that scream. "I hate to mend," she shouted to the walls, to Mother, to anyone. "It's not making anything."

Father stepped into the room, looked at Mother and then scowled at Magdalena. It had been her job to keep her little brothers quiet for him, or shoo them out of doors, and here she was, the noisy one. No one moved. Even the boys were still. At first she looked only at Father's hand smeared with ultramarine powder, not in his eyes, too surprised by the echo of her voice to fling out any additional defiance. She loved him, loved what he did with that hand, and even, she suspected, loved what he loved, though they had not spoken of it. When that thought lifted her face to his, she saw his cheeks grow softer, as if he noticed her in his house for the first time. He drew her over to the table by the window, brought the sewing basket, placed on her lap her brother's shirt that needed buttons, adjusted the chair, opened the window, a little more, then less, and discovered that at a certain angle, it reflected her face. "If you sit here mending, I will paint you, Magdalena. But only if you stop that shouting." He positioned her shoulders, and his hands resting a moment were warm through the muslin[10] of her smock and seemed to settle her.

Mother rushed over to take away Geertruida's glass of milk.

"No, leave it, Catharina. Right there in the light."

For days she sat there, still as she could for Father, and yet sewing a few stitches every so often to satisfy Mother. In that mood of stillness, all the things within her line of vision touched her deeply. The tapestry laid across the table, the sewing basket, the same glass repoured each day to the same level, the amber-toned map of the world on the wall-it plucked a lute string in her heart that these things she'd touched, grown as familiar to her as her own skin, would be looked at, marveled at, maybe even loved by viewers of his painting.

Vocabulary Development defiance (di FY uhns) *n.* the act of defying; open resistance to authority

---

9. **chartreuse** (shahr TROOZ) pale yellowish green.
10. **muslin** (MUZ lin) stong, plain cotton cloth.

On sunny days the panes of window glass glistened before her. Like jewels melted into flat squares, she thought. Each one was slightly different in its pale transparent color—ivory, parchment, the lightest of wines and the palest of tulips. She wondered how glass was made, but she didn't ask. It would disturb him.

Outside the window the market chattered with the selling of apples and lard and brooms and wooden buckets. She liked the cheese porters in their flat-brimmed red hats and stark white clothes. Their curved yellow carrying platforms stacked neatly with cheese rounds were suspended on ropes between pairs of them, casting brown shadows on the paving stones. Two platforms diagonally placed in the midground between their carriers would make a nice composition with the repeated shapes of those bulging cheese rounds. She'd put a delivery boy wheeling his cart of silver cod in the background against the guild hall, and maybe in the foreground a couple of lavender gray pigeons pecking crumbs. The carillon[11] from Nieuwe Kerk ringing out the hour sounded something profound in her chest. All of it is ordinary to everyone but me, she thought.

All that month she did not speak, the occasion too momentous to dislodge it with words. He said he'd paint her as long as she didn't shout, and so she did not speak a word. Her chest ached like a dull wound when she realized that her silence did not cause him a moment's reflection or curiosity. When she looked out the corner of her eye at him, she could not tell what she meant to him. Slowly, she came to understand that he looked at her with the same interest he gave to the glass of milk.

Maybe it was because she wasn't pretty like Maria. She knew her jaws protruded and her watery, pale eyes were too widely set. She had a mole on her forehead that she always tried to hide by tugging at her cap. What if no one would want the painting? What then? It might be her fault, because she wasn't pretty. She wished he'd say something about her, but all he said, not to her directly, more to himself, was how the sunlight whitened her cap at the forehead, how the shadow at the nape of her neck reflected blue from her collar, or how the sienna of her skirt deepened to Venetian red[12] in the folds. It was never

---

Vocabulary Development **parchment** (PARCH muhnt) *adj.* creamy or yellowish color of the paper used for special documents, letters, or artwork

---

11. **carillon** (KAR uh lahn) a set of tuned church bells.
12. **sienna** (see EN uh) . . . **Venetian** (vah NEE shuhn) **red** Colors; sienna is a reddish or yellowish brown, and Venetian red is a brownish red.

TAKE NOTES

Fiction

Read the first bracketed passage. What is Magdalena doing in this passage? What does this passage show about her as a **character**?

_____

_____

_____

_____

Fiction

How would the second bracketed paragraph be different if it were told from Magdalena's father's **point of view**?

_____

_____

_____

_____

Reading Check

Why does Magdalena decide not to ask her father about how glass is made? Circle the text that tells you.

Why do you think Magdalena does not express her feelings to her father?

_____

_____

_____

What does the bracketed paragraph tell you about the **character** of Magdalena's father?

_____

_____

_____

Read the underlined sentences. What do these sentences tell you about Magdalena's **conflict**? What do you think will prevent her from trying to paint?

_____

_____

_____

_____

Magdalena tries to look calm for her father while he is painting her. When she sees the painting, Magdalena does not think she looks calm. How does she think she looks? Underline the text that tells you.

her, she cried to herself, only something surrounding her that she did not make or even contribute to knowingly. Another wish that never would come true, she saw then, even if she lived forever, was that he, that someone, would look at her not as an artistic study, but with love. If two people love the same thing, she reasoned, then they must love each other, at least a little, even if they never say it. Nevertheless, because he painted with such studied concentration, and because she held him in awe, she practiced looking calm for him as she looked out the window, but when she saw the canvas, what she intended as calm looked more like wistfulness.[13]

The painting was not bought by the brewer, Pieter Claesz van Ruijven,[14] who bought most of her father's work. He saw it, but passed over it for another. Disgrace seared her so that she could not speak that night. The painting hung without a frame in the outer kitchen where the younger children slept. Eventually the family had to give up their lodgings at Mechelen on the square, and take smaller rooms with Grandmother Maria on the Oude Langendijck.[15] Her father stopped taking the iceboat out to the Schie, sold it, in fact. He rarely painted, the rooms were so cramped and dark, the younger children boisterous, and a few years later, he died.

When she washed him in his bed that last time, his fingers already cold, she had a thought, the shame of which prevented her from uttering: It would make a fine painting, a memorial, the daughter with towel and blue-figured washing bowl at bedside, her hand covering his, the wife exhausted on the Spanish chair clutching a crucifix, the father-husband, eyes glazed, looking to another landscape. While he painted everyone else, no one was there to paint him, to make him remembered. She yearned to do it, but the task was too fearsome. She lacked the skill, and the one to teach her had never offered.

Even though she asked for them, Mother sold his paints and brushes to the Guild of St. Luke. It helped to pay a debt. When Mother became sick with worry, Magdalena had the idea to take the painting to Hendrick van Buyten, the baker, because she knew he liked her. And he accepted it, along with one of a lady playing a guitar, for the debt of six hundred seventeen guilders, six stuivers,[16] more than

---

13. **wistfulness** a mood of wishfulness or vague longing.
14. **Pieter Claesz van Ruijven** (PEE ter KLAHS fahn RY fen)
15. **Mechelen** (ME khe len) . . . **Oude Langendijck** (OW de LAHNG jen dyk) The Mechelen was an inn owned by the Vermeer family. The Oude Langendijck is a canal in Delft.
16. **stuivers** (STY ferz) coins worth a fraction of a guilder; roughly, a dime.

two years' worth of bread. He smiled at her and gave her a bun.

Within a year, she married a saddlemaker named Nicolaes, the first man to notice her, a hard worker whose pores smelled of leather and grease, who taught her a pleasure not of the eyes, but, she soon realized, a man utterly without imagination. They moved to Amsterdam and she didn't see the painting again for twenty years.

In 1696, just after their only living child, Magritte, damp with fever, stopped breathing in her arms, Magdalena read in the *Amsterdamsche Courant* of a public auction of one hundred thirty-four paintings by various artists. "Several outstandingly artful paintings," the notice said, "including twenty-one works most powerfully and splendidly painted by the late J. Vermeer of Delft, will be auctioned May 16, 1:00, at the Oude Heeren Logement."[17] Only a week away. She thought of Hendrick. Of course he couldn't be expected to keep those paintings forever. Hers might be there. The possibility kept her awake nights.

Entering the auction gallery, she was struck again by that keenest of childhood wishes—to make a record not only of what she saw, but how. The distance she'd come from that, and not even a child to show for it! She shocked herself by asking, involuntarily, what had been the point of having lived? Wishing had not been enough. Was it a mistake that she didn't beg him to teach her? Maybe not. If she'd seen that eventually, with help, she could paint, it might have made the years of birthing and dying harder. But then the birthing and dying would have been painted and the pain given. It would have served a purpose. Would that have been enough—to tell a truth in art?

She didn't know.

To see again so many of Father's paintings was like walking down an avenue of her childhood. The honey-colored window, the Spanish chair, the map she'd stared at, dreaming, hanging on the wall, Grandmother Maria's golden water pitcher, Mother's pearls and yellow satin jacket—they commanded such a reverence for her now that she felt they all had souls.

And suddenly there she was on canvas, framed. Her knees went weak.

Hendrick hadn't kept it. Even though he liked her, he hadn't kept it.

Almost a child she was, it seemed to her, gazing out the window instead of doing her mending, as if by the mere act of looking she could send her spirit out into the world. And those shoes! She had forgotten. How she loved the buckles, and thought they made her such a

---

17. **Oude Heeren Logement** (OW de HER en LOHZ mohn)

Magdalena Looking **11**

TAKE NOTES

Fiction

Underline the words the author uses to show a change in the **setting** in the bracketed paragraph.

Fiction

Think about how the **character** Magdalena's life has changed. How does her adult life differ from her childhood wishes? How does this difference make you feel about her and the life that she lives?

_____

_____

_____

Stop to Reflect

What changes would you notice about yourself if you saw a picture that was taken when you were very young?

_____

_____

Read the bracketed passage. What does this passage tell you about how the **character** Magdalena has changed over the years?

_____

_____

_____

Do you believe that Magdalena has the talent to paint the pain out of her life? Explain.

_____

_____

_____

How does Magdalena feel when she sees her childhood shoes in the painting? Circle the text that tells you.

Do you think that the new owners of the painting would have wanted Magdalena to introduce herself to them? Why or why not?

_____

_____

_____

_____

_____

lady. Eventually she'd worn the soles right through, but now, brand-new, the buckles glinted on the canvas, each with a point of golden light. A bubble of joy surged upward right through her.

No, she wasn't beautiful, she owned, but there was a simplicity in her young face that she knew the years had eroded, a stilled longing in the forward lean of her body, a wishing in the intensity of her eyes. The painting showed she did not yet know that lives end abruptly, that much of living is repetition and separation, that buttons forever need resewing no matter how ferociously one works the thread, that nice things almost happen. Still a woman overcome with wishes, she wished Nicolaes would have come with her to see her in the days of her sentry post wonder when life and hope were new and full of possibility, but he had seen no reason to close up the shop on such a whim.

She stood on tiptoe and didn't breathe when her painting was announced. Her hand in her pocket closed tight around the twenty-four guilders, some of it borrowed from two neighbor women, some of it taken secretly from the box where Nicolaes kept money for leather supplies. It was all she could find, and she didn't dare ask for more. He would have thought it foolish.

"Twenty," said a man in front of her.

"Twenty-two," said another.

"Twenty-four," she said so loud and fast the auctioneer was startled. Did he see something similar in her face? He didn't call for another bid. The painting was hers!

"Twenty-five."

Her heart cracked.

The rest was a blur of sound. It finally went to a man who kept conferring with his wife, which she took as a good sign that it was going to a nice family. Forty-seven guilders. Most of the paintings sold for much more, but forty-seven was fine, she thought. In fact, it filled her momentarily with what she'd been taught was the sin of pride. Then she thought of Hendrick and a pain lashed through her. Forty-seven guilders minus the auctioneer's fee didn't come close to what her family had owed him.

She followed the couple out into the drizzle of Herengracht,[18] wanting to make herself known to them, just to have a few words, but then dropped back. She had such bad teeth now, and they were people of means. The woman wore stockings. What would she say to them? She didn't want them to think she wanted anything.

---

18. **Herengracht** (HER en krahkt) the "Gentleman's Canal"; one of the three main canals in the center of the city of Amsterdam.

She walked away slowly along a wet stone wall that shone iridescent, and the wetness of the street reflected back the blue of her best dress. Water spots appeared fast, turning the cerulean[19] to deep ultramarine, Father's favorite blue. Light rain pricked the charcoal green canal water into delicate, dark lace, and she wondered if it had ever been painted just that way, or if the life of something as inconsequential as a water drop could be arrested and given to the world in a painting, or if the world would care.

She thought of all the people in all the paintings she had seen that day, not just Father's, in all the paintings of the world, in fact. Their eyes, the particular turn of a head, their loneliness or suffering or grief was borrowed by an artist to be seen by other people throughout the years who would never see them face to face. People who would be that close to her, she thought, a matter of a few arms' lengths, looking, looking, and they would never know her.

---

19. cerulean (suh ROO lee uhn) sky-blue.

Reader's Response: What could Magdalena now do to make her life a happier one?

_____

_____

_____

_____

Fiction

This story does not contain much **dialogue**. The lack of dialogue keeps other characters from becoming very involved in the story. Why might the author have kept dialogue out of the story?

_____

_____

_____

_____

Fiction

The **resolution** is the conclusion of the story. Do you think the resolution of this story is positive or negative? Circle details in the text that support your answer.

_____

Fiction

The **theme** of a story is the message the writer wants to tell you about life or human nature. What is one theme of this story?

_____

_____

Artful Research

Susan Vreeland

Summary Susan Vreeland explains why she does so much research. She also explains how she goes about finding information. What she found helped her write *Girl in Hyacinth Blue*, from which "Magdalena Looking" was taken. She also includes a list of her favorite reference materials.

Note-taking Guide

Fill in this cluster diagram to record the types of resources you can use when you research a topic.

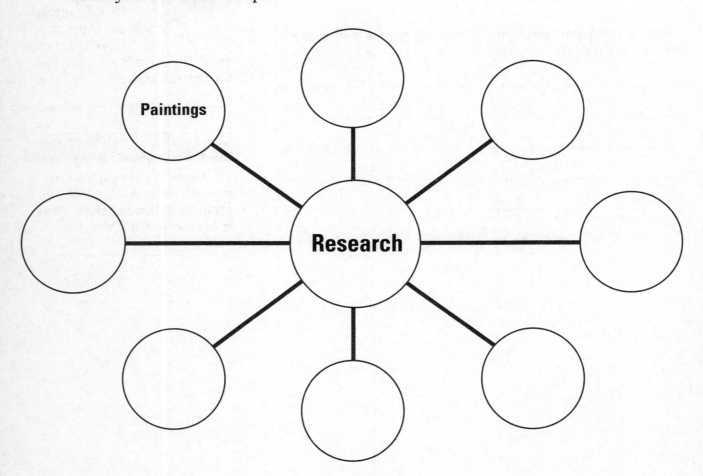

Artful Research
Susan Vreeland

Is it possible for an ordinary person to climb over the area railings of #7 Eccles Street, either from the path or the steps, lower himself down from the lowest part of the railings till his feet are within two feet or three of the ground and drop unhurt? I saw it done myself but by a man of rather athletic build. I require this information in detail in order to determine the wording of a paragraph.

James Joyce[1] wrote this to his aunt once when he was out of Dublin. Can't you just imagine her muttering, "That boy! What will he think of next?" as she looks for her umbrella to go out in the rain and take the trolley to Eccles Street?

Excessive? Unnecessary? Stalling from the act of writing? Joyce's letter is instructive and revealing.

Similarly, I must admit that I sent my French translator on a mission to find out whether the carvings of heads on the façade of the Ministère de la Défense[2] on Boulevard Saint-Germain in Paris are repeats of the same face or different faces. Among other things, she told me I had the wrong street!

While some writers may be more cavalier, claiming that it's fiction, after all, I hold with the meticulous Joyce, not wholly out of allegiance to a recognized master, but for the sake of the richness of story that results. For me, research gives direction, depth, and authority to the writing; it doesn't just decorate a preconceived story with timely trivia.

Early research tends to be scattered, while one searches for the story, but later, usually during or after a first draft when one discovers in the work some needed information, it becomes pinpoint precise. At either time, an array of interesting material, some of it crucial, some merely useable, will emerge—and sometimes leap off the page. The results can be exciting. A single unexpected line can prompt a whole story. For example, the line in Jacob Presser's grim history, *Ashes in the Wind: The Destruction of Dutch Jewry*, indicating that in 1941, Jews were not allowed to keep pigeons, provided the genesis of my story "A Night Different from All Other Nights."

That story is one of eight linked narratives comprising my composite novel, *Girl in Hyacinth Blue*, which traces an alleged Vermeer[3] painting in reverse chronology

---

1. **James Joyce** (1882–1941) famed Irish writer noted for *Dubliners* (1914), a collection of short stories, and *Ulysses* (1922), a novel, among other works.
2. **Ministère de la Défense** (meen ee STAYR duh lah day FAHNS) the Ministry of Defense building in Paris, France.
3. **Vermeer** (vuhr MEER) Jan (yahn) Vermeer (1632–1675), renowned Dutch painter.

TAKE NOTES

Activate Prior Knowledge

What resources do you normally use when you research a topic?

_____

_____

_____

Nonfiction

Perspective is the author's point of view on a subject. Read the bracketed passage. What does this passage tell you about Vreeland's perspective?

_____

_____

_____

Reading Check

Does Vreeland think that early research is usually scattered or organized? Circle the text that tells you.

Perspective is based on personal experience or general research. Is Vreeland's perspective based on personal experience or general research? Explain.

_____
_____
_____
_____

Read the bracketed passage. If Vreeland had not acquired all of this information, how would her novel have been different?

_____
_____
_____
_____

When doing research for *Girl in Hyacinth Blue*, how many books did Vreeland consult? Circle the text that tells you.

through the centuries, showing how defining moments in people's lives are lived under its influence. Besides the present, six time periods and numerous locales in the Netherlands are evoked: 1942 in Amsterdam; 1896 in Vreeland (yes, a real village located between Amsterdam and Utrecht); 1798 in The Hague during French rule; 1717 in Oling, Delfzijl, Westerbork, and Groningen (which I learned had been a university town since 1614, prompting my focal character to be a student); 1665 in Delft; and 1685 in Amsterdam. Naive in understanding what such a project entailed, I found that by the end, I had consulted seventy-six books.

I'd been to the Netherlands only once, twenty-five years ago for three days, and I had never seen a Vermeer painting face to face. Blithely, I went ahead. I read books on Vermeer, Dutch art and social and cultural history, the Holocaust[4] as experienced in the Netherlands, the changing geography of the Netherlands as more land was reclaimed from the sea,[5] Erasmus' adages,[6] the history of costume, Passover and the practice of Jewish customs, Amsterdam's diamond trade, Dutch superstitions and treatment of witches, the French occupation, and the engineering of windmills and dikes.

Twenty printout pages from the Internet on the engineering of windmills (they vary regionally), on gears, wallowers, Archimedean screws, and drive shafts yielded one paragraph establishing the authority of my character the windmill engineer. More importantly, the research also suggested a metaphor appropriate for him:

> I had fancied love a casual adjunct and not the central turning shaft making all parts move.
> I had not stood astonished at the power of its turning.

I would not have arrived at his critical self-assessment and the epiphany of the story without meandering through gears and drive shafts.

Here are ten research sources and approaches, beginning with the most obvious and ending with the ultimate—travel—that I used for either *Girl in Hyacinth Blue* or my subsequent novel, *The Passion of Artemisia*, which takes place in seventeenth-century Italy.

---

4. **the Holocaust** (HAHL uh kawst) the persecution, imprisonment, and mass murder of Jews by Nazi Germany before and during the Second World War (1939–1945).
5. **reclaimed from the sea** Significant portions of the Netherlands were originally covered by water. To drain water from this land, the Dutch built a system of dikes (dams) and canals.
6. **Erasmus' adages** (i RAZ muhs A di juhz) the sayings or brief observations of Desiderius (des uh DIR ee uhs) Erasmus (1455–1536), an influential Dutch scholar.

1. **Works on history, politics, and social conditions** A couple of titles might serve to show how I approached possible narratives from different angles: on the one hand, *Daily Life in Rembrandt's Holland;* on the other, *An Embarrassment of Riches: An Interpretation of Dutch Culture in the Golden Age.* Some I used as browser books; others, for specific information. Their bibliographies proved to be good sources for characters' names.

2. **Biography, autobiography, personal narrative, and oral history** The mere memory of Anne Frank's *Diary of a Young Girl* suggested that I create a young character the antithesis of Anne in terms of self expression, yet suffering similar revelations.

3. **Geography books** These can give information about weather, topography, crops, industry, indigenous plants, birds, and other animals.

4. **Maps** Besides those available in travel bookstores, universities often have historical map collections. This was essential for *Girl* because I had to know if certain villages and canals existed at the time of each of the stories.

5. **Travel books** Those of the descriptive sort, the older the better, provide visual and cultural detail.

6. **Novels** Novels written at the time, written about the time, or set in the same place can be helpful in revealing attitudes, concerns, expressions, syntax, and diction.

7. **Paintings** Paintings done in the same time and place as one's fiction are excellent sources of information about costume, hairstyles, jewelry, household furnishings, landscape, available foods, flowers typical of the region, even the quality of light in a region, Vermeer's "trademark."

8. **Children's and juvenile fiction and nonfiction** Works for younger readers are sufficient in some cases and have the advantages of providing evocative illustrations and simplifying complicated political histories.

9. **Interviews and phone calls** Don't neglect the importance of interviews and phone calls. People are intrigued by novelists and are usually delighted to be consulted. For *Girl in Hyacinth Blue,* I consulted a pigeon breeder to learn why the owning of pigeons was prohibited to Jews under the German occupation and how homing pigeons "worked."

10. **Going there!** While travel is not always practical (I wrote *Girl in Hyacinth Blue* entirely while undergoing cancer treatment and could not travel), it will yield unexpected insights.

TAKE NOTES

Nonfiction

The purpose of nonfiction can be **to persuade, to inform,** or **to entertain.** How successful is Vreeland in fulfilling each purpose with this article? Explain.

_____

_____

Nonfiction

Tone expresses an author's attitude toward the subject and the readers. Tone is shown through choice of words and details. On this page, Vreeland writes many long sentences and uses difficult words such as *antithesis, indigenous,* and *evocative.* Underline two other difficult words. What does the use of these sentences and words say about Vreeland's attitude toward her readers?

_____

_____

Nonfiction

Do you think a list like the one on this page would work better to **inform, persuade,** or **entertain** a reader? Why?

_____

_____

Nonfiction

Read the first brack-eted passage. In this passage, Vreeland talks directly to the reader. Circle an example from this passage that shows Vreeland directly talking to the reader. What does this style of writing do to the **tone** of the piece?

_____

_____

_____

Stop to Reflect

Read the second bracketed pas-sage. Why do you think Vreeland includes this tip? Why is it important?

_____

_____

_____

_____

Reading Check

What does Vreeland think is safer, research or writing? Underline the text that tells you.

So when does one stop researching and start writing? You write when the story comes to life, when it assumes some structure, when you can't help but start, not when you know everything you'll need to know. That's impossible to anticipate before you get into the heart of the writing. You might need to push yourself away from the safer act of research and leap into a first draft.

Don't get bogged down with fears of historical inaccuracy when writing a first draft. In one of the flood stories in *Girl in Hyacinth Blue*, the student needs to write a note. He's in a rowboat. He can't dip a pen in an inkwell. Did they have pencils in 1717? Look it up later. Keep writing. Keep the momentum going. If you don't know what they ate, leave it blank and get down the more important elements of the scene.

One caveat: Even if you put into your manuscript some fact delectable to you, recalling your delight in discovering it, if the story does not justify it, take it out. Type it up. Pin it on your wall. Use it elsewhere. But don't include it! The book is about characters, not about research.

Reader's Response: Do you agree with Vreeland that research is important when writing? Explain.

_____

_____

_____

_____

_____

Fiction and Nonfiction

1. **Evaluate:** Are Magdalena's disappointments because of her **character** and behavior or because of happenings that are beyond her control? Explain.

   _____

   _____

2. **Support:** Complete the chart below. Find two passages from "Magdalena Looking" that show how Vreeland's research gave "direction, depth, and authority" to the story.

How Research Helps in Fiction	
"Magdalena Looking" Passage	**Why You Chose It**

3. **Fiction:** Would Magdalena experience the same problem if she lived today? Explain.

   _____

   _____

4. **Nonfiction:** Which part of **nonfiction** is discussed more in "Artful Research," exploration of ideas or sharing information? Support your answer.

   _____

   _____

   _____

RESEARCH THE AUTHOR

Bulletin Board Display

Prepare a **bulletin board display** that centers around Vreeland's other works that focus on art. Use your answers to these prompts to create your display.

- Susan Vreeland's short fiction has appeared in journals such as *The Missouri Review, Confrontation, Calyx,* and *Alaska Quarterly Review.* Susan Vreeland's other novels are *What Love Sees, The Forest Lover,* and *The Passion of Artemisia.* Her nonfiction includes the student writing handbook, *What English Teachers Want,* and the essays "Nothing Lost" and "The Balm of Creative Endeavor."

  What I learned from Vreeland's writing:

  _____

  _____

  _____

- Search the Internet. Use phrases such as "Susan Vreeland article" or "Susan Vreeland interview."

  What I learned from information about Vreeland:

  _____

  _____

- Watch the video interview with Susan Vreeland, and review your source material. Use this information to answer the following questions.
  - How does art affect Vreeland's choice of material?

    _____

  - Why was Vreeland drawn to Vermeer's paintings?

    _____

  - How did Vreeland come up with the idea of writing *Girl in Hyacinth Blue*?

    _____

BUILD SKILLS

The Monkey's Paw • The Leap

LITERARY ANALYSIS

A **plot** is the sequence of related events in a story. A typical plot concerns a **conflict**—a struggle between opposing forces—and follows a pattern like the one shown. Use the chart below to record events in the plot.

- **Exposition:** The writer gives background on the characters and situation.
- **Rising action:** Events intensify the conflict.
- **Climax:** The tension reaches its highest point because the outcome of the conflict is about to be revealed.
- **Falling action:** The tension lessens because the outcome is clear.
- **Resolution:** The resolution, or final outcome, often involves a change or an insight.

Writers use various techniques to add tension to a story. One technique is **foreshadowing**—giving details that hint at upcoming events.

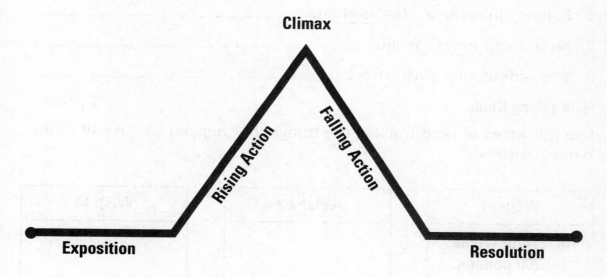

READING SKILL

A **prediction** is a logical idea about what will happen. To make predictions, pay attention to story details and **use your prior knowledge**.

- Knowledge of stories with similar plots can help you predict events.
- Knowledge of human nature can help you predict how characters will act.

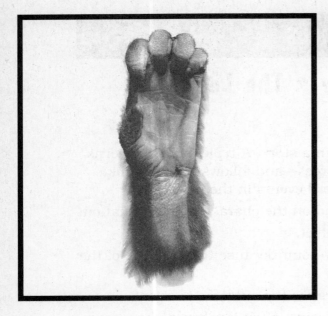

The Monkey's Paw

W.W. Jacobs

Summary An old friend visits the White family. He shows them a monkey's paw. He says that it can grant wishes. He warns the family not to take the monkey's paw. The Whites take it anyway and wish on it. The results are not what they expected.

Reading/Writing Connection

Complete the following sentences. Explain what you might do if you could make wishes. Your wishes may have consequences.

1. Before you make a wish, <u>evaluate</u> _____.

2. No one can <u>intervene</u> later to _____.

3. You cannot <u>alter</u> your wish if _____.

Note-taking Guide

Use this chart to keep track of the things that happen as a result of the Whites' wishes.

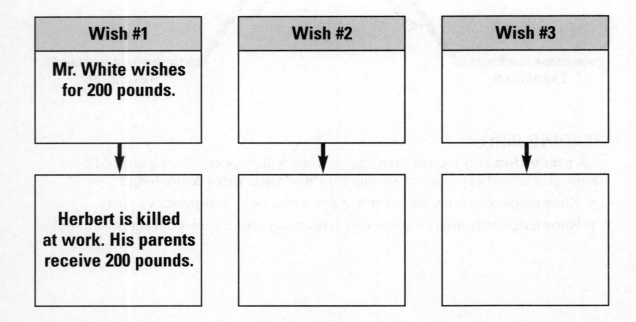

Wish #1	Wish #2	Wish #3
Mr. White wishes for 200 pounds.		
↓	↓	↓
Herbert is killed at work. His parents receive 200 pounds.		

The Monkey's Paw

W.W. Jacobs

I

Without, the night was cold and wet, but in the small parlor of Laburnam Villa the blinds were drawn and the fire burned brightly. Father and son were at chess, the former, who possessed ideas about the game involving radical changes, putting his king into such sharp and unnecessary perils that it even provoked comment from the white-haired old lady knitting placidly by the fire.

"Hark at the wind," said Mr. White, who, having seen a fatal mistake after it was too late, was amiably desirous of preventing his son from seeing it.

"I'm listening," said the latter, grimly surveying the board as he stretched out his hand. "Check."

"I should hardly think that he'd come tonight," said his father, with his hand poised over the board.

"Mate,"[1] replied the son.

"That's the worst of living so far out," bawled Mr. White, with sudden and unlooked-for violence; "of all the beastly, slushy, out-of-the-way places to live in, this is the worst. Pathway's a bog, and the road's a torrent. I don't know what people are thinking about. I suppose because only two houses on the road are let, they think it doesn't matter."

"Never mind, dear," said his wife, soothingly; "perhaps you'll win the next one."

Mr. White looked up sharply, just in time to intercept a knowing glance between mother and son. The words died away on his lips, and he hid a guilty grin in his thin gray beard.

"There he is," said Herbert White, as the gate banged to loudly and heavy footsteps came toward the door.

The old man rose with hospitable haste, and opening the door, was heard condoling with the new arrival. The new arrival also condoled with himself, so that Mrs. White said, "Tut, tut!" and coughed gently as her husband entered the room, followed by a tall, burly man, beady of eye and rubicund of visage.[2]

"Sergeant Major Morris," he said, introducing him.

The sergeant major shook hands, and taking the proffered seat by the fire, watched contentedly while his host got out tumblers and stood a small copper kettle on the fire.

At the third glass his eyes got brighter, and he began to talk, the little family circle regarding with eager interest

---

1. **mate** *n.* checkmate, a chess move that prevents the opponent's king from escaping capture and so ends the game.
2. **rubicund** (ROO buh kund) **of visage** (VIS ij) having a red face.

© Pearson Education, Inc., publishing as Pearson Prentice Hall.

TAKE NOTES

Activate Prior Knowledge

You probably have heard the expression "Be careful what you wish for." Explain what the sentence means. Why should someone be careful about wishing?

_____

_____

_____

_____

Literary Analysis

The **exposition** of a story gives background information. What important background information about the characters and their home is given in the exposition of this story?

_____

_____

_____

Reading Skill

A **prediction** is a logical idea about what will happen in a story. What can you predict will happen between the Whites and their visitor?

_____

_____

_____

Reading Check

Who has arrived at the Whites' house? Underline the text that tells you.

What do the details about Sergeant Major Morris's body language and gestures reveal about him?

_____

_____

_____

Literary Analysis

What two reactions does Mrs. White have to the monkey's paw? Underline the words or phrases that describe her behavior when she sees the monkey's paw.

_____

_____

Foreshadowing is giving details that hint at upcoming events. What might these reactions foreshadow?

_____

_____

Reading Skill

What **prediction** can you make about the monkey's paw? **Use your prior knowledge and story details** to make your prediction.

_____

_____

_____

this visitor from distant parts, as he squared his broad shoulders in the chair and spoke of wild scenes and doughty deeds; of wars and plagues and strange peoples.

"Twenty-one years of it," said Mr. White, nodding at his wife and son. "When he went away he was a slip of a youth in the warehouse. Now look at him."

"He don't look to have taken much harm," said Mrs. White, politely.

"I'd like to go to India myself," said the old man, "just to look round a bit, you know."

"Better where you are," said the sergeant major, shaking his head. He put down the empty glass, and sighing softly, shook it again.

"I should like to see those old temples and fakirs and jugglers," said the old man. "What was that you started telling me the other day about a monkey's paw or something, Morris?"

"Nothing," said the soldier, hastily. "Leastways nothing worth hearing."

"Monkey's paw?" said Mrs. White, curiously.

"Well, it's just a bit of what you might call magic, perhaps," said the sergeant major, offhandedly.

His three listeners leaned forward eagerly. The visitor absent-mindedly put his empty glass to his lips and then set it down again. His host filled it for him.

"To look at," said the sergeant major, fumbling in his pocket, "it's just an ordinary little paw, dried to a mummy."

He took something out of his pocket and proffered it. Mrs. White drew back with a grimace, but her son, taking it, examined it curiously.

"And what is there special about it?" inquired Mr. White as he took it from his son, and having examined it, placed it upon the table.

"It had a spell put on it by an old fakir," said the sergeant major, "a very holy man. He wanted to show that fate ruled people's lives, and that those who interfered with it did so to their sorrow. He put a spell on it so that three separate men could each have three wishes from it."

His manner was so impressive that his hearers were conscious that their light laughter jarred somewhat.

"Well, why don't you have three, sir?" said Herbert White, cleverly.

The soldier regarded him in the way that middle age is wont to regard presumptuous youth. "I have," he said, quietly, and his blotchy face whitened.

"And did you really have the three wishes granted?" asked Mrs. White.

"I did," said the sergeant major, and his glass tapped against his strong teeth.

"And has anybody else wished?" persisted the old lady.

"The first man had his three wishes, yes," was the reply; "I don't know what the first two were, but the third was for death. That's how I got the paw."

His tones were so grave that a hush fell upon the group.

"If you've had your three wishes, it's no good to you now, then, Morris," said the old man at last. "What do you keep it for?"

The soldier shook his head. "Fancy, I suppose," he said, slowly. "I did have some idea of selling it, but I don't think I will. It has caused enough mischief already. Besides, people won't buy. They think it's a fairy tale, some of them, and those who do think anything of it want to try it first and pay me afterward."

"If you could have another three wishes," said the old man, eyeing him keenly, "would you have them?"

"I don't know," said the other. "I don't know."

He took the paw, and dangling it between his forefinger and thumb, suddenly threw it upon the fire. White, with a slight cry, stooped down and snatched it off.

"Better let it burn," said the soldier, solemnly.

"If you don't want it, Morris," said the other, "give it to me."

"I won't," said his friend doggedly. "I threw it on the fire. If you keep it, don't blame me for what happens. Pitch it on the fire again, like a sensible man."

The other shook his head and examined his new possession closely. "How do you do it?" he inquired.

"Hold it up in your right hand and wish aloud," said the sergeant major, "but I warn you of the consequences."

"Sounds like the *Arabian Nights*,"[3] said Mrs. White, as she rose and began to set the supper. "Don't you think you might wish for four pairs of hands for me?"

Her husband drew the talisman from his pocket, and then all three burst into laughter as the sergeant major, with a look of alarm on his face, caught him by the arm. "If you must wish," he said, gruffly, "wish for something sensible."

Mr. White dropped it back in his pocket, and placing chairs, motioned his friend to the table. In the business of supper the talisman was partly forgotten, and afterward the three sat listening in an enthralled fashion to a second installment of the soldier's adventures in India.

"If the tale about the monkey's paw is not more truthful than those he has been telling us," said Herbert, as the door closed behind their guest, just in time for him to catch the last train, "we shan't make much out of it."

"Did you give him anything for it, Father?" inquired Mrs. White, regarding her husband closely.

---

3. *Arabian Nights* collection of stories from the ancient Near East telling of fantastical adventures and supernatural beings.

TAKE NOTES

Literary Analysis

A **plot** is the sequence of events in a story. The sergeant major tells the Whites the history of the monkey's paw. What part of the plot is this history?

_____

_____

Stop to Reflect

What is your opinion about the sergeant major's behavior toward the Whites and the monkey's paw? Do you think he is tempting the Whites, or is he trying to warn them against using the paw to make a wish? Explain your response.

_____

_____

_____

Literary Analysis

How does the information about the previous wishers **foreshadow** danger?

_____

_____

_____

Reading Check

What does Sergeant Major Morris tell Mr. White to wish for? Underline the sentence that tells you.

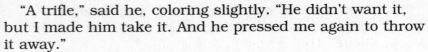

TAKE NOTES

Literary Analysis

A **conflict** is a struggle. What is Mr. White's conflict in the first bracketed passage?

_____

_____

Reading Skill

Predict the results of Mr. White's wish. **Use your prior knowledge** about characters in stories about wishes.

_____

_____

Stop to Reflect

Read the second bracketed passage. How does the mood of the story change after the wish has been made?

_____

_____

Reading Check

What is the first wish Mr. White makes? Underline the text that tells you.

"A trifle," said he, coloring slightly. "He didn't want it, but I made him take it. And he pressed me again to throw it away."

"Likely," said Herbert, with pretended horror. "Why, we're going to be rich, and famous and happy. Wish to be an emperor, Father, to begin with; then you can't be bossed around."

He darted round the table, pursued by the <u>maligned</u> Mrs. White armed with an antimacassar.[4]

Mr. White took the paw from his pocket and eyed it dubiously. "I don't know what to wish for, and that's a fact," he said, slowly. "It seems to me I've got all I want."

"If you only cleared the house, you'd be quite happy, wouldn't you?" said Herbert, with his hand on his shoulder. "Well, wish for two hundred pounds,[5] then; that'll just do it."

His father, smiling shamefacedly at his own credulity, held up the talisman, as his son, with a solemn face somewhat marred by a wink at his mother, sat down at the piano and struck a few impressive chords.

"I wish for two hundred pounds," said the old man distinctly.

A fine crash from the piano greeted the words, interrupted by a shuddering cry from the old man. His wife and son ran toward him.

"It moved," he cried, with a glance of disgust at the object as it lay on the floor. "As I wished it twisted in my hand like a snake."

"Well, I don't see the money," said his son as he picked it up and placed it on the table, "and I bet I never shall."

"It must have been your fancy, Father," said his wife, regarding him anxiously.

He shook his head. "Never mind, though; there's no harm done, but it gave me a shock all the same."

They sat down by the fire again while the two men finished their pipes. Outside, the wind was higher than ever, and the old man started nervously at the sound of a door banging upstairs. A silence unusual and depressing settled upon all three, which lasted until the old couple rose to retire for the night.

"I expect you'll find the cash tied up in a big bag in the middle of your bed," said Herbert, as he bade them good night, "and something horrible squatting up on top of the wardrobe watching you as you pocket your ill-gotten gains."

Vocabulary Development maligned (muh LYND) *adj.* spoken ill of

---

4. **antimacassar** (an ti muh KAS er) *n.* small cover for the arms or back of a chair or sofa.
5. **pounds** *n.* units of English currency, roughly comparable to dollars.

26 Reader's Notebook

© Pearson Education, Inc., publishing as Pearson Prentice Hall.

Herbert sat alone in the darkness, gazing at the dying fire, and seeing faces in it. The last face was so horrible and so simian[6] that he gazed at it in amazement. It got so vivid that, with a little uneasy laugh, he felt on the table for a glass containing a little water to throw over it. His hand grasped the monkey's paw, and with a little shiver he wiped his hand on his coat and went up to bed.

II

In the brightness of the wintry sun next morning as it streamed over the breakfast table Herbert laughed at his fears. There was an air of prosaic wholesomeness about the room which it had lacked on the previous night, and the dirty, shriveled little paw was pitched on the sideboard with a carelessness which betokened no great belief in its virtues.

"I suppose all old soldiers are the same," said Mrs. White. "The idea of our listening to such nonsense! How could wishes be granted in these days? And if they could, how could two hundred pounds hurt you, Father?"

"Might drop on his head from the sky," said the frivolous Herbert.

"Morris said the things happened so naturally," said his father, "that you might if you so wished attribute it to coincidence."

"Well, don't break into the money before I come back," said Herbert, as he rose from the table. "I'm afraid it'll turn you into a mean, avaricious[7] man, and we shall have to disown you."

His mother laughed, and following him to the door, watched him down the road, and, returning to the breakfast table, was very happy at the expense of her husband's credulity. All of which did not prevent her from scurrying to the door at the postman's knock, nor prevent her from referring somewhat shortly to retired sergeant majors of bibulous habits when she found that the post brought a tailor's bill.

"Herbert will have some more of his funny remarks, I expect, when he comes home," she said, as they sat at dinner.

"I dare say," said Mr. White, "but for all that, the thing moved in my hand; that I'll swear to."

"You thought it did," said the old lady soothingly.

"I say it did," replied the other. "There was no thought about it; I had just—What's the matter?"

His wife made no reply. She was watching the mysterious movements of a man outside, who, peering in an undecided fashion at the house, appeared to be trying to make up his mind to enter. In mental connection with

---

6. **simian** (SIM ee uhn) *adj.* monkeylike.
7. **avaricious** (av uh RISH uhs) *adj.* greedy for wealth.

TAKE NOTES

Literary Analysis

Read the first bracketed passage. Circle words in the passage that **foreshadow** that something bad may happen with regard to the monkey's paw.

Reading Skill

Read the second bracketed passage. **Use your prior knowledge** and think about human nature. Why might Herbert say this to his father?

_____

_____

_____

_____

Reading Check

What does Mrs. White think about Mr. White's insistence that the monkey's paw moved in his hand when he made his first wish? Underline the sentence that tells you.

Do you think that the monkey's paw has anything to do with the arrival of the stranger? Why or why not?

_____

_____

_____

What do you **predict** the stranger outside the Whites' home is there to do?

_____

_____

_____

What information does the stranger give to Mr. and Mrs. White? Underline the sentence that tells you.

the two hundred pounds, she noticed that the stranger was well dressed, and wore a silk hat of glossy newness. Three times he paused at the gate, and then walked on again. The fourth time he stood with his hand upon it, and then with sudden resolution flung it open and walked up the path. Mrs. White at the same moment placed her hands behind her, and hurriedly unfastening the strings of her apron, put that useful article of apparel beneath the cushion of her chair.

She brought the stranger, who seemed ill at ease, into the room. He gazed at her <u>furtively</u>, and listened in a preoccupied fashion as the old lady apologized for the appearance of the room, and her husband's coat, a garment which he usually reserved for the garden. She then waited patiently for him to broach his business, but he was at first strangely silent.

"I—was asked to call," he said at last, and stooped and picked a piece of cotton from his trousers. "I come from 'Maw and Meggins.'"

The old lady started. "Is anything the matter?" she asked, breathlessly. "Has anything happened to Herbert? What is it? What is it?"

Her husband interposed. "There, there, mother," he said, hastily. "Sit down, and don't jump to conclusions. You've not brought bad news, I'm sure, sir," and he eyed the other wistfully.

"I'm sorry—" began the visitor.

"Is he hurt?" demanded the mother, wildly.

The visitor bowed in assent. "Badly hurt," he said quietly, "but he is not in any pain."

"Oh, thank God!" said the old woman, clasping her hands. "Thank God for that! Thank—"

She broke off suddenly as the sinister meaning of the assurance dawned upon her and she saw the awful confirmation of her fears in the other's averted face. She caught her breath, and turning to her husband, laid her trembling old hand upon his. There was a long silence.

"He was caught in the machinery," said the visitor at length, in a low voice.

"Caught in the machinery," repeated Mr. White, in a dazed fashion, "yes."

He sat staring blankly out at the window, and taking his wife's hand between his own, pressed it as he had been wont to do in their old courting days nearly forty years before.

"He was the only one left to us," he said, turning gently to the visitor. "It is hard."

Vocabulary Development furtively (FER tiv lee) *adv.* secretively; sneakily; stealthily

The other coughed, and, rising, walked slowly to the window. "The firm wished me to convey their sincere sympathy with you in your great loss," he said, without looking round. "I beg that you will understand I am only their servant and merely obeying orders."

There was no reply; the old woman's face was white, her eyes staring, and her breath inaudible; on the husband's face was a look such as his friend the sergeant might have carried into his first action.

"I was to say that Maw and Meggins disclaim all responsibility," continued the other. "They admit no liability at all, but in consideration of your son's services they wish to present you with a certain sum as compensation."

Mr. White dropped his wife's hand, and rising to his feet, gazed with a look of horror at his visitor. His dry lips shaped the words, "How much?"

"Two hundred pounds," was the answer.

Unconscious of his wife's shriek, the old man smiled faintly, put out his hands like a sightless man, and dropped, a senseless heap, to the floor.

III

In the huge new cemetery, some two miles distant, the old people buried their dead, and came back to a house steeped in shadow and silence. It was all over so quickly that at first they could hardly realize it, and remained in a state of expectation as though of something else to happen—something else which was to lighten this load, too heavy for old hearts to bear.

But the days passed, and expectation gave place to resignation—the hopeless resignation of the old, sometimes miscalled apathy. Sometimes they hardly exchanged a word, for now they had nothing to talk about, and their days were long to weariness.

It was about a week after that the old man, waking suddenly in the night, stretched out his hand and found himself alone. The room was in darkness, and the sound of subdued weeping came from the window. He raised himself in bed and listened.

"Come back," he said, tenderly. "You will be cold."

"It is colder for my son," said the old woman, and wept afresh.

The sound of her sobs died away on his ears. The bed was warm, and his eyes heavy with sleep. He dozed fitfully, and then slept until a sudden wild cry from his wife awoke him with a start.

Vocabulary Development apathy (AP uh thee) *n.* lack of emotion or interest

---

Reading Skill

From the foreshadowing in the bracketed paragraph, make a logical **prediction** about where the Whites' money will come from.

_____

_____

Literary Analysis

Read the underlined sentence. In what way does the stranger's answer increase the tension of the **rising action**?

_____

_____

_____

_____

Stop to Reflect

How is the mood in the White's home different without Herbert?

_____

_____

_____

What do you **predict** the second wish will be?

_____

_____

_____

What does Mrs. White want her husband to wish for? Underline the words that tell you what she asks Mr. White to do.

If you could advise the Whites, what would you tell them?

_____

_____

_____

What consequences might you warn them about?

_____

_____

_____

"The paw!" she cried wildly. "The monkey's paw!"

He started up in alarm. "Where? Where is it? What's the matter?"

She came stumbling across the room toward him. "I want it," she said quietly. "You've not destroyed it?"

"It's in the parlor, on the bracket," he replied, marveling. "Why?"

She cried and laughed together, and bending over, kissed his cheek.

"I only just thought of it," she said hysterically. "Why didn't I think of it before? Why didn't *you* think of it?"

"Think of what?" he questioned.

"The other two wishes," she replied rapidly. "We've only had one."

"Was not that enough?" he demanded, fiercely.

"No," she cried triumphantly; "we'll have one more. Go down and get it quickly, and wish our boy alive again."

The man sat up in bed and flung the bedclothes from his quaking limbs. "You are mad!" he cried, aghast.

"Get it," she panted; "get it quickly, and wish—Oh, my boy, my boy!"

Her husband struck a match and lit the candle. "Get back to bed," he said unsteadily. "You don't know what you are saying."

"We had the first wish granted," said the old woman feverishly; "why not the second?"

"A coincidence," stammered the old man.

"Go and get it and wish," cried his wife, quivering with excitement.

The old man turned and regarded her, and his voice shook. "He has been dead ten days, and besides he—I would not tell you else, but—I could only recognize him by his clothing. If he was too terrible for you to see then, how now?"

"Bring him back," cried the old woman, and dragged him toward the door. "Do you think I fear the child I have nursed?"

He went down in the darkness, and felt his way to the parlor, and then to the mantelpiece. The talisman was in its place, and a horrible fear that the unspoken wish might bring his mutilated son before him ere he could escape from the room seized upon him, and he caught his breath as he found that he had lost the direction of the door. His brow cold with sweat, he felt his way round the table, and groped along the wall until he found himself in the small passage with the unwholesome thing in his hand.

Even his wife's face seemed changed as he entered the room. It was white and expectant, and to his fears seemed to have an unnatural look upon it. He was afraid of her.

"Wish!" she cried, in a strong voice.

"It is foolish and wicked," he faltered.

"Wish!" repeated his wife.

He raised his hand. "I wish my son alive again."

The talisman fell to the floor, and he regarded it fearfully. Then he sank trembling into a chair as the old woman, with burning eyes, walked to the window and raised the blind.

He sat until he was chilled with the cold, glancing occasionally at the figure of the old woman peering through the window. The candle-end, which had burned below the rim of the china candlestick, was throwing pulsating shadows on the ceiling and walls, until, with a flicker larger than the rest, it expired. The old man, with an unspeakable sense of relief at the failure of the talisman, crept back to his bed, and a minute or two afterward the old woman came silently and apathetically beside him.

Neither spoke, but lay silently listening to the ticking of the clock. A stair creaked, and a squeaky mouse scurried noisily through the wall. The darkness was oppressive, and after lying for some time screwing up his courage, he took the box of matches, and striking one, went downstairs for a candle.

At the foot of the stairs the match went out, and he paused to strike another; and at the same moment a knock, so quiet and stealthy as to be scarcely audible, sounded on the front door.

The matches fell from his hand and spilled in the passage. He stood motionless, his breath suspended until the knock was repeated. Then he turned and fled swiftly back to his room, and closed the door behind him. A third knock sounded through the house.

"What's that?" cried the old woman, starting up.

"A rat," said the old man in shaking tones—"a rat. It passed me on the stairs."

His wife sat up in bed listening. A loud knock resounded through the house.

"It's Herbert!" she screamed. "It's Herbert!"

She ran to the door, but her husband was before her, and catching her by the arm, held her tightly.

"What are you going to do?" he whispered hoarsely.

"It's my boy; it's Herbert!" she cried, struggling mechanically. "I forgot it was two miles away. What are you holding me for? Let go. I must open the door."

"Don't let it in," cried the old man, trembling.

"You're afraid of your own son," she cried, struggling. "Let me go. I'm coming, Herbert; I'm coming."

There was another knock, and another. The old woman with a sudden wrench broke free and ran from the room. Her husband followed to the landing, and called after her appealingly as she hurried downstairs. He heard the

TAKE NOTES

Reading Skill

Make a **prediction** about the outcome of the second wish.

_____
_____
_____
_____

Reading Check

What does Mr. White hear when he pauses to strike another match? Underline the sentence that tells you.

Reading Skill

What do you **predict** the Whites will do about the third wish?

_____
_____
_____
_____

The **climax** occurs when the tension reaches the highest point. How does the difference between what Mr. and Mrs. White are trying to do bring events to a climax?

_____

_____

_____

What do you think Mr. White's last wish is?

_____

_____

_____

chain rattle back and the bottom bolt drawn slowly and stiffly from the socket. Then the old woman's voice, strained and panting.

"The bolt," she cried, loudly. "Come down. I can't reach it."

But her husband was on his hands and knees groping wildly on the floor in search of the paw. If he could only find it before the thing outside got in. A perfect fusillade[9] of knocks reverberated through the house, and he heard the scraping of a chair as his wife put it down in the passage against the door. He heard the creaking of the bolt as it came slowly back, and at the same moment he found the monkey's paw, and frantically breathed his third and last wish.

The knocking ceased suddenly, although the echoes of it were still in the house. He heard the chair drawn back and the door opened. A cold wind rushed up the staircase, and a long loud wail of disappointment and misery from his wife gave him courage to run down to her side, and then to the gate beyond. The street lamp flickering opposite shone on a quiet and deserted road.

Vocabulary Development reverberated (ri VER buh rayt id) *v.*
resounded, reechoed

---

9. **fusillade** (FYOO suh lahd) *n.* rapid firing, as of gunshots.

Reader's Response: What wishes would you make if you were Mr. or Mrs. White?

_____

_____

_____

_____

The Monkey's Paw

1. **Infer:** What painful outcome seems to follow from the wording of Mr. White's wish for 200 pounds?

   _____

   _____

2. **Draw Conclusions:** Explain whether you think the events of the story prove the fakir's point that "fate ruled people's lives, and that those who interfered with it did so to their sorrow."

   _____

   _____

3. **Literary Analysis:** Identify two details that **foreshadow** the tragic outcome of the first wish.

   _____

   _____

4. **Reading Skill:** Use this chart to indicate how you used your prior knowledge to **make a prediction** about one of the wishes.

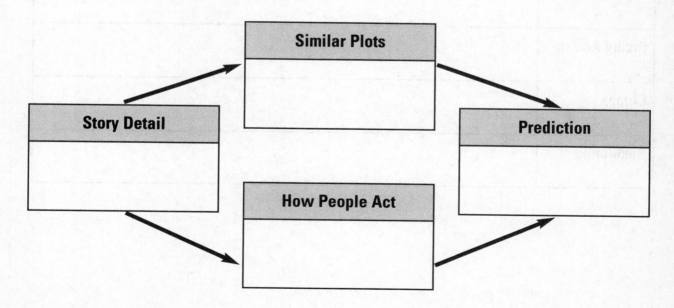

SUPPORT FOR WRITING AND EXTEND YOUR LEARNING

Writing: Sequel

Write a brief **sequel** to this tale in which someone else finds the paw. Answer the questions below to help you plan. Use your notes to help you write your sequel.

- How does the new person get the monkey's paw?

  _____

- How will he or she learn about the history of the monkey's paw?

  _____

- What does this person have, and what does he or she want?

  _____

- Will the person make a wish?

  _____

- What consequences will this person's wishes bring?

Listening and Speaking: Interview

Conduct an **interview** between a reporter and the Whites after the tragedy. Use this chart to plan. Think of a question you could ask about each of these story parts.

Exposition	
Rising Action	
Climax	
Resolution	

The Leap

Louise Erdrich

Summary The narrator tells of her mother's life as a trapeze artist. An accident injures her and kills her first husband. She later marries a doctor and settles on his farm. While the narrator is a child, their house catches fire. The narrator is trapped in her bedroom. Her mother makes a brave attempt to save her.

Reading/Writing Connection

Complete these sentences. Describe emotional gifts you have given or received.

1. A teacher could demonstrate _____.

2. A good coach can help athletes devote _____.

3. Emotional gifts enrich the lives of _____.

Note-taking Guide

Use this chart to recall the different parts of the story's plot.

Exposition	One Event in the Rising Action	Climax	One Event in the Falling Action	Resolution
The narrator's mother was once a circus performer.				

The Leap

1. **Respond:** Which event in Anna's life surprised you the most? Why?

   _____

   _____

2. **Infer:** Why does the mother make the leap at the end of the story?

   _____

   _____

3. **Literary Analysis:** Describe three events in the **rising action** that increase the tension in the **plot**.

   _____

   _____

4. **Reading Skill:** Fill in the chart below to show how you **used prior knowledge** to **make a prediction** about the outcome of the story.

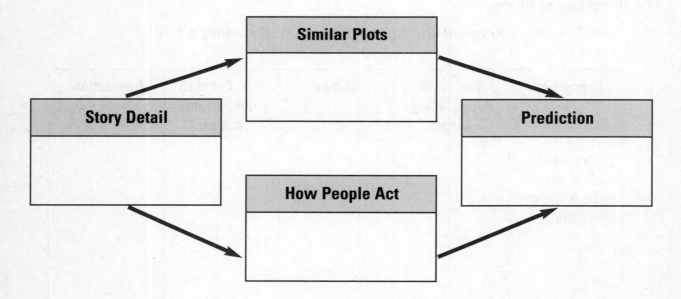

SUPPORT FOR WRITING AND EXTEND YOUR LEARNING

Writing: Sequel

Write a brief **sequel** to "The Leap." Tell another exciting episode in which the narrator's mother uses her circus skills to rescue someone. Answer the following questions. Use your notes to help you write the sequel.

- Where will you set your sequel? List details about the place and time.

_____

- Which characters will you use in the sequel?

_____

- What are the characters doing and thinking in this sequel?

_____

- What is the climax of the story?

_____

Research and Technology: Scene Proposal

Imagine that you are the director of a film version of this story. Write a **scene proposal** for your movie. Fill in the chart below with notes about the story. Decide which part would work best as a movie scene. Use your notes to help you plan.

Scene Title:				
Exposition	**Rising Action**	**Climax**	**Falling Action**	**Resolution**

from Swimming to Antarctica • Occupation: Conductorette from I Know Why the Caged Bird Sings

LITERARY ANALYSIS

The **author's perspective** in a literary work includes the judgments, attitudes, and experiences the author brings to the subject. An author's perspective determines which details he or she includes, as in these examples:

- A writer with firsthand experience of an event might report his or her own reactions as well as generally known facts.
- A writer with a positive view of a subject may emphasize its benefits.

A work may combine several perspectives. For example, a writer may tell what it felt like to live through an event. In addition, the writer may express his or her present views of the experience. As you read, look for details that suggest the author's perspective.

READING SKILL

As you read, **make predictions**, or educated guesses, about what will happen next. Then, check your predictions as you read.

- **Revise**, or adjust, your predictions as you gather more information.
- **Verify**, or confirm, predictions by comparing the outcome you predicted with the actual outcome.

To help you make, verify, and revise predictions, **ask questions**. Use the chart below to record your predictions and findings.

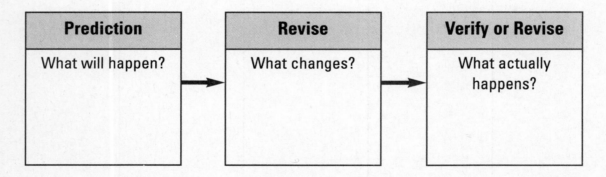

Prediction		Revise		Verify or Revise
What will happen?	→	What changes?	→	What actually happens?

from Swimming to Antarctica

Lynne Cox

Summary Lynne Cox, a record-breaking swimmer, describes how she prepared herself to swim a mile in the freezing Antarctic water. Many obstacles along the way test the limits of both her body and her mind.

Reading/Writing Connection

Complete the following sentences by thinking about ways to prepare mentally and physically for a challenge.

1. Relaxing and breathing deeply can help you <u>focus</u> on _____.

2. Practicing beforehand can <u>minimize</u> _____.

3. When the time comes, you will want to <u>maximize</u> _____.

Note-taking Guide

Use this diagram to list details that show how different people in the story saw Lynne's swim. In the left oval, list details that only Lynne Cox could describe. In the right oval, list the details that only the crewmembers could have noticed. In the overlapping area, list any details that both Lynne and the crewmembers could describe.

Lynne Cox　　　　　　　　　　　　　　**Crewmembers**

The pressure of the cold water feels like a tourniquet.

Both

Activate Prior Knowledge

Describe a time when you undertook a challenging project or activity. What steps did you take to prepare yourself?

_____

_____

_____

Literary Analysis

The **author's perspective** includes the judgments, attitudes, and experiences the author brings to the subject. What do the underlined sentences indicate about the author's attitude toward her swim?

_____

_____

_____

Reading Skill

A **prediction** is an educated guess about what will happen next. Underline details in the text that support a prediction that Cox will succeed at her swim. Draw a box around details that support a prediction that she will fail. What is your prediction?

_____

_____

Reading Check

What temperature will the water be when Cox swims? Circle the answer.

from Swimming to Antarctica
Lynne Cox

In 2002, swimmer Lynne Cox attempted an ambitious feat—swimming a mile in the frigid waters of Antarctica. Cox sailed on the ship Orlova with a team of seven friends, including team leader Barry Binder and her physicians, Susan Sklar, Gabriella Miotta, and Laura King. Bob Griffith and Martha Kaplan, Cox's agent, would scout for danger as Cox swam, while Dan Cohen stood by as a rescue swimmer. Scott Pelley, a television producer, also came. The ship's crew included Dr. Anthony Block and expedition leader Susan Adie. Before attempting a mile, Cox tested her reactions on a shorter swim.

When I returned to my cabin, I thought for a long time about what I was about to attempt.

I had mixed feelings about the test swim. In some ways, it had given me confidence; I now knew that I could swim for twenty-two minutes in thirty-three-degree water. But it had also made me feel uncertain. It had been the most difficult and probably the most dangerous swim I had ever done. Part of me wanted to be satisfied with it. Part of me didn't want to attempt the mile. I was afraid. The water temperature on the big swim would be a degree colder. Thirty-two degrees. That was a magic number, the temperature at which freshwater froze. I wondered if in thirty-two-degree water the water in my cells would freeze, if my body's tissues would become permanently damaged. I wondered if my mind would function better this time, if I would be able to be more aware of what was happening, or if it would be further dulled by the cold. Would my core temperature drop faster, more quickly than I could recognize? Would I be able to tell if I needed to get out? Did I really want to risk my life for this? Or did I want to risk failure?

The other part of me wanted to try, wanted to do what I had trained for, wanted to explore and reach beyond what I had done. That part of me was excited about venturing into the unknown. That part of me knew I would have felt a tremendous letdown if I didn't get a chance to try. I wanted to do it now.

The next morning, on December 15, 2002, Susan called me up to the bridge. She pointed out Water Boat Point. The tiny gray beach between steep glaciers was completely blocked by icebergs and brash ice.[1] There was no place to land.

We continued sailing south through the Gerlache Strait, past mountain-high glaciers and by ship-sized icebergs ranging in shades of blue from juniper berry to robin's-egg

---

1. **brash ice** *n.* floating fragments of ice.

to light powder blue. In the protection of the Antarctic Peninsula, the wind dropped off and the sea grew calmer. When we reached Neko Harbor, about an hour later, Susan called me up to the bridge. She was excited. The beach was free of icebergs and brash ice. A landing was possible.

Now I would have a chance to swim the first Antarctic mile. I was thrilled and scared, but I tried to remain calm; I knew that the weather could suddenly change and the swim would be off. I met with Barry Binder, who said, "I'll get the crew into the Zodiacs[2] and come and get you when everything's set."

I walked to the ship's library, drank four eight-ounce cups of hot water, and ate two small croissants for breakfast—they were high in fat and carbohydrates, two sources of energy I would need for the swim. Then I started through the hallway to my cabin, where many of the *Orlova's* passengers were waiting, eager to find out if I was going to swim. They wished me luck and said they would wait for me at the finish. I stopped by Dan's cabin to ask him if he would jump into the water with me at the end of the swim. He was already in his dry suit, prepared to go. Everyone was doing what we had practiced. All I could do was to go back to my room and wait. Gabriella came in to take a core temperature; it was up to 100.4 degrees. Knowing I was venturing into unknown waters, I must have psyched myself up so much that I increased my body temperature. Gabriella left me alone while I put on my swimsuit and sweats. I rubbed sunscreen on my face, but not on my arms or legs; it could make my skin slippery, and if my crew needed me to get out of the water quickly, that would create a problem. The night before, three of the crew had spotted a pod of eight killer whales swimming into the Gerlache Strait. They hadn't been moving fast. I hoped they were still north of us.

I stared out the window at the brown crescent-shaped beach. There were snow-covered hills directly above the beach, and massive glaciers on either side. I picked out landmarks, places I could aim for, so I'd know if I was on or off course.

Dr. Block caught me at the top of the stairs, just before we stepped out the door and onto the ramp, and asked if I would sit down on a step so he could trace two veins on my hands with a blue Magic Marker. It was just a precaution, he said, in case I needed emergency assistance; this way he would easily be able to find a vein to start an IV. I gave him my right hand and watched him draw the blue lines for the television camera. It gave me the creeps. Why did he have to do this now, right before I swam?

---

2. **Zodiacs** *n.* speedboats.

TAKE NOTES

Reading Skill

As you read this narrative, you may need to **revise**, or adjust, your original **prediction** as you gather more information. Read the underlined passage. Explain whether and how details in the passage lead you to **revise** your **prediction** about the outcome of Cox's swim.

_____

_____

_____

Literary Analysis

How has the **author's perspective** changed since the beginning of this narrative?

_____

_____

Stop to Reflect

The body's core includes the heart, lungs, and brain. Why do you think having a high core temperature is important for Cox?

_____

_____

Reading Check

Underline what Cox eats for breakfast on the morning of the swim. How does this choice help her prepare for the challenge?

_____

_____

Underline two dangers Cox faces on her swim.

How does the bracketed passage reflect the **author's perspective** both during the event and after it?

_____

_____

_____

_____

Do you think that Cox would have attempted her swim if she had known all the dangers she faced?

_____

_____

_____

_____

As you **make** and **revise predictions**, you **ask questions**. What questions might you ask after reading this page?

_____

_____

_____

_____

_____

Didn't he realize this kind of stuff psychs people out? I know the swim is dangerous, but he could have done this hours ago, not just before I swam. Get over it, I told myself. Shake it off. Take a deep breath. Refocus. Take another breath. Good. Now think about the swim. I smiled. *I'm so ready for this.*

Walking to the door, I peeked out and felt a blast of icy wind hit my face from the northwest. It was blowing in off the glaciers in gusts to twenty-five knots,[3] and the air temperature was thirty-two degrees. I felt the hair rising on my arms and my jaw tighten to suppress a shiver. I was much more nervous than I had been during my first swim. I had greater expectations of myself now. I wanted to swim the first Antarctic mile, and I knew I would be very disappointed if I didn't succeed.

I stared across the icy water at Neko Harbor's beach and felt excitement building within me. Quickly, before I could lose my chance, I pulled off my sweat suit and shoes and stuck them in a corner of the ship, climbed down the gangway, sat on the platform, and dangled my feet in the water. Surprisingly, it didn't feel any colder than it had two days before. I didn't realize then that the nerves on my skin's surface had been damaged from the first swim. I didn't know that the nerves that signaled danger weren't firing. I wasn't aware that my first line of defense was gone. I had no idea that <u>prolonged</u> exposure in thirty-two-degree water could cause permanent nerve and muscle damage. And I didn't know then that when an untrained person is immersed in water colder than forty degrees, their nerves are cooled down so they can't fire at the neuromuscular level. After only seven or eight minutes the person's body seizes up and (he or she) can't move. It was a good thing I didn't know any of this. All I knew was that I was ready. I took a deep breath, leaned back, and threw myself forward into the thirty-two-degree water.

When I hit the water, I went all the way under. I hadn't intended to do that; I hadn't wanted to immerse my head, which could over-stimulate my vagus nerve[4] and cause my heart to stop beating. Dog-paddling as quickly as I could, I popped up in the water, gasping for air. I couldn't catch my breath. I was swimming with my head up,

---

Vocabulary Development prolonged (proh LONGD) *adj.*
extended; lengthy

---

3. **knots** (nahts) *n.* a rate of speed. One knot equals one nautical mile (6,076.12 feet) per hour.
4. **vagus** (VAY gus) **nerve** *n.* either of a pair of nerves running from the brain to the heart that regulate the heartbeat.

hyperventilating.[5] I kept spinning my arms, trying to get warm, but I couldn't get enough air. I felt like I had a corset tightening around my chest. I told myself to relax, take a deep breath, but I couldn't slow my breath. And I couldn't get enough air in. I tried again. My body wanted air, and it wanted it now. I had to override that reaction of hyperventilating. I had to concentrate on my breath, to press my chest out against the cold water and draw the icy air into my lungs.

My body resisted it. The air was too cold. My body didn't want to draw the cold air deep into my lungs and cool myself from the inside. It wanted to take short breaths so the cold air would be warmed in my mouth before it reached my lungs. I was fighting against myself.

I noticed my arms. They were bright red, and I felt like I was swimming through slush. My arms were thirty-two degrees, as cold as the sea. They were going numb, and so were my legs. I pulled my hands right under my chest so that I was swimming on the upper inches of the sea, trying to minimize my contact with the water. I was swimming fast and it was hard to get enough air. I began to notice that the cold was pressurizing my body like a giant tourniquet. It was squeezing the blood from the exterior part of my body and pushing it into the core. Everything felt tight. *Focus on your breath,* I told myself. *Slow it down. Let it fill your lungs. You're not going to be able to make it if you keep going at this rate.*

It wasn't working. I was laboring for breath harder than on the test swim. I was in oxygen debt,[6] panting, gasping. My breath was inefficient, and the oxygen debt was compounding. In an attempt to create heat, I was spinning my arms wildly, faster than I'd ever turned them over before. Laura later told me that I was swimming at a rate of ninety strokes per minute, thirty strokes per minute quicker than my normal rate. My body was demanding more oxygen, but I couldn't slow down. Not for a nanosecond. Or I would freeze up and the swim would be over.

An icy wave slapped my face: I choked and felt a wave of panic rise within me. My throat tightened. I tried to clear my throat and breathe. My breath didn't come out. I couldn't get enough air in to clear my throat. I glanced at the crew. They couldn't tell I was in trouble. If I stopped, Dan would jump in and pull me out. I still couldn't get a good breath. I thought of rolling on my back to give myself time to breathe, but I couldn't. It was too cold. I closed my mouth, overrode everything my body was telling me to do, held my breath, and gasped, coughed, cleared my windpipe,

---

5. **hyperventilating** v. breathing rapidly or deeply enough to cause dizziness or fainting.
6. **oxygen debt** n. an increased need for oxygen in the body brought on by intensive activity.

TAKE NOTES

Reading Skill

Do the details in the bracketed passage support your **prediction** about the outcome of Cox's swim or lead you to **revise** it? Explain.

_____

_____

_____

Literary Analysis

From the **author's perspective**, what is the biggest obstacle in the way of reaching her goal?

_____

_____

Reading Check

Underline Cox's description of how the cold affects her body. To what does she compare the feeling?

_____

Stop to Reflect

Why do you think Cox wants to do something which is causing her so much physical pain?

_____

_____

_____

Name one way in which the details in the underlined passage might be different if presented by a crew member on the boat.

_____

_____

What does Cox's **perspective** add to this account of her Antarctic swim?

_____

_____

_____

_____

Cox is finally able to gain control of her breathing. Explain how this information could lead you to **revise** your **prediction** about the outcome of the swim.

_____

_____

_____

What does Cox think about to avoid thinking about how cold she is? Circle the answer.

and relaxed just a little, just enough to let my guard down and catch another wave in the face. I choked again. I put my face down into the water, hoping this time I could slow my heart rate down. I held my face in the water for two strokes and told myself, *Relax, just turn your head and breathe.*

It was easier to breathe in a more horizontal position. I thought it might be helping. I drew in a deep breath and put my face down again. I knew I couldn't do this for long. I was losing too much heat through my face. The intensity of the cold was as sharp as broken glass. I'd thought that swimming across the Bering Strait[7] in thirty-eight-degree water had been tough, but there was a world of difference between thirty-eight degrees and thirty-two. In a few seconds, the cold pierced my skin and penetrated into my muscles. It felt like freezer burn, like touching wet fingers to frozen metal.

Finally I was able to gain control of my breath. I was inhaling and exhaling so deeply I could hear the breath moving in and out of my mouth even though I was wearing earplugs. I kept thinking about breathing, working on keeping it deep and even; that way I didn't have time to think about the cold.

My brain wasn't working as it normally did. It wasn't flowing freely from one idea to another—it was moving mechanically, as if my awareness came from somewhere deep inside my brain. Maybe it was because my body was being assaulted with so many sensations, too different and too complex to recognize. Or maybe it was because my blood and oxygen were going out to the working muscles. I didn't know.

For the next five or six minutes, I continued swimming, telling myself that I was doing well, telling myself that this was what I had trained for. Then something clicked, as if my body had gained equilibrium. It had fully closed down the blood flow in my skin and fingers and toes. My arms and legs were as cold as the water, but I could feel the heat radiating deep within my torso and head, and this gave me confidence. I knew that my body was protecting my brain and vital organs. Staring through the clear, silver-blue water, I examined my fingers; they were red and swollen. They were different than when I'd been swimming in the Bering Strait, when they'd looked like the fingers of a dead person. They looked healthy, and

---

Vocabulary Development equilibrium (ee kwuh LIB ree uhm) *n.* a state of balance

---

7. **Bering Strait** (BER ing strayt) the body of water between Russia and Alaska, joining the Pacific and Arctic oceans.

I thought their swollenness would give me more surface area, more to pull with.

I smiled and looked up at the crew, who were in the Zodiacs on either side of me. Each of them was leaning forward, willing me ahead. Their faces were filled with tension. Gabriella, Barry, Dan, and Scott were leaning so far over the Zodiac's pontoon I felt as if they were swimming right beside me. I was sprinting faster than I ever had before, moving faster than the Zodiac, and I was getting fatigued quickly. The water was thicker than on the test swim, and it took more force to pull through on each stroke. My arms ached. I didn't feel right; I couldn't seem to get into any kind of a rhythm. Then I sensed that something was wrong.

We were heading to the left, toward some glaciers. This didn't make sense; we couldn't land there. It was too dangerous. The glaciers could calve[8] and kill us.

"Barry, where are we going?" I shouted, using air I needed for breathing.

He pointed out our direction—right toward the glaciers. I didn't understand. I didn't want to go that way. I wanted to aim for the beach. I was confused. I was moving my arms as fast as they would go, and it was taking all I had. From each moment to the next, I had to tell myself to keep going. The water felt so much colder than on the test swim. It had already worked its way deep into my muscles. My arms and legs were stiff. My strokes were short and choppy. But I kept going, telling myself to trust the crew and focus on the glaciers to watch the outcropping of rocks that was growing larger. I couldn't get into any kind of pace.

Abruptly the Zodiacs zagged to the right. I looked up and thought, *Wow, okay; we're heading for the beach now.* For a moment, I started to feel better. I was able to extend my reach farther, and I could see passengers from the *Orlova* walking along the snowbanks. In the distance, their clothes lost their color and they looked black, like giant penguins. I saw smaller black figures, too—real penguins nesting near the edge of the shore. For a few moments, I felt like I was going to be okay, like I was going to make it in to shore, but then the Zodiacs abruptly turned farther to the right, and we were headed past the beach for another range of glaciers.

Finally, it occurred to me that the *Orlova* had anchored too close to shore for me to swim a mile, so Barry was adding distance by altering the course. And the ship's captain was on the bridge monitoring our course on his GPS[9] and radioing our Zodiacs, updating them on the

---

8. **calve** (kav) *v.* to give birth to young; used here to refer to the "birth" of a new ice mass when a piece of a glacier splits off.
9. **GPS** "Global Positioning System," referring here to a portable device that provides information about the bearer's location and speed.

TAKE NOTES

Literary Analysis

The Zodiacs guide Cox through the water. In what way does the crew's perspective differ from the **author's perspective** about the direction they are going?

_____

_____

_____

Stop to Reflect

What does the first bracketed passage reveal about Cox?

_____

_____

_____

Reading Skill

Do the details in the second bracketed paragraph support or lead you to **revise** your **prediction** about whether Cox will succeed? Explain.

_____

_____

_____

Reading Check

Circle two effects of the cold water on Cox.

Literary Analysis

What do you learn from the **author's perspective** that you could not learn from the crew's perspective?

_____

_____

_____

_____

Reading Skill

Underline the **prediction** that Cox makes about the effect of the current on her swim.

Reading Check

How far has Cox swum so far? How long has it taken her? Circle the answers.

distance we had traveled. One of the passengers, Mrs. Stokie, who was on the bridge with him, told me later, "The captain was watching you and he was shaking his head. He was an older man, and he had experienced everything. And now he was seeing something new. It was good for him. Still, I think he couldn't believe it."

We continued on right past the beach, toward more glaciers.

"How long have I been swimming?" I asked.

"Fifteen minutes," Barry said.

I had swum a little more than half a mile. I looked up at the shore. If I turned left, I could make it in. I could reach the shore. This struggle could be over. But I wouldn't complete the mile. I had swum farther two days before. But I was tired now, and this was so much harder. I just didn't feel right. I couldn't figure out what the problem was. I kept talking to myself, coaching myself to keep going. Then I felt it; it was the water pressure, and it was increasing on my back. It meant there was a strong current behind me. I looked at the glaciers onshore, using the fixed points to gauge how fast the current was flowing. It was flowing at over a knot. I wondered if I would have enough strength to fight it when we turned around and headed back for the beach. It would cut my speed by half and could cause me to lose heat more rapidly.

Barry and the crew in the Zodiacs couldn't feel what was happening. They had no idea we were moving into a risky area. If the current grew any stronger, it could cost us the swim. Barry motioned for me to swim past a peninsula and across a narrow channel. I lifted my head and pulled my hands directly under my chest, to gain more lift, so I could look across the bay and see if we had any other options for landing. There were no alternatives. This made me very uncomfortable. Chances were good that there would be a strong current flowing into or out of the narrow bay. And if we got caught in that current, all would be lost.

We started across the inlet, and within a moment I could feel that second current, slamming into our right side at two knots, pushing us into the inlet. Without any explanation, I spun around, put my head down, dug my arms into the water, and crabbed[10] into the current. I focused on repositioning myself so I could parallel shore again and head toward Neko Harbor. Barry knew I knew what I was doing. But the abrupt course change caught the Zodiac drivers by surprise. They scattered in different directions, trying to avoid ramming into each other and trying to catch up with me. The motor on the lead Zodiac on my left sputtered and stopped. The second Zodiac

---

10. **crabbed** v. moved sideways or diagonally.

immediately pulled up beside me. I sprinted against the current.

"How long have I been swimming?"

"Twenty-one minutes," Barry said. He and all the crew were watching me intently, their faces filled with tension and concern.

I put my head down, and something suddenly clicked. Maybe it was because I knew shore was within reach, or maybe because I got a second wind; I don't know. But I was finally swimming strongly, stretching out and moving fluidly. My arms and legs were as cold as the sea, but I felt the heat within my head and contained in my torso and I thrilled to it, knowing my body had carried me to places no one else had been in only a bathing suit. I looked down into the water; it was a bright blue-gray and so clear that it appeared as if I were swimming through air. The viscosity of the water was different, too; it was thicker than any I had ever swum in. It felt like I was swimming through gelato. And I got more push out of each arm stroke than I ever had before. I looked at the crew. They were leaning so far over the pontoons, as if they were right there with me. I needed to let them know I was okay.

I lifted my head, took a big breath, and shouted, "Barry, I'm swimming to Antarctica!"

I saw the smiles, heard the cheers and laughs, and I felt their energy lift me. They were as thrilled as I was. I swam faster, extending my arms, pulling more strongly, reaching for the shores of Antarctica. Now I knew we were almost there.

The crew was shouting warnings about ice. I swerved around two icebergs. Some chunks looked sharp, but I was too tired to care. I swam into whatever was in my path. It hurt, but all I wanted now was to finish.

As we neared shore, I lifted my head and saw the other passengers from the *Orlova*, in their bright red and yellow hats and parkas, tromping down the snowbanks, spreading their feet and arms wide for balance, racing to the water's edge to meet us. I lifted my foot and waved and saw my crew break into bigger smiles.

I'm almost done, I thought. I feel okay. I feel strong. I feel *warm inside. My arms and legs are thirty-two degrees. But* *I feel good. I can stretch out my strokes and put my face in* *the water. Maybe I can go a little farther. Maybe I can see* what more I can do. Maybe I can swim five or ten more minutes. Or maybe I should be happy with what I've done. My skin is so cold I can't feel it, and when I stop swimming, I don't know how far my temperature's going to drop. I looked at my watch. Twenty-three minutes. I'd been in a minute longer than two days before. *How much difference* *would a minute make?* I asked myself. *How much*

Literary Analysis

How does the **author's perspective** on her swim change as she nears the shore?

_____

_____

_____

Reading Skill

What effect does the underlined passage have on your first **prediction**?

_____

_____

_____

_____

Reading Check

How is this water different from other water Cox has swum in? Circle the answer.

Underline the prediction
Dr. Keatinge
made.

difference is there between thirty-two-degree and thirty-three-degree water? Remember what Dr. Keatinge[11] said: once your temperature starts to drop, it will drop very fast. If you continue swimming, you're going to cool down even more. Remember how hard you shivered last time? Remember how much work it was? Remember how uncomfortable you were? This is the place where people make mistakes, when they're tired and cold and they push too far into the unknown. You could really hurt yourself. Finish now. You've done a good job. Be satisfied with what you've done. Go celebrate with your friends.

Turning in toward shore, I again lifted my foot and waved it, and my friends waved back and cheered. One hundred yards from shore, I saw chinstrap penguins sliding headfirst, like tiny black toboggans, down a steep snowbank. When they reached the base of the hill, they used their bristly tails like brakes, sticking them into the snow to stop their momentum. They waddled across the beach at full tilt, holding their wings out at their sides for balance. Reaching the water, they dove in headfirst, then porpoised across it, clearing it by one or two feet with each surface dive. They tucked their wings back by their sides so they would be more aerodynamic. When they neared the Zodiacs, they dove and flapped their wings under the water as if they were flying through air. It was amazing to think this was the only place they would fly. They zoomed under me in bursts of speed, and their bubbles exploded like white fireworks. More penguins joined in. One cannonballed off a ledge, another slipped on some ice and belly flopped, and three penguins swam within inches of my hands. I reached out to touch one, but he swerved and flapped his wings, so he moved just beyond my fingertips. I had no idea why they were swimming with me, but I knew it was a good sign; it meant there were no killer whales or leopard seals in the area.

When I reached knee-deep water, Dan jumped in, ran through the water, looped his arm through mine, and helped me stand. "Are you okay?" he asked.

"Yes. We made it!" I said.

Everyone around me was crying. Susan Adie helped Dan pull me up the incline. Martha wrapped a towel around my shoulders. Barry hugged me tightly. Laura and Susan began drying me off. I was so cold I was already starting to shiver hard. My legs were stiffer than after the other swim. The crew helped me into the Zodiac and I flopped onto the floor. Laura and Susan piled on top of me to protect me from the wind, and we pounded across the water, my head slamming into the Zodiac's floor. I managed to lift my head so that someone could place a

Rewrite the underlined sentence
from Dan's **perspective**.

_____

_____

_____

Three penguins swim with
Cox. Why is this a good
sign? Underline
the answer.

---

11. **Dr. Keatinge** Cox's doctor on her swim across the Bering Strait.

hand under it to buffer the impact. I was so cold and stiff and shaking harder than before.

When we reached the *Orlova*, it took me a minute to stand, to gain my balance, and as I climbed the ramp's steps I clung to the railing and pulled myself up, shaking hard. By the time I reached the top of the ramp, my teeth were chattering and I was breathing harder and faster than when I had been swimming. I didn't like being so cold. I didn't like my body having to work so hard. My temperature had dropped to 95.5 degrees, and I couldn't control my shaking. I just let go, and my body bounced up and down with shakes and shivers.

Quickly Martha and Dan and the three doctors huddled around me like emperor penguins, and their combined comfort and body heat began to warm me. It seemed as if I would never stop shaking, and I was completely exhausted. Within half an hour my shivering had subsided to small body shudders. Once I was able to stand and maintain my balance, the doctors helped me pull on a special top and pants that had been designed by a friend. She had sewn pockets under the arms, in the groin area, and into a scarf and had placed chemical packs that emitted heat inside the pockets. Their placement in the clothing warmed the major blood-flow areas of my body so that I was heated from the inside out. It was effective, and within an hour my temperature was back to normal.

That night we celebrated with everyone aboard the *Orlova*. I had swum the first Antarctic mile—a distance of 1.06 miles, in fact—in thirty-two-degree water in twenty-five minutes. I had been able to do what had seemed impossible because I'd had a crew who believed in me and in what we as human beings were capable of. It was a great dream, swimming to Antarctica.

Vocabulary Development   buffer (BUF er) *v.* lessen a shock; cushion

---

Reader's Response: Explain whether the physical or the emotional challenges seemed more difficult for Cox to overcome during her swim.

_____

_____

_____

_____

Reading Skill

Does the outcome **verify** your initial or **revised prediction**? Explain.

_____

_____

_____

Reading Check

How far did Cox swim? How long did it take her? Underline the answers.

Stop to Reflect

Do you think Cox made a good decision in swimming the Antarctic? Explain your answer.

_____

_____

_____

_____

Literary Analysis

From the **author's perspective**, what was the most helpful tool she had in attaining her goal?

_____

_____

_____

from Swimming to Antarctica

1. **Analyze:** At the start of her swim, Cox cannot control her breathing. What does Cox's ability to overcome this challenge reveal about her?

_____

2. **Evaluate:** Explain whether you think the swim was worth the effort.

_____

_____

3. **Literary Analysis:** Fill in this chart to analyze the **author's perspective** in this selection.

Author's Perspective	
Types of Details Included	**Examples of Each**
❏ researched facts	
❏ personal experiences	
❏ opinions	
❏ attitudes	

4. **Reading Skill:** Summarize and explain one **prediction** you made and revised as you read.

_____

_____

SUPPORT FOR WRITING AND EXTEND YOUR LEARNING

Writing: Description

Prepare to write a brief **description** of a scene in Antarctica. Answer the following questions to help write your description:

- What mood, or atmosphere, would you like to create? For instance, you could create a mood of awe, danger, beauty, or isolation.

_____

- Details help create the mood. For example, if you want to create a dangerous atmosphere, you should not describe playful penguins. Instead, you could describe the dangerous animals of the sea and the difficult landscape. What details would help create your mood?

_____

_____

- Precise words help make descriptions clear. For example, instead of writing "the penguins ran," you could write "the penguins wobbled." What precise words describe your details?

_____

_____

Listening and Speaking: Group Discussion

Plan a **group discussion** about Cox's extraordinary achievement. Summarize your thoughts and opinions about Cox's swim. Record details from the text that support your thoughts.

My Thoughts	Supporting Details

Use the chart to help you prepare for the group discussion.

Occupation: Conductorette from I Know Why the Caged Bird Sings

Maya Angelou

Summary As a teenager, the author decides to get a job. She wants to be a streetcar conductorette. The streetcar company does not employ African Americans, but Angelou is determined to get the job. In her battle to succeed, she learns about herself and about the society in which she lives.

Reading/Writing Connection

Complete this paragraph to describe how people reach their goals.

Some people <u>aspire</u> to _____. Even

though _____, these people <u>persist</u>. If they

_____, they will probably <u>attain</u> their goals.

Note-taking Guide

Fill in this character wheel with terms that describe Maya Angelou's character.

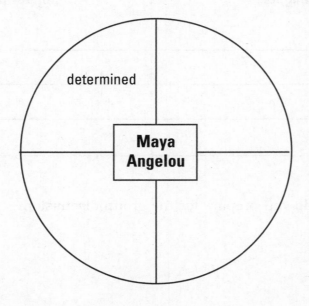

determined

Maya Angelou

Occupation: Conductorette
from I Know Why the Caged Bird Sings

1. **Interpret:** Why does Angelou insist on becoming a conductorette? List details to support your answer.

_____

_____

2. **Draw Conclusions:** In what ways does Angelou's mother contribute to her success?

_____

_____

3. **Literary Analysis:** Fill in the chart below to analyze the **author's perspective** in this selection.

Author's Perspective	
Types of Details Included	**Examples of Each**
❑ researched facts	
❑ personal experiences	
❑ opinions	
❑ attitudes	

4. **Reading Skill:** Summarize and explain one **prediction** you made and revised as you read.

_____

_____

SUPPORT FOR WRITING AND EXTEND YOUR LEARNING

Writing: Description

Write a **description** of a streetcar ride in the 1940s. Use your own experiences with public transportation to imagine what it may have been like to ride on a streetcar in the 1940s.

- In the word web below. record the sensory details you have experienced on a bus or train.

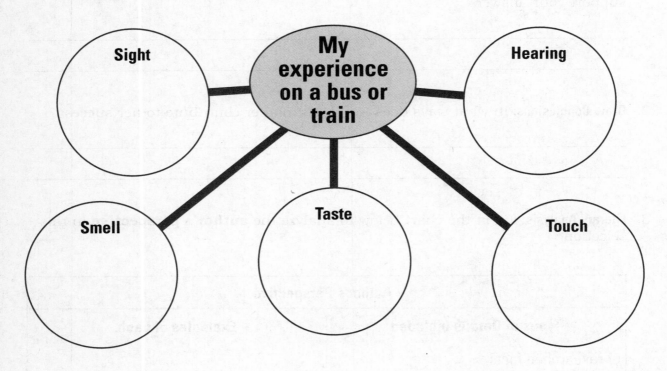

Listening and Speaking: Group Discussion

Prepare for a **group discussion** about Angelou's experiences. Answer the following questions:

- What does Angelou try to do?

_____

- What does she experience while trying to reach her goal?

_____

- Does she meet the goal? Explain why or why not.

_____

- Do the results match her hopes? Explain your answer.

_____

Job Applications

ABOUT JOB APPLICATIONS

A **job application** is a form that gathers information about a person who is looking for a job. This information helps the employer make predictions about the person. It tells the employer whether the person is likely to be good at the job. Most job applications ask for the following kinds of information:

- Name and address
- Social Security number
- Schools attended
- Work experience
- Useful skills
- References

READING SKILL

Predict which information you will be asked to give on an application. **Use prior knowledge** to decide what might appear on the job application. What have you seen on other applications? What did the job posting or ad say? What do you know about the type of job and its needs?

Predicting will help you prepare. Use a checklist like the one below:

Items for Completing a Job Application
❑ Driver's license and Social Security card (or another form of identification)
❑ Names, addresses, dates, and contact information for schools attended, previous employers, volunteer work, and references
❑ List of special skills, such as knowledge of foreign languages, typing ability, and knowledge of computer programs

DURHAM

1869

Summer Employment
City of Durham, NC

Mayor's Youth Works Summer Program
Are you between the ages of 14 and 21?
Yes____ No____

Please Print or Type - Use Blue or Black Ink

Check One (1) I am applying for:

☐ Impact Team   ☐ Parks & Recreation   ☐ Private Sector   ☐ OEED

Name _____
              (Last)   (First)   (MI)

Address _____
            (Street)   (City/State)   (Zip Code)

Driver's License # _____ Class _____

Telephone # _____ (Work) _____

Are you related by blood or marriage to any person now employed by the City? __No __Yes

If yes, give name/relationship/and work location of relatives(s) _____

EDUCATION

School Name and Location	From/to Attended	Completed # of Years	Diploma or Degree	Year Received
Middle School				
High School				
College/Other				

EMPLOYMENT HISTORY

May we contact your present or last employer regarding your experience and qualifications?
__Yes __No

Work History: List below all employment for the last 5 years; use an additional sheet if needed.

Job Title: _____ Dates Employed _____

Reason for Leaving: _____

Employer's Name _____ Address _____

Supervisor's Name _____ Describe Work Duties/Responsibilities _____

_____

_____

(Cont'd)

SKILLS INVENTORY

Check all certificates, skills, or experience which you possess and indicate the length of experience.

General

___ Record keeping _____
___ Working with Senior Citizens _____
___ Working with young children (5–12)_____
___ Working with adolescents (13–19)_____

Pool Positions

___ AED Certification _____
___ CPR Certification _____
___ Water Safety Instructor_____
___ Pool Supervision_____
___ Pool Maintenance_____
___ ARC-01 Lifeguard Certification _____
    (NM or Lifesaving Instructor)

Athletics

___ Volleyball_____
___ Soccer_____
___ Softball_____
___ Racquetball_____
___ Baseball_____
___ Basketball_____
___ Tennis_____
___ Other_____

Special Populations
(Working with Disabled Persons)

___ Physically Disabled _____
___ Hearing Impaired_____
___ Visually Impaired_____
___ Multi-Disabled _____
___ Developmentally Disabled_____
___ Adapted Aquatics Certificates_____

Programs/Day Camps
(Planned Activities as Group Leader or Instructor)

___ Sports_____
___ Gymnastics _____
___ Arts and Crafts _____
___ Drama_____
___ Music_____
___ Baton_____
___ Pre-Schoolers _____
___ Supervision_____

VOLUNTEER EXPERIENCE

Organization/Volunteer Site	Year Volunteered	# of Hours	Duties/Responsibilities

ADDITIONAL INFORMATION - List any additional skills or knowledge you possess which relate to this position

_____

CERTIFICATION AND RELEASE (PLEASE READ CAREFULLY BEFORE SIGNING BELOW)

I hereby certify that all statements on this application and applicant flow sheet are true and complete to the best of my knowledge and belief. I understand that falsification (including omission) regarding this record may be considered cause for immediate termination of employment or disqualification from the application process, if discovered before employment. I authorize the City to use the information provided and to review my background including but not limited to reference checks, education, driving record verification, and credit history. This information may also be used for internal data and record keeping. I authorize persons, schools, and current and previous employers to provide the City with any relevant information needed to consider me for employment.

_____
                         Signature/Date

THINKING ABOUT THE JOB APPLICATION

1. What are two jobs that you could apply for with this application? Give details to support your choices.

   _____

   _____

2. Why do you think the employer asks for volunteer experience, as well as work experience?

   _____

READING SKILL

3. Why would you NOT need to bring a credit card to fill out this application?

   _____

4. What is a volunteer experience that is appropriate to put on this application? Explain why it is appropriate.

   _____

   _____

TIMED WRITING: PERSUASION (20 minutes)

Write a letter recommending yourself to the person hiring for the City of Durham. Write notes about yourself on the lines below.

- Education _____

- Employment History _____

- Skills Inventory _____

- Volunteer Experience _____

- Additional Information _____

Contents of the Dead Man's Pocket •
Games at Twilight

LITERARY ANALYSIS

The **conflict** in a short story is a struggle between two forces.

- In an **external conflict**, a character struggles against an outside force, such as an element of nature or another character.
- In an **internal conflict**, a character struggles with his or her own opposing desires, beliefs, or needs.
- In many stories, the conflict intensifies until one force wins and a **resolution** of the conflict occurs.

To build interest in a conflict, writers may hint at events to come or "stretch out" episodes that lead up to a crucial moment. In these ways, they create **suspense**, a rising curiosity or anxiety in readers. As you read, use a chart like this one to record conflicts.

READING SKILL

A **cause** is an event, an action, or a situation that produces a result. An **effect** is the result produced. To better follow a story, **analyze causes and effects** as you read. Determine which earlier events lead to which later events. Many stories are chains of cause and effect. One event leads to the next.

To analyze causes and effects, **reflect on key details** that the writer spends time explaining or describing. For example, a writer's description of a dangerous coastline prepares you to understand the cause-and-effect relationships leading to the sinking of a ship.

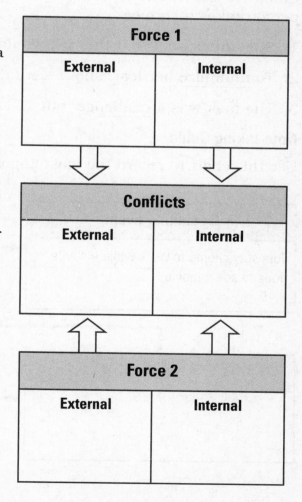

Contents of the Dead Man's Pocket

Jack Finney

Summary Tom Benecke thinks getting ahead at work is the most important thing in his life. While trying to retrieve a piece of paper for work, he finds himself in a life-threatening situation. This situation forces him to reexamine his life and to reconsider what is truly most important.

Reading/Writing Connection

Complete the following sentences to describe what happens when a person takes a chance.

1. She <u>anticipated</u> that the risk would lead to _____.

2. To <u>minimize</u> her fear, she _____.

3. The task was a <u>challenge</u>, but _____.

Note-taking Guide

Use this chart to record the most important events in the story.

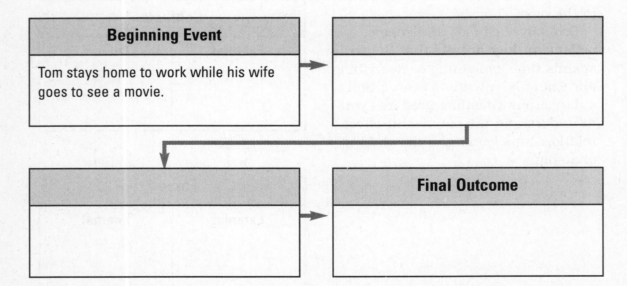

Beginning Event	
Tom stays home to work while his wife goes to see a movie.	

	Final Outcome

Contents of the Dead Man's Pocket
Jack Finney

At the little living-room desk Tom Benecke rolled two sheets of flimsy[1] and a heavier top sheet, carbon paper sandwiched between them, into his portable. Interoffice Memo, the top sheet was headed, and he typed tomorrow's date just below this; then he glanced at a creased yellow sheet, covered with his own handwriting, beside the typewriter. "Hot in here," he muttered to himself. Then, from the short hallway at his back, he heard the muffled clang of wire coat hangers in the bedroom closet, and at this reminder of what his wife was doing he thought: Hot, no—guilty conscience.

He got up, shoving his hands into the back pockets of his gray wash slacks, stepped to the living-room window beside the desk and stood breathing on the glass, watching the expanding circle of mist, staring down through the autumn night at Lexington Avenue, eleven stories below. He was a tall, lean, dark-haired young man in a pullover sweater, who looked as though he had played not football, probably, but basketball in college. Now he placed the heels of his hands against the top edge of the lower window frame and shoved upward. But as usual the window didn't budge, and he had to lower his hands and then shoot them hard upward to jolt the window open a few inches. He dusted his hands, muttering.

But still he didn't begin his work. He crossed the room to the hallway entrance and, leaning against the doorjamb, hands shoved into his back pockets again, he called, "Clare?" When his wife answered, he said, "Sure you don't mind going alone?"

"No." Her voice was muffled, and he knew her head and shoulders were in the bedroom closet. Then the tap of her high heels sounded on the wood floor and she appeared at the end of the little hallway, wearing a slip, both hands raised to one ear, clipping on an earring. She smiled at him—a slender, very pretty girl with light brown, almost blonde, hair—her prettiness emphasized by the pleasant nature that showed in her face. "It's just that I hate you to miss this movie; you wanted to see it too."

"Yeah, I know." He ran his fingers through his hair. "Got to get this done though."

She nodded, accepting this. Then, glancing at the desk across the living room, she said, "You work too much, though, Tom—and too hard."

---

1. **flimsy** (FLIM zee) *n.* thin typing paper for making carbon copies. Carbon copies are created by placing carbon paper, a sheet coated with an inklike substance, between two pieces of typing paper.

TAKE NOTES

Activate Prior Knowledge

Describe a time when you took a chance and tried something new. Did you regret it, or were you glad you tried? List three things you tried, and describe each outcome.

_____

_____

_____

Reading Skill

A **cause** is an event, an action, or a situation that makes something else happen. What happens is called the **effect**. Read the first bracketed passage. Underline the **cause** of Tom's attempt to open the window.

Literary Analysis

The **conflict** in a story is a struggle between two forces. Conflict is crucial to the development of a story. Often, a writer will hint at an outcome or prolong a moment to add **suspense** to the story. Read the second bracketed paragraph. What hints do you see about future events in the story?

_____

_____

_____

Reading Check

Where is Clare going? Underline the sentence that tells you.

TAKE NOTES

Literary Analysis

In an **internal conflict**, a character struggles with his or her opposing desires, beliefs, or needs. Read the first bracketed paragraph. What is Tom's internal conflict?

_____

_____

_____

_____

Reading Skill

Read the second bracketed passage. What is the **effect** of Tom's closing the door after Clare leaves?

_____

_____

_____

_____

_____

Reading Check

Why does Tom think Clare will not mind that he works so much? Underline the sentence that tells you.

He smiled. "You won't mind though, will you, when the money comes rolling in and I'm known as the Boy Wizard of Wholesale Groceries?"

"I guess not." She smiled and turned back toward the bedroom.

At his desk again, Tom lighted a cigarette, then a few moments later as Clare appeared, dressed and ready to leave, he set it on the rim of the ash tray. "Just after seven," she said. "I can make the beginning of the first feature."

He walked to the front-door closet to help her on with her coat. He kissed her then and, for an instant, holding her close, smelling the perfume she had used, he was tempted to go with her; it was not actually true that he had to work tonight, though he very much wanted to. This was his own project, unannounced as yet in his office, and it could be postponed. But then they won't see it till Monday, he thought once again, and if I give it to the boss tomorrow he might read it over the weekend . . . "Have a good time," he said aloud. He gave his wife a little swat and opened the door for her, feeling the air from the building hallway, smelling faintly of floor wax, stream gently past his face.

He watched her walk down the hall, flicked a hand in response as she waved, and then he started to close the door, but it resisted for a moment. As the door opening narrowed, the current of warm air from the hallway, channeled through this smaller opening now, suddenly rushed past him with accelerated force. Behind him he heard the slap of the window curtains against the wall and the sound of paper fluttering from his desk, and he had to push to close the door.

Turning, he saw a sheet of white paper drifting to the floor in a series of arcs, and another sheet, yellow, moving toward the window, caught in the dying current flowing through the narrow opening. As he watched, the paper struck the bottom edge of the window and hung there for an instant, plastered against the glass and wood. Then as the moving air stilled completely, the curtains swinging back from the wall to hang free again, he saw the yellow sheet drop to the window ledge and slide over out of sight.

He ran across the room, grasped the bottom edge of the window and tugged, staring through the glass. He saw the yellow sheet, dimly now in the darkness outside, lying on the ornamental ledge a yard below the window. Even as he watched, it was moving, scraping slowly along the ledge, pushed by the breeze that pressed steadily against the building wall. He heaved on the window with all his strength and it shot open with a bang, the window weight rattling in the casing. But the paper was past his reach and, leaning out into the night, he watched it scud steadily along the ledge to the south, half plastered against the building wall. Above the muffled sound of the street traffic far below, he could hear the dry scrape of its movement, like a leaf on the pavement.

The living room of the next apartment to the south projected a yard or more farther out toward the street than this one; because of this the Beneckes paid seven and a half dollars less rent than their neighbors. And now the yellow sheet, sliding along the stone ledge, nearly invisible in the night, was stopped by the projecting blank wall of the next apartment. It lay motionless, then, in the corner formed by the two walls—a good five yards away, pressed firmly against the ornate corner ornament of the ledge, by the breeze that moved past Tom Benecke's face.

He knelt at the window and stared at the yellow paper for a full minute or more, waiting for it to move, to slide off the ledge and fall, hoping he could follow its course to the street, and then hurry down in the elevator and retrieve it. But it didn't move, and then he saw that the paper was caught firmly between a projection of the convoluted corner ornament and the ledge. He thought about the poker from the fireplace, then the broom, then the mop—discarding each thought as it occurred to him. There was nothing in the apartment long enough to reach that paper.

It was hard for him to understand that he actually had to abandon it—it was ridiculous—and he began to curse. Of all the papers on his desk, why did it have to be this one in particular! On four long Saturday afternoons he had stood in supermarkets counting the people who passed certain displays, and the results were scribbled on that yellow sheet. From stacks of trade publications, gone over page by page in snatched half hours at work and during evenings at home, he had copied facts, quotations, and figures onto that sheet. And he had carried it with him to the Public Library on Fifth Avenue, where he'd spent a dozen lunch hours and early evenings adding more. All were needed to support and lend authority to his idea for a new grocery-store display method; without them his idea was a mere opinion. And there they all lay, in his own improvised shorthand—countless hours of work—out there on the ledge.

For many seconds he believed he was going to abandon the yellow sheet, that there was nothing else to do. The work could be duplicated. But it would take two months, and the time to present this idea . . . was *now*, for use in the spring displays. He struck his fist on the window ledge. Then he shrugged. Even if his plan were adopted, he told himself, it wouldn't bring him a raise in pay—not

---

Vocabulary Development convoluted (KAHN vuh loot id) *adj.*
intricate; twisted

Contents of the Dead Man's Pocket **63**

TAKE NOTES

Reading Skill

What **causes** the yellow paper to stop sliding along the stone ledge? Underline the sentence that tells you.

Literary Analysis

In an **external conflict**, a character struggles against an outside force, such as an element of nature. Read the bracketed passage. Explain how external conflict helps create **suspense** in the passage.

_____

_____

_____

_____

_____

Stop to Reflect

What do you think is going through Tom's mind as he looks out the window and sees his paper?

_____

_____

_____

_____

Reading Check

How far away is the paper from Tom? Underline the sentence that tells you.

How is Tom's **conflict** now different from the conflict at the beginning of the story?

_____

_____

_____

Read the bracketed paragraph. What **effect** does Tom hope the story of his adventure will have on listeners?

_____

_____

_____

_____

_____

How do you think Tom feels about going out on the ledge?

_____

_____

_____

_____

_____

What details about the ledge make Tom think he will be able to retrieve his paper? Underline the text that tells you.

immediately, anyway, or as a direct result. It won't bring me a promotion either, he argued—not of itself.

But just the same, and he couldn't escape the thought, this and other independent projects, some already done and others planned for the future, would gradually mark him out from the score of other young men in his company. They were the way to change from a name on the payroll to a name in the minds of the company officials. They were the beginning of the long, long climb to where he was determined to be, at the very top. And he knew he was going out there in the darkness, after the yellow sheet fifteen feet beyond his reach.

By a kind of instinct, he instantly began making his intention acceptable to himself by laughing at it. The mental picture of himself sidling along the ledge outside was absurd—it was actually comical—and he smiled. He imagined himself describing it; it would make a good story at the office and, it occurred to him, would add a special interest and importance to his memorandum, which would do it no harm at all.

To simply go out and get his paper was an easy task—he could be back here with it in less than two minutes—and he knew he wasn't deceiving himself. The ledge, he saw, measuring it with his eye, was about as wide as the length of his shoe, and perfectly flat. And every fifth row of brick in the face of the building, he remembered—leaning out, he verified this—was indented half an inch, enough for the tips of his fingers, enough to maintain balance easily. It occurred to him that if this ledge and wall were only a yard aboveground—as he knelt at the window staring out, this thought was the final confirmation of his intention—he could move along the ledge indefinitely.

On a sudden impulse, he got to his feet, walked to the front closet and took out an old tweed jacket; it would be cold outside. He put it on and buttoned it as he crossed the room rapidly toward the open window. In the back of his mind he knew he'd better hurry and get this over with before he thought too much, and at the window he didn't allow himself to hesitate.

He swung a leg over the sill, then felt for and found the ledge a yard below the window with his foot. Gripping the bottom of the window frame very tightly and carefully, he slowly ducked his head under it, feeling on his face the sudden change from the warm air of the room to the chill outside. With infinite care he brought out his other leg, his mind concentrating on what he was doing. Then he slowly stood erect. Most of the putty, dried out and brittle, had dropped off the bottom edging of the window frame, he found, and the flat wooden edging provided a good gripping surface, a half inch or more deep, for the tips of his fingers.

Now, balanced easily and firmly, he stood on the ledge outside in the slight, chill breeze, eleven stories above the street, staring into his own lighted apartment, odd and different-seeming now.

First his right hand, then his left, he carefully shifted his fingertip grip from the puttyless window edging to an indented row of bricks directly to his right. It was hard to take the first shuffling sideways step then—to make himself move—and the fear stirred in his stomach, but he did it, again by not allowing himself time to think. And now—with his chest, stomach, and the left side of his face pressed against the rough cold brick—his lighted apartment was suddenly gone, and it was much darker out here than he had thought.

Without pause he continued—right foot, left foot, right foot, left—his shoe soles shuffling and scraping along the rough stone, never lifting from it, fingers sliding along the exposed edging of brick. He moved on the balls of his feet, heels lifted slightly; the ledge was not quite as wide as he'd expected. But leaning slightly inward toward the face of the building and pressed against it, he could feel his balance firm and secure, and moving along the ledge was quite as easy as he had thought it would be. He could hear the buttons of his jacket scraping steadily along the rough bricks and feel them catch momentarily, tugging a little, at each mortared crack. He simply did not permit himself to look down, though the compulsion to do so never left him; nor did he allow himself actually to think. Mechanically—right foot, left foot, over and again—he shuffled along crabwise, watching the projecting wall ahead loom steadily closer . . .

Then he reached it, and, at the corner—he'd decided how he was going to pick up the paper—he lifted his right foot and placed it carefully on the ledge that ran along the projecting wall at a right angle to the ledge on which his other foot rested. And now, facing the building, he stood in the corner formed by the two walls, one foot on the ledging of each, a hand on the shoulder-high indentation of each wall. His forehead was pressed directly into the corner against the cold bricks, and now he carefully lowered first one hand, then the other, perhaps a foot farther down, to the next indentation in the rows of bricks.

Very slowly, sliding his forehead down the trough of the brick corner and bending his knees, he lowered his body toward the paper lying between his outstretched feet. Again he lowered his fingerholds another foot and bent his knees still more, thigh muscles taut, his forehead sliding and bumping down the brick V. Half squatting now, he dropped his left hand to the next indentation and then

TAKE NOTES

Literary Analysis

Describe one **internal conflict** and one **external conflict** Tom faces in this situation.

_____

_____

_____

_____

_____

Reading Skill

Describe how Tom's movement along the ledge away from his apartment window **causes** him to think differently about what he is doing. Underline details in the bracketed passage that support your answer.

_____

_____

_____

_____

_____

Stop to Reflect

After reading the bracketed passage, why do you think Tom will not let himself look down?

_____

_____

_____

_____

Read the bracketed passage. Explain the **external conflict** Tom struggles with in this passage.

_____

_____

_____

Do you think the paper Tom is trying to retrieve is worth the dangerous position in which he has put himself? Why or why not?

_____

_____

_____

Describe the **effect** of Tom's glimpse of the avenue below.

_____

_____

_____

How does Tom prevent himself from losing consciousness? Underline the sentence that tells you.

slowly reached with his right hand toward the paper between his feet.

He couldn't quite touch it, and his knees now were pressed against the wall; he could bend them no farther. But by ducking his head another inch lower, the top of his head now pressed against the bricks, he lowered his right shoulder and his fingers had the paper by a corner, pulling it loose. At the same instant he saw, between his legs and far below, Lexington Avenue stretched out for miles ahead.

He saw, in that instant, the Loew's theater sign, blocks ahead past Fiftieth Street; the miles of traffic signals, all green now; the lights of cars and street lamps; countless neon signs; and the moving black dots of people. And a violent instantaneous explosion of absolute terror roared through him. For a motionless instant he saw himself externally—bent practically double, balanced on this narrow ledge, nearly half his body projecting out above the street far below—and he began to tremble violently, panic flaring through his mind and muscles, and he felt the blood rush from the surface of his skin.

In the fractional moment before horror paralyzed him, as he stared between his legs at that terrible length of street far beneath him, a fragment of his mind raised his body in a spasmodic jerk to an upright position again, but so violently that his head scraped hard against the wall, bouncing off it, and his body swayed outward to the knife edge of balance, and he very nearly plunged backward and fell. Then he was leaning far into the corner again, squeezing and pushing into it, not only his face but his chest and stomach, his back arching; and his fingertips clung with all the pressure of his pulling arms to the shoulder-high half-inch indentation in the bricks.

He was more than trembling now; his whole body was racked with a violent shuddering beyond control, his eyes squeezed so tightly shut it was painful, though he was past awareness of that. His teeth were exposed in a frozen grimace, the strength draining like water from his knees and calves. It was extremely likely, he knew, that he would faint, to slump down along the wall, his face scraping, and then drop backward, a limp weight, out into nothing. And to save his life he concentrated on holding onto consciousness, drawing deliberate deep breaths of cold air into his lungs, fighting to keep his senses aware.

Then he knew that he would not faint, but he could neither stop shaking nor open his eyes. He stood where he was, breathing deeply, trying to hold back the terror of the glimpse he had had of what lay below him; and he knew he had made a mistake in not making himself stare down at the street, getting used to it and accepting it, when he had first stepped out onto the ledge.

It was impossible to walk back. He simply could not do it. He couldn't bring himself to make the slightest movement. The strength was gone from his legs; his shivering hands—numb, cold and desperately rigid—had lost all <u>deftness</u>; his easy ability to move and balance was gone. Within a step or two, if he tried to move, he knew that he would stumble clumsily and fall.

Seconds passed, with the chill faint wind pressing the side of his face, and he could hear the toned-down volume of the street traffic far beneath him. Again and again it slowed and then stopped, almost to silence; then presently, even this high, he would hear the click of the traffic signals and the subdued roar of the cars starting up again. During a lull in the street sounds, he called out. Then he was shouting *"Help!"* so loudly it rasped his throat. But he felt the steady pressure of the wind, moving between his face and the blank wall, snatch up his cries as he uttered them, and he knew they must sound directionless and distant. And he remembered how habitually, here in New York, he himself heard and ignored shouts in the night. If anyone heard him, there was no sign of it, and presently Tom Benecke knew he had to try moving; there was nothing else he could do.

Eyes squeezed shut, he watched scenes in his mind like scraps of motion-picture film—he could not stop them. He saw himself stumbling suddenly sideways as he crept along the ledge and saw his upper body arc outward, arms flailing. He saw a dangling shoestring caught between the ledge and the sole of his other shoe, saw a foot start to move, to be stopped with a jerk, and felt his balance leaving him. He saw himself falling with a terrible speed as his body revolved in the air, knees clutched tight to his chest, eyes squeezed shut, moaning softly.

Out of utter necessity, knowing that any of these thoughts might be reality in the very next seconds, he was slowly able to shut his mind against every thought but what he now began to do. With fear-soaked slowness, he slid his left foot an inch or two toward his own impossibly distant window. Then he slid the fingers of his shivering left hand a corresponding distance. For a moment he could not bring himself to lift his right foot from one ledge to the other; then he did it, and became aware of the harsh exhalation of air from his throat and realized that he was panting. As his right hand, then, began to slide along the brick edging, he was astonished to feel the yellow paper pressed to the bricks underneath his stiff fingers, and he uttered a terrible, abrupt bark that might have been

Vocabulary Development deftness (DEFT nis) *n.* skillfulness

© Pearson Education, Inc., publishing as Pearson Prentice Hall.

Contents of the Dead Man's Pocket **67**

TAKE NOTES

Reading Skill

Does Tom think his cries for help will **cause** his situation to change? Explain. Under-line the details that support your answer.

_____

_____

_____

Stop to Reflect

Why do you think the author spends so much time describing Tom's thoughts and feelings, rather than focusing entirely on the action?

_____

_____

_____

_____

Reading Skill

Read the bracketed passage. Explain what **causes** Tom to begin moving.

_____

_____

_____

_____

What **effect** does closing his eyes have on Tom?

_____

_____

_____

Read the bracketed passage. What does this **conflict** reveal about Tom's character?

_____

_____

_____

_____

What **causes** Tom to panic and nearly lose his balance on the ledge? Explain. Underline details in the bracketed passage that support your answer.

_____

_____

_____

_____

What method does Tom use to grasp the yellow paper without losing his grip on the ledge? Underline the text that tells you.

a laugh or a moan. He opened his mouth and took the paper in his teeth, pulling it out from under his fingers.

By a kind of trick—by concentrating his entire mind on first his left foot, then his left hand, then the other foot, then the other hand—he was able to move, almost imperceptibly, trembling steadily, very nearly without thought. But he could feel the terrible strength of the pent-up horror on just the other side of the flimsy barrier he had erected in his mind; and he knew that if it broke through he would lose this thin artificial control of his body.

During one slow step he tried keeping his eyes closed; it made him feel safer, shutting him off a little from the fearful reality of where he was. Then a sudden rush of giddiness swept over him and he had to open his eyes wide, staring sideways at the cold rough brick and angled lines of mortar, his cheek tight against the building. He kept his eyes open then, knowing that if he once let them flick outward, to stare for an instant at the lighted windows across the street, he would be past help.

He didn't know how many dozens of tiny sidling steps he had taken, his chest, belly, and face pressed to the wall; but he knew the slender hold he was keeping on his mind and body was going to break. He had a sudden mental picture of his apartment on just the other side of this wall—warm, cheerful, incredibly spacious. And he saw himself striding through it, lying down on the floor on his back, arms spread wide, reveling in its unbelievable security. The impossible remoteness of this utter safety, the contrast between it and where he now stood, was more than he could bear. And the barrier broke then, and the fear of the awful height he stood on coursed through his nerves and muscles.

A fraction of his mind knew he was going to fall, and he began taking rapid blind steps with no feeling of what he was doing, sidling with a clumsy desperate swiftness, fingers scrabbling along the brick, almost hopelessly resigned to the sudden backward pull and swift motion outward and down. Then his moving left hand slid onto not brick but sheer emptiness, an impossible gap in the face of the wall, and he stumbled.

His right foot smashed into his left anklebone; he staggered sideways, began falling, and the claw of his hand cracked against glass and wood, slid down it, and his fingertips were pressed hard on the puttyless edging

Vocabulary Development imperceptibly (im per SEP tuh blee) *adv.* so slowly or slightly as to be barely noticeable

of his window. His right hand smacked gropingly beside it as he fell to his knees; and, under the full weight and direct downward pull of his sagging body, the open window dropped shudderingly in its frame till it closed and his wrists struck the sill and were jarred off.

For a single moment he knelt, knee bones against stone on the very edge of the ledge, body swaying and touching nowhere else, fighting for balance. Then he lost it, his shoulders plunging backward, and he flung his arms forward, his hands smashing against the window casing on either side; and—his body moving backward—his fingers clutched the narrow wood stripping of the upper pane.

For an instant he hung suspended between balance and falling, his fingertips pressed onto the quarter-inch wood strips. Then, with utmost delicacy, with a focused concentration of all his senses, he increased even further the strain on his fingertips hooked to these slim edgings of wood. Elbows slowly bending, he began to draw the full weight of his upper body forward, knowing that the instant his fingers slipped off these quarter-inch strips he'd plunge backward and be falling. Elbows imperceptibly bending, body shaking with the strain, the sweat starting from his forehead in great sudden drops, he pulled, his entire being and thought concentrated in his fingertips. Then suddenly, the strain slackened and ended, his chest touching the window sill, and he was kneeling on the ledge, his forehead pressed to the glass of the closed window.

Dropping his palms to the sill, he stared into his living room—at the red-brown davenport[2] across the room, and a magazine he had left there; at the pictures on the walls and the gray rug; the entrance to the hallway; and at his papers, typewriter and desk, not two feet from his nose. A movement from his desk caught his eye and he saw that it was a thin curl of blue smoke; his cigarette, the ash long, was still burning in the ash tray where he'd left it—this was past all belief—only a few minutes before.

His head moved, and in faint reflection from the glass before him he saw the yellow paper clenched in his front teeth. Lifting a hand from the sill he took it from his mouth; the moistened corner parted from the paper, and he spat it out.

For a moment, in the light from the living room, he stared wonderingly at the yellow sheet in his hand and then crushed it into the side pocket of his jacket.

He couldn't open the window. It had been pulled not completely closed, but its lower edge was below the level of the outside sill; there was no room to get his fingers underneath it. Between the upper sash and the lower was a gap not wide enough—reaching up, he tried—to get his

---

2. **davenport** (DAV uhn pawrt) *n.* large couch.

TAKE NOTES

Literary Analysis

Read the first bracketed passage. Why does this lengthy description at a moment of excitement add to the **suspense**?

_____

_____

_____

_____

Reading Skill

Read the second bracketed passage. What **causes** Tom to move so slowly on the ledge?

_____

_____

_____

_____

Reading Check

What happens when Tom reaches the window? Underline the text that tells you.

Reading Skill

What is the **effect** of Tom's seeing his reflection in the window's glass?

_____

_____

_____

_____

What **key detail** from the beginning of the story helps you understand the **cause** of Tom's situation?

_____

_____

_____

_____

Read the bracketed passage. What **external conflict** does Tom face? How does Tom try to **resolve** the conflict?

_____

_____

_____

_____

_____

_____

What new **internal conflict** does Tom experience?

_____

_____

_____

_____

fingers into; he couldn't push it open. The upper window panel, he knew from long experience, was impossible to move, frozen tight with dried paint.

Very carefully observing his balance, the fingertips of his left hand again hooked to the narrow stripping of the window casing, he drew back his right hand, palm facing the glass, and then struck the glass with the heel of his hand.

His arm rebounded from the pane, his body tottering, and he knew he didn't dare strike a harder blow.

But in the security and relief of his new position, he simply smiled; with only a sheet of glass between him and the room just before him, it was not possible that there wasn't a way past it. Eyes narrowing, he thought for a few moments about what to do. Then his eyes widened, for nothing occurred to him. But still he felt calm: the trembling, he realized, had stopped. At the back of his mind there still lay the thought that once he was again in his home, he could give release to his feelings. He actually _would_ lie on the floor, rolling, clenching tufts of the rug in his hands. He would literally run across the room, free to move as he liked, jumping on the floor, testing and reveling in its absolute security, letting the relief flood through him, draining the fear from his mind and body. His yearning for this was astonishingly intense, and somehow he understood that he had better keep this feeling at bay.

He took a half dollar from his pocket and struck it against the pane, but without any hope that the glass would break and with very little disappointment when it did not. After a few moments of thought he drew his leg up onto the ledge and picked loose the knot of his shoelace. He slipped off the shoe and, holding it across the instep, drew back his arm as far as he dared and struck the leather heel against the glass. The pane rattled, but he knew he'd been a long way from breaking it. His foot was cold and he slipped the shoe back on. He shouted again experimentally, and then once more, but there was no answer.

The realization suddenly struck him that he might have to wait here till Clare came home, and for a moment the thought was funny. He could see Clare opening the front door, withdrawing her key from the lock, closing the door behind her, and then glancing up to see him crouched on the other side of the window. He could see her rush across the room, face astounded and frightened, and hear himself shouting instructions: "Never mind how I got here! Just open the wind—" She couldn't open it, he remembered, she'd never been able to; she'd always had to call him. She'd have to get the building superintendent or a neighbor, and he pictured himself smiling and answering their questions as he climbed in. "I just wanted to get a breath of fresh air, so—"

He couldn't possibly wait here till Clare came home. It was the second feature she'd wanted to see, and she'd left in time to see the first. She'd be another three hours or—He glanced at his watch; Clare had been gone eight minutes. It wasn't possible, but only eight minutes ago he had kissed his wife goodbye. She wasn't even at the theater yet!

It would be four hours before she could possibly be home, and he tried to picture himself kneeling out here, fingertips hooked to these narrow strippings, while first one movie, preceded by a slow listing of credits, began, developed, reached its climax and then finally ended. There'd be a newsreel next, maybe, and then an animated cartoon, and then interminable scenes from coming pictures. And then, once more, the beginning of a full-length picture—while all the time he hung out here in the night.

He might possibly get to his feet, but he was afraid to try. Already his legs were cramped, his thigh muscles tired; his knees hurt, his feet felt numb and his hands were stiff. He couldn't possibly stay out here for four hours, or anywhere near it. Long before that his legs and arms would give out; he would be forced to try changing his position often—stiffly, clumsily, his coordination and strength gone—and he would fall. Quite realistically, he knew that he would fall; no one could stay out here on this ledge for four hours.

A dozen windows in the apartment building across the street were lighted. Looking over his shoulder, he could see the top of a man's head behind the newspaper he was reading; in another window he saw the blue-gray flicker of a television screen. No more than twenty-odd yards from his back were scores of people, and if just one of them would walk idly to his window and glance out. . . . For some moments he stared over his shoulder at the lighted rectangles, waiting. But no one appeared. The man reading his paper turned a page and then continued his reading. A figure passed another of the windows and was immediately gone.

In the inside pocket of his jacket he found a little sheaf of papers, and he pulled one out and looked at it in the light from the living room. It was an old letter, an advertisement of some sort; his name and address, in purple ink, were on a label pasted to the envelope. Gripping one end of the envelope in his teeth, he twisted it into a tight curl. From his shirt pocket he brought out a book of matches. He didn't dare let go the casing with both hands, but, with the twist of paper in his teeth, he opened the matchbook with his free hand; then he bent one of the matches in two without tearing it from the folder, its red-tipped end now touching the striking surface. With his thumb, he rubbed the red tip across the striking area.

How does Tom's **external conflict** with the match add to the **suspense**?

_____

_____

_____

_____

_____

What **effect** does Tom hope the burning papers and the falling coins will have?

_____

_____

_____

_____

_____

How many times did Tom burn letters in his attempt to get someone's attention? Circle the text that tells you.

He did it again, then again, and still again, pressing harder each time, and the match suddenly flared, burning his thumb. But he kept it alight, cupping the matchbook in his hand and shielding it with his body. He held the flame to the paper in his mouth till it caught. Then he snuffed out the match flame with his thumb and forefinger, careless of the burn, and replaced the book in his pocket. Taking the paper twist in his hand, he held it flame down, watching the flame crawl up the paper, till it flared bright. Then he held it behind him over the street, moving it from side to side, watching it over his shoulder, the flame flickering and guttering in the wind.

There were three letters in his pocket and he lighted each of them, holding each till the flame touched his hand and then dropping it to the street below. At one point, watching over his shoulder while the last of the letters burned, he saw the man across the street put down his paper and stand—even seeming, to Tom, to glance toward his window. But when he moved, it was only to walk across the room and disappear from sight.

There were a dozen coins in Tom Benecke's pocket and he dropped them, three or four at a time. But if they struck anyone, or if anyone noticed their falling, no one connected them with their source, and no one glanced upward.

His arms had begun to tremble from the steady strain of clinging to this narrow perch, and he did not know what to do now and was terribly frightened. Clinging to the window stripping with one hand, he again searched his pockets. But now—he had left his wallet on his dresser when he'd changed clothes—there was nothing left but the yellow sheet. It occurred to him irrelevantly that his death on the sidewalk below would be an eternal mystery; the window closed—why, how, and from where could he have fallen? No one would be able to identify his body for a time, either—the thought was somehow unbearable and increased his fear. All they'd find in his pockets would be the yellow sheet. *Contents of the dead man's pockets,* he thought, *one sheet of paper bearing penciled notations— incomprehensible.*

He understood fully that he might actually be going to die; his arms, maintaining his balance on the ledge, were trembling steadily now. And it occurred to him then with all the force of a revelation that, if he fell, all he was ever going to have out of life he would then, abruptly, have had. Nothing, then, could ever be changed; and nothing more—no least experience or pleasure—could ever be added to his life. He wished, then, that he had not allowed his wife to go off by herself tonight—and on similar nights. He thought of all the evenings he had spent away from her, working; and he regretted them. He thought wonderingly of his fierce ambition and of the direction his life had taken; he thought of the hours he'd spent by himself, filling the yellow sheet that had brought him out here. *Contents of the dead man's pockets*, he thought with sudden fierce anger, *a wasted life.*

He was simply not going to cling here till he slipped and fell; he told himself that now. There was one last thing he could try; he had been aware of it for some moments, refusing to think about it, but now he faced it. Kneeling here on the ledge, the fingertips of one hand pressed to the narrow strip of wood, he could, he knew, draw his other hand back a yard perhaps, fist clenched tight, doing it very slowly till he sensed the outer limit of balance, then, as hard as he was able from the distance, he could drive his fist forward against the glass. If it broke, his fist smashing through, he was safe; he might cut himself badly, and probably would, but with his arm inside the room, he would be secure. But if the glass did not break, the rebound, flinging his arm back, would topple him off the ledge. He was certain of that.

He tested his plan. The fingers of his left hand clawlike on the little stripping, he drew back his other fist until his body began teetering backward. But he had no leverage now—he could feel that there would be no force to his swing—and he moved his fist slowly forward till he rocked forward on his knees again and could sense that his swing would carry its greatest force. Glancing down, however, measuring the distance from his fist to the glass, he saw that it was less than two feet.

It occurred to him that he could raise his arm over his head, to bring it down against the glass. But, experimenting in slow motion, he knew it would be an awkward . . . blow without the force of a driving punch, and not nearly enough to break the glass.

Facing the window, he had to drive a blow from the shoulder, he knew now, at a distance of less than two feet; and he did not know whether it would break through the heavy glass. It might; he could picture it happening, he could feel it in the nerves of his arm. And it might not; he could feel that too—feel his fist striking this glass and being instantaneously flung back by the unbreaking pane, feel the fingers of his other hand breaking loose, nails scraping along the casing as he fell.

He waited, arm drawn back, fist balled, but in no hurry to strike; this pause, he knew, might be an extension of his life. And to live even a few seconds longer, he felt, even out here on this ledge in the night, was infinitely better than to die a moment earlier than he had to. His arm grew tired, and he brought it down and rested it.

Then he knew that it was time to make the attempt. He could not kneel here hesitating indefinitely till he lost all courage to act, waiting till he slipped off the ledge. Again

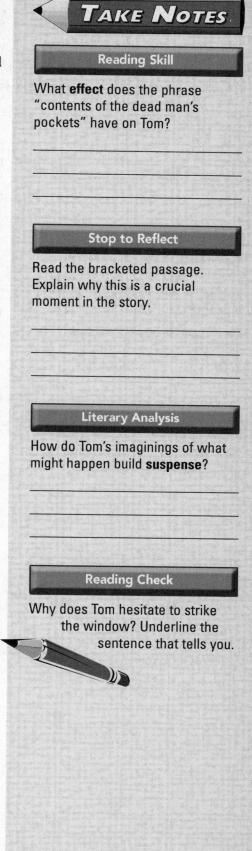

TAKE NOTES

Reading Skill

What **effect** does the phrase "contents of the dead man's pockets" have on Tom?

_____

_____

_____

Stop to Reflect

Read the bracketed passage. Explain why this is a crucial moment in the story.

_____

_____

_____

Literary Analysis

How do Tom's imaginings of what might happen build **suspense**?

_____

_____

_____

Reading Check

Why does Tom hesitate to strike the window? Underline the sentence that tells you.

Literary Analysis

Name one **conflict** that is resolved in the story's **resolution**.

_____

_____

_____

_____

Reading Skill

Explain the different **effect** the yellow paper has on Tom the second time that it goes out the window.

_____

_____

_____

Stop to Reflect

How do you think this experience will affect Tom in the future?

_____

_____

Reading Check

What does Tom shout as he breaks the window? Underline the text that tells you.

he drew back his arm, knowing this time that he would not bring it down till he struck. His elbow protruding over Lexington Avenue far below, the fingers of his other hand pressed down bloodlessly tight against the narrow stripping, he waited, feeling the sick tenseness and terrible excitement building. It grew and swelled toward the moment of action, his nerves tautening. He thought of Clare—just a wordless, yearning thought—and then drew his arm back just a bit more, fist so tight his fingers pained him, and knowing he was going to do it. Then with full power, with every last scrap of strength he could bring to bear, he shot his arm forward toward the glass, and he said, _"Clare!"_

He heard the sound, felt the blow, felt himself falling forward, and his hand closed on the living-room curtains, the shards and fragments of glass showering onto the floor. And then, kneeling there on the ledge, an arm thrust into the room up to the shoulder, he began picking away the protruding slivers and great wedges of glass from the window frame, tossing them in onto the rug. And, as he grasped the edges of the empty window frame and climbed into his home, he was grinning in triumph.

He did not lie down on the floor or run through the apartment, as he had promised himself; even in the first few moments it seemed to him natural and normal that he should be where he was. He simply turned to his desk, pulled the crumpled yellow sheet from his pocket and laid it down where it had been, smoothing it out; then he absently laid a pencil across it to weight it down. He shook his head wonderingly, and turned to walk toward the closet.

There he got out his topcoat and hat and, without waiting to put them on, opened the front door and stepped out, to go find his wife. He turned to pull the door closed and the warm air from the hall rushed through the narrow opening again. As he saw the yellow paper, the pencil flying, scooped off the desk and, unimpeded by the glassless window, sail out into the night and out of his life, Tom Benecke burst into laughter and then closed the door behind him.

Reader's Response: Did you predict what would happen to Tom the first time the yellow paper flew out the window? Explain your answer.

_____

_____

_____

Contents of the Dead Man's Pocket

1. **Compare and Contrast:** Contrast Tom's attitude toward life at the beginning of the story and his attitude at the end.

   _____

   _____

   _____

2. **Speculate**: What changes do you think Tom will make because of this experience?

   _____

   _____

3. **Literary Analysis:** How are Tom's **conflicts resolved?**

   _____

   _____

4. **Reading Skill:** Use the diagram below to identify a single **cause** of a situation in the story. Then, write down two key **effects** that happen because of it. One effect should have short-term effects, and the other should have possible long-term

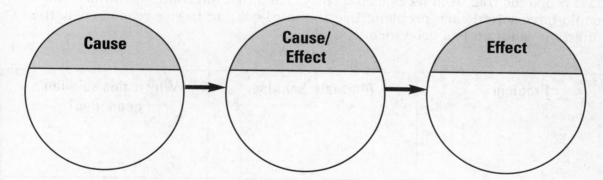

SUPPORT FOR WRITING AND EXTEND YOUR LEARNING

Writing: Anecdote

"Contents of the Dead Man's Pocket" has an **ironic** ending. Irony is a strong difference between a character's efforts and what actually happens. Write an **anecdote**, or brief story, with an ironic ending. Use the sequence-of-events chart below to write the order of the main events in your story.

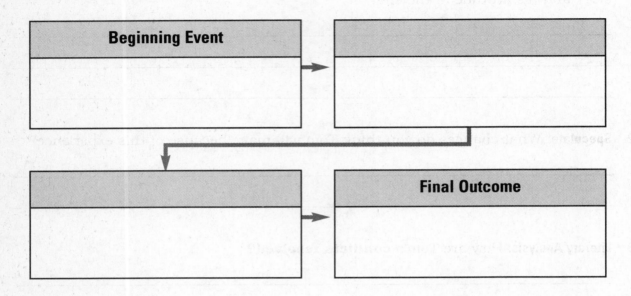

Listening and Speaking: Problem-Solving Group

Form a **problem-solving group** to find solutions to Tom's problem. Use the chart below to decide how Tom could have dealt with his situation differently.

- List problems that Tom faces in the story. Then, list alternate ways that Tom could have solved each problem. Use the third column to give reasons why the alternate solution is a good idea.

Problem	Alternate Solution	Why is this solution a good idea?

Games at Twilight

Anita Desai

Summary Ravi plays hide-and-seek with his friends. He hides all afternoon in a dark shed to win. Finally, he runs out at twilight to claim victory. He discovers that he waited too long.

Reading/Writing Connection

Complete these sentences to describe an older child who is admired by a younger child.

1. When children are little, they <u>identify</u> with _____.

2. They do not <u>differentiate</u> between _____.

3. They <u>appreciate</u> the _____ of older children.

Note-taking Guide

Use this chart to record Ravi's conflicts and resolutions in "Games at Twilight."

Conflict	Resolution
Ravi wants to find a good hiding place.	He hides in a dark shed.

Games at Twilight

1. **Draw Conclusions:** What do Ravi's feelings show about his view of other children and his view of himself?

   _____

   _____

   _____

2. **Infer:** Why do the other children stop searching for Ravi?

   _____

   _____

   _____

3. **Literary Analysis:** Are Ravi's **conflicts resolved** by the end of the story? Explain.

   _____

   _____

   _____

4. **Reading Skill:** Which **cause** do you think sets the story's cause-and-effect chain in motion? Identify two **effects** that depend on the cause you named. Use the diagram below to record your answer.

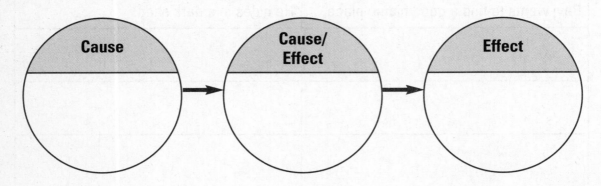

SUPPORT FOR WRITING AND EXTEND YOUR LEARNING

Writing: Anecdote

Write an **anecdote** with an **ironic** ending. Write several possible endings to your anecdote in the web below. Label each ending "expected" or "unexpected." Then, highlight the unexpected ending you want to use in your anecdote.

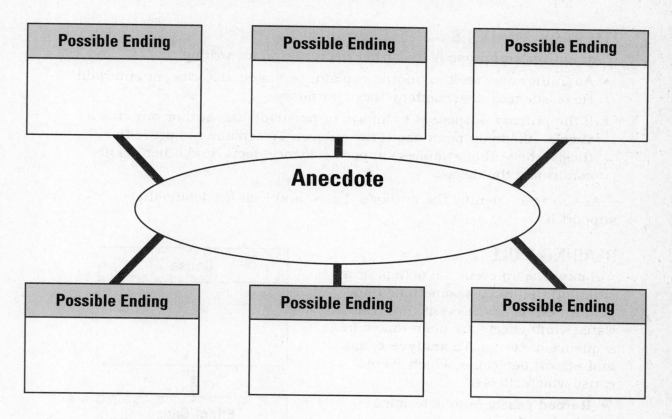

Research and Technology: Outline for a Multimedia Report

Plan a report about the history of a children's game such as hide-and-seek. Then, create an **outline for a multimedia report**. Answer these questions to help you plan your report.

- What game will I research? _____

- What information do I want to research? _____

  _____

  _____

- What sources will I use? _____

  _____

Making History With Vitamin C •
The Marginal World

LITERARY ANALYSIS

An **author's purpose** is his or her main reason for writing.

- An author may seek to inform, explain, persuade, describe, or entertain. He or she may also combine these purposes.

- If the primary purpose is to inform or persuade, the author presents a **thesis**—the main point about the subject. To explain and prove the thesis, the author supplies support: evidence, facts, and other details confirming the thesis.

As you read, identify the author's thesis, and look for details that support it.

READING SKILL

A **cause** is an event, an action, or a situation that makes something happen. An **effect** is the event that results. Causes and effects are often linked in a sequence of events. To **analyze cause and effect**, determine which events cause which effects.

- **Reread** passages to determine whether they involve sequences of events. Ask whether the writer indicates causes and effects in these sequences. Look for cause-and-effect terms such as *because, as a result, for that reason,* and so on.

- As you read, use this diagram to record causes and effects.

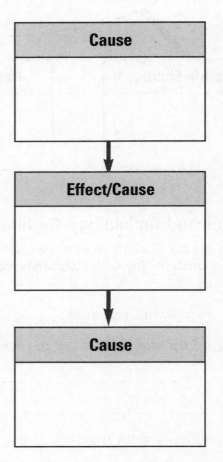

Making History With Vitamin C

Penny Le Couteur and Jay Burreson

Summary A pair of chemists examine how early sea captains often failed to reach their goals because of the disease called scurvy. Scurvy is an ancient disease caused by a lack of vitamin C in one's diet.

Reading/Writing Connection

Complete these sentences to describe a small thing that is key to the success of your day or week.

1. It is easy to rely on _____ first thing in the morning.

2. One benefit of depending on it is _____.

3. _____ would reinforce how important it is.

Note-taking Guide

Fill in this chart to record the important facts that support the conclusion below.

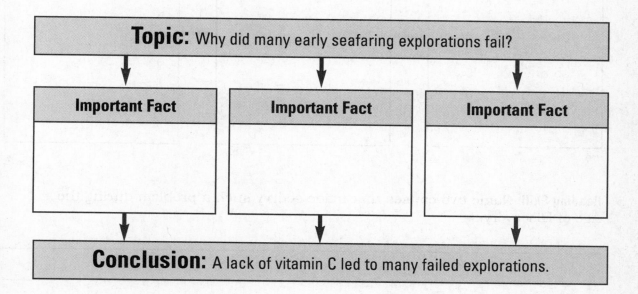

Topic: Why did many early seafaring explorations fail?

Important Fact	Important Fact	Important Fact

Conclusion: A lack of vitamin C led to many failed explorations.

Making History With Vitamin C

1. **Analyze Cause and Effect:** Before the eighteenth century, why did a typical sailor's diet lead to illness?

_____

2. **Interpret:** What did the delay in correcting the problem reveal about human nature?

_____

_____

3. **Literary Analysis:** Write one sentence describing the authors' subject and their **thesis**, or main point.

_____

_____

4. **Literary Analysis:** Fill in the diagram below to record two details that support the authors' **thesis**.

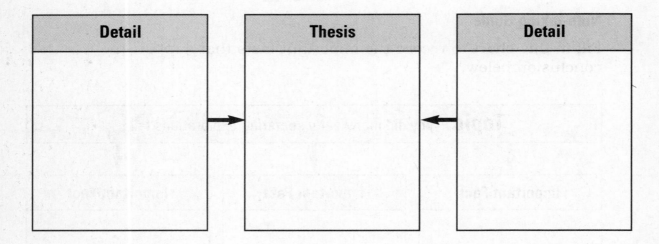

5. **Reading Skill:** Name two **causes** that made scurvy such a problem during the Age of Discovery.

_____

_____

SUPPORT FOR WRITING AND EXTEND YOUR LEARNING

Writing: Proposal for a Documentary

Write a **proposal for a documentary** on Cook's efforts to solve the problem of scurvy. Watch a documentary, such as *4 Little Girls* (1997) or *Winged Migration* (2001). Make notes regarding how the story is told.

- What is the main topic of the film? What is the filmmaker trying to prove?

    _____

- Who is interviewed? What is the purpose of each interview?

    _____

Research and Technology: Diet Spreadsheet

Use computer software to create a diet spreadsheet. Record information about the foods you eat during a typical week, in the chart below. Then, transfer the information to your diet spreadsheet.

	Sunday	Monday	Tuesday	Wednesday	Thursday	Friday	Saturday
Breakfast							
Snack							
Lunch							
Snack							
Dinner							

- List the items that sailors during the Age of Discovery ate.

    _____

    _____

- How is your diet different from the sailors' typical diet? How is it the same?

    _____

    _____

    _____

    _____

    _____

The Marginal World

Rachel Carson

Summary Marine biologist Rachel Carson describes places between land and water, such as different types of coastlines, tidal pools, and caves. Carson discusses the biological traits of these places and explains why these places are significant and meaningful to her.

Reading/Writing Connection

Complete the following sentences to describe a place that has meaning to you.

1. This place <u>appeals</u> to _____.

2. In order to <u>appreciate</u> the beauty _____.

3. This place pleasantly <u>contrasts</u> with _____.

Note-taking Guide

Use this diagram to write reasons why Rachel Carson admires and enjoys shores.

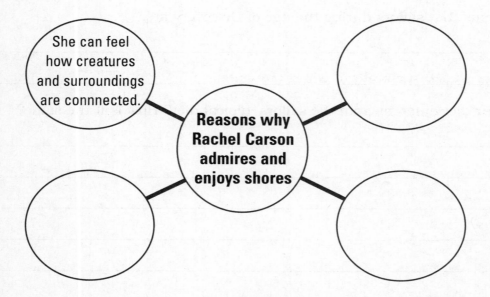

She can feel how creatures and surroundings are connnected.

Reasons why Rachel Carson admires and enjoys shores

The Marginal World
By Rachel Carson

The edge of the sea is a strange and beautiful place. All through the long history of Earth it has been an area of unrest where waves have broken heavily against the land, where the tides have pressed forward over the continents, receded, and then returned. For no two successive days is the shoreline precisely the same. Not only do the tides advance and retreat in their eternal rhythms, but the level of the sea itself is never at rest. It rises or falls as the glaciers melt or grow, as the floor of the deep ocean basins shifts under its increasing load of sediments, or as the earth's crust along the continental margins warps up or down in adjustment to strain and tension. Today a little more land may belong to the sea, tomorrow a little less. Always the edge of the sea remains an elusive and indefinable boundary.

The shore has a dual nature, changing with the swing of the tides, belonging now to the land, now to the sea. On the ebb tide it knows the harsh extremes of the land world, being exposed to heat and cold, to wind, to rain and drying sun. On the flood tide it is a water world, returning briefly to the relative stability of the open sea.

Only the most hardy and adaptable can survive in a region so mutable, yet the area between the tide lines is crowded with plants and animals. In this difficult world of the shore, life displays its enormous toughness and vitality by occupying almost every conceivable niche. Visibly, it carpets the intertidal rocks; or half hidden, it descends into fissures and crevices, or hides under boulders, or lurks in the wet gloom of sea caves. Invisibly, where the casual observer would say there is no life, it lies deep in the sand, in burrows and tubes and passageways. It tunnels into solid rock and bores into peat and clay. It encrusts weeds or drifting spars[1] or the hard, chitinous[2] shell of a lobster. It exists minutely, as the film of bacteria that spreads over a rock surface or a wharf piling; as spheres of protozoa, small as pinpricks, sparkling at the surface of the sea; and as Lilliputian[3] beings swimming through dark pools that lie between the grains of sand.

Vocabulary Development mutable (MYOOT uh buhl) *adj.* changeable

---

1. **spars** (sparz) *n.* pieces of wood or metal, such as masts or booms, for supporting sails on a ship.
2. **chitinous** (KY tuhn uhs) *adj.* of the material that forms the tough outer covering of insects, crustaceans, and so on.
3. **Lilliputian** (lil uh PYOO shuhn) *adj.* tiny (from the name of the tiny people who inhabit Lilliput in *Gulliver's Travels* by Jonathan Swift).

TAKE NOTES

Activate Prior Knowledge

Human beings are faced with environmental challenges all the time. A new environment could be a swimming pool, a new school, or a different country. Consider things you do to adapt to new environments. Describe some strategies that have helped you.

_____

_____

_____

_____

Literary Analysis

Underline the sentence in the opening paragraph that states the author's **thesis**, or main point.

Reading Skill

A **cause** is an event, an action, or a situation that makes something else happen. What happens is called the **effect**. One way to **analyze cause and effect** is to **reread** passages, looking for a sequence of events and cause-and-effect terms. **Reread** the second paragraph. What causes the "dual nature" of the shore?

_____

_____

_____

An **author's purpose** is his or her main reason for writing. What do you think Carson's purpose is in the first bracketed paragraph?

_____

_____

What would **cause** the sea level to drop below the entrance to the pool? Underline the explanation in the second bracketed paragraph.

How do you think it would feel to stand in the pool Carson describes? Describe the sounds you might hear.

_____

_____

_____

What kind of weather does Carson need to view the pool on the day she chooses? Circle the text that tells you.

The shore is an ancient world, for as long as there has been an earth and sea there has been this place of the meeting of land and water. Yet it is a world that keeps alive the sense of continuing creation and of the relentless drive of life. Each time that I enter it, I gain some new awareness of its beauty and its deeper meanings, sensing that intricate fabric of life by which one creature is linked with another, and each with its surroundings.

In my thoughts of the shore, one place stands apart for its revelation of exquisite beauty. It is a pool hidden within a cave that one can visit only rarely and briefly when the lowest of the year's low tides fall below it, and perhaps from that very fact it acquires some of its special beauty. Choosing such a tide, I hoped for a glimpse of the pool. The ebb was to fall early in the morning. I knew that if the wind held from the northwest and no interfering swell ran in from a distant storm the level of the sea should drop below the entrance to the pool. There had been sudden ominous showers in the night, with rain like handfuls of gravel flung on the roof. When I looked out into the early morning the sky was full of a gray dawn light but the sun had not yet risen. Water and air were pallid. Across the bay the moon was a luminous disc in the western sky, suspended above the dim line of distant shore—the full August moon, drawing the tide to the low, low levels of the threshold of the alien sea world. As I watched, a gull flew by, above the spruces. Its breast was rosy with the light of the unrisen sun. The day was, after all, to be fair.

Later, as I stood above the tide near the entrance to the pool, the promise of that rosy light was sustained. From the base of the steep wall of rock on which I stood, a moss-covered ledge jutted seaward into deep water. In the surge at the rim of the ledge the dark fronds of oarweeds swayed, smooth and gleaming as leather. The projecting ledge was the path to the small hidden cave and its pool. Occasionally a swell, stronger than the rest, rolled smoothly over the rim and broke in foam against the cliff. But the intervals between such swells were long enough to admit me to the ledge and long enough for a glimpse of that fairy pool, so seldom and so briefly exposed.

And so I knelt on the wet carpet of sea moss and looked back into the dark cavern that held the pool in a shallow basin. The floor of the cave was only a few inches below the roof, and a mirror had been created in which all that grew on the ceiling was reflected in the still water below.

Under water that was clear as glass the pool was carpeted with green sponge. Gray patches of sea squirts glistened on the ceiling and colonies of soft coral were a pale apricot color. In the moment when I looked into the cave a little elfin starfish hung down, suspended by the merest thread, perhaps by only a single tube foot. It reached down to touch its own reflection, so perfectly delineated that there might have been, not one starfish, but two. The beauty of the reflected images and of the limpid pool itself was the poignant beauty of things that are <u>ephemeral</u>, existing only until the sea should return to fill the little cave.

Whenever I go down into this magical zone of the low water of the spring tides, I look for the most delicately beautiful of all the shore's inhabitants—flowers that are not plant but animal, blooming on the threshold of the deeper sea. In that fairy cave I was not disappointed. Hanging from its roof were the pendent[4] flowers of the hydroid Tubularia, pale pink, fringed and delicate as the wind flower. Here were creatures so exquisitely fashioned that they seemed unreal, their beauty too fragile to exist in a world of crushing force. Yet every detail was functionally useful, every stalk and hydranth[5] and petallike tentacle fashioned for dealing with the realities of existence. I knew that they were merely waiting, in that moment of the tide's ebbing, for the return of the sea. Then in the rush of water, in the surge of surf and the pressure of the incoming tide, the delicate flower heads would stir with life. They would sway on their slender stalks, and their long tentacles would sweep the returning water, finding in it all that they needed for life.

And so in that enchanted place on the threshold of the sea the realities that possessed my mind were far from those of the land world I had left an hour before. In a different way the same sense of remoteness and of a world apart came to me in a twilight hour on a great beach on the coast of Georgia. I had come down after sunset and walked far out over sands that lay wet and gleaming, to the very edge of the retreating sea. Looking back across that immense flat, crossed by winding, waterfilled gullies and here and there holding shallow pools left by the tide, I was filled with awareness that this intertidal area, although abandoned briefly and rhythmically by the sea, is always reclaimed by the rising tide. There at the edge of low water the beach with its reminders of the land seemed far away. The only sounds were those of the wind and the sea and the birds. There was one sound of wind moving over water, and another of water sliding over the sand and tumbling down the faces of its own wave forms. The flats were astir with birds, and the voice of the willet[6] rang

---

Vocabulary Development ephemeral (i FEM uhr uhl) *adj.* short-lived

---

4. **pendent** (PEN dent) *adj.* dangling; hanging like a pendant on a necklace or charm.
5. **hydranth** (HY dranth) *n.* one of the feeding individuals in a hydroid colony; the individuals are all attached at the base to a common tube.
6. **willet** (WILL it) *n.* shorebird, about 16 inches long, with a long bill, found by shallow shores and other waters of North and South America.

Reread the first bracketed paragraph, focusing on the changes Carson describes. What **effect** does the coming of dusk have on the flats?

_____

_____

What is the **author's purpose** in the second bracketed paragraph?

_____

_____

How has Carson's essay changed the way you think about these "marginal" places?

_____

_____

How did skimmers get their name? Underline the text that tells you.

insistently. One of them stood at the edge of the water and gave its loud, urgent cry; an answer came from far up the beach and the two birds flew to join each other.

The flats took on a mysterious quality as dusk approached and the last evening light was reflected from the scattered pools and creeks. Then birds became only dark shadows, with no color discernible. Sanderlings[7] scurried across the beach like little ghosts, and here and there the darker forms of the willets stood out. Often I could come very close to them before they would start up in alarm—the sanderlings running, the willets flying up, crying. Black skimmers[8] flew along the ocean's edge silhouetted against the dull, metallic gleam, or they went flitting above the sand like large, dimly seen moths. Sometimes they "skimmed" the winding creeks of tidal water, where little spreading surface ripples marked the presence of small fish.

The shore at night is a different world, in which the very darkness that hides the distractions of daylight brings into sharper focus the elemental realities. Once, exploring the night beach, I surprised a small ghost crab in the searching beam of my torch. He was lying in a pit he had dug just above the surf, as though watching the sea and waiting. The blackness of the night possessed water, air, and beach. It was the darkness of an older world, before Man. There was no sound but the all-enveloping, primeval sounds of wind blowing over water and sand, and of waves crashing on the beach. There was no other visible life— just one small crab near the sea. I have seen hundreds of ghost crabs in other settings, but suddenly I was filled with the odd sensation that for the first time I knew the creature in its own world—that I understood, as never before, the essence of its being. In that moment time was suspended; the world to which I belonged did not exist and I might have been an onlooker from outer space. The little crab alone with the sea became a symbol that stood for life itself—for the delicate, destructible, yet incredibly vital force that somehow holds its place amid the harsh realities of the inorganic world.

The sense of creation comes with memories of a southern coast, where the sea and the mangroves,[9] working together, are building a wilderness of thousands of small islands off the southwestern coast of Florida, separated from each other by a tortuous[10] pattern of bays, lagoons, and narrow waterways. I remember a winter day when the sky was

7. **sanderlings** (SAN duhr lingz) *n.* small, gray-and-white shorebirds.
8. **skimmers** (SKIM erz) *n.* shorebirds with bladelike bills, which they use to skim the surface of the water for small fish and crustaceans.
9. **mangroves** (MANG grohvz) *n.* tropical trees that grow in swampy ground with spreading branches. The branches send down additional roots, forming a cluster of trunks for each tree.
10. **tortuous** (TAWR choo uhs) *adj.* full of twists and turns.

blue and drenched with sunlight; though there was no wind one was conscious of flowing air like cold clear crystal. I had landed on the surf-washed tip of one of those islands, and then worked my way around to the sheltered bay side. There I found the tide far out, exposing the broad mud flat of a cove bordered by the mangroves with their twisted branches, their glossy leaves, and their long prop roots reaching down, grasping and holding the mud, building the land out a little more, then again a little more.

The mud flats were strewn with the shells of that small, exquisitely colored mollusk,[11] the rose tellin, looking like scattered petals of pink roses. There must have been a colony nearby, living buried just under the surface of the mud. At first the only creature visible was a small heron in gray and rusty plumage—a reddish egret that waded across the flat with the stealthy, hesitant movements of its kind. But other land creatures had been there, for a line of fresh tracks wound in and out among the mangrove roots, marking the path of a raccoon feeding on the oysters that gripped the supporting roots with projections from their shells. Soon I found the tracks of a shore bird, probably a sanderling, and followed them a little; then they turned toward the water and were lost, for the tide had erased them and made them as though they had never been.

Looking out over the cove I felt a strong sense of the interchangeability of land and sea in this marginal world of the shore, and of the links between the life of the two. There was also an awareness of the past and of the continuing flow of time, obliterating much that had gone before, as the sea had that morning washed away the tracks of the bird.

The sequence and meaning of the drift of time were quietly summarized in the existence of hundreds of small snails—the mangrove periwinkles—browsing on the branches and roots of the trees. Once their ancestors had been sea dwellers, bound to the salt waters by every tie of their life processes. Little by little over the thousands and millions of years the ties had been broken, the snails had adjusted themselves to life out of water, and now today they were living many feet above the tide to which they only occasionally returned. And perhaps, who could say how many ages hence, there would be in their descendants not even this gesture of remembrance for the sea.

Vocabulary Development marginal (MAHR juh nuhl) *adj.* at, on, or near the edge

---

11. **mollusk** (MAHL uhsk) *n.* one of a large group of soft-bodied animals with shells, including clams and snails.

TAKE NOTES

Reading Skill

Analyze cause and effect by circling the effects of the underlined cause in the text.

Literary Analysis

How does the bracketed paragraph contribute to the **author's purpose** for writing?

_____

_____

_____

Reading Check

What does Carson show with her example of the small snails? Underline the text that tells you.

What **causes** Carson to imagine flocks of flamingos?

_____

_____

_____

Read the bracketed paragraph. Underline the text that most clearly restates the author's **thesis**. Restate the thesis in your own words.

_____

_____

_____

What do you think Carson foresees in the future for all creatures?

_____

_____

_____

The spiral shells of other snails—these quite minute—left winding tracks on the mud as they moved about in search of food. They were horn shells, and when I saw them I had a nostalgic moment when I wished I might see what Audubon[12] saw, a century and more ago. For such little horn shells were the food of the flamingo, once so numerous on this coast, and when I half closed my eyes I could almost imagine a flock of these magnificent flame birds feeding in that cove, filling it with their color. It was a mere yesterday in the life of the earth that they were there; in nature, time and space are relative matters, perhaps most truly perceived subjectively in occasional flashes of insight, sparked by such a magical hour and place.

There is a common thread that links these scenes and memories—the spectacle of life in all its varied manifestations as it has appeared, evolved, and sometimes died out. Underlying the beauty of the spectacle there is meaning and significance. It is the elusiveness of that meaning that haunts us, that sends us again and again into the natural world where the key to the riddle is hidden. It sends us back to the edge of the sea, where the drama of life played its first scene on earth and perhaps even its prelude; where the forces of evolution are at work today, as they have been since the appearance of what we know as life; and where the spectacle of living creatures faced by the cosmic realities of their world is crystal clear.

Vocabulary Development   manifestations (man uh fes TAY shuhnz) *n.* appearances or showings (of); forms (of)

---

12. **Audubon** (AWD uh bahn) John James Audubon (1785–1851), an ornithologist, a naturalist, and a painter famous for his paintings of North American birds.

Reader's Response: Although Rachel Carson is a scientist, many people think that her writing style is more like a poet's or a philosopher's. What effect do you think this style has on her audience?

_____

_____

_____

The Marginal World

1. **Infer:** Carson first visits a pool hidden in a cave in the early morning. Which details make this place special to her?

   _____

   _____

2. **Interpret:** What lesson about life does Carson draw from the "marginal world"? Support your answer with details from the work.

   _____

   _____

3. **Literary Analysis:** Use the diagram below to record details that support the author's **thesis**.

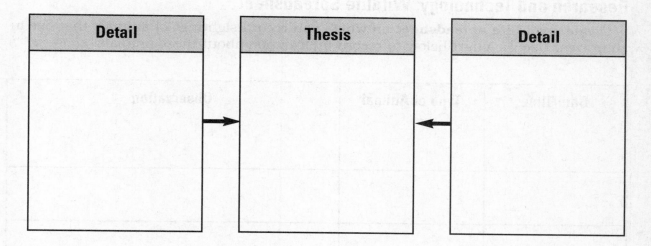

Detail	Thesis	Detail

4. **Reading Skill:** Identify the **cause** of changes in the water level of the "marginal world."

   _____

   _____

SUPPORT FOR WRITING AND EXTEND YOUR LEARNING

Writing: Proposal for a Documentary

Write a **proposal for a documentary** on the "marginal world." A proposal is a suggestion for how to do something. Use the chart below to record details about the places where the documentary should be filmed. Use vivid language for your details.

Places to Film	Details About the Places

Use these notes to help write your proposal.

Research and Technology: Wildlife Spreadsheet

Create a **wildlife spreadsheet** on which you record sightings of animals that live in your area. Use the chart below to record information about these animals.

Date/Time	Type of Animal	Observation

Use these notes to create your wildlife spreadsheet.

About Technical Articles

ABOUT TECHNICAL ARTICLES

A **technical article** is an article that explains a special process. Some technical articles give step-by-step instructions. Others give specific information. Technical articles usually include the following:

- Main headings that divide the article into sections
- Subheadings that organize the information in each section
- Boldface words, phrases, or sentences that contain key ideas
- Diagrams or charts to show or summarize information
- Captions that explain how to use the diagrams

READING SKILL

Diagrams are a very important part of a technical article. Diagrams help make difficult information easier to understand. Read the following article. **Use charts and diagrams** to help you understand the article. They will help you **analyze the causes and effects** the article tells about. Follow these steps:

- Read the text. Notice important situations and events.
- Look for notes in the text that tell you where to find diagrams.
- Study each diagram. Ask yourself whether the diagram tells about a cause or an effect. Also, ask whether it tells about the relationship between a cause and an effect.

Use the chart below to help you use the diagrams in "Tides."

Text: Cause and Effects	Related Diagram	What Diagram Shows
moon's gravity tides	Figure 1	

Tides

Joseph D. Exline, Ed.D., Jay M. Pasachoff, Ph.D., et al.

Y ou're standing on a riverbank in the town of Saint John, Canada. In the distance there's a loud roaring sound, like a train approaching. Suddenly a wall of water twice your height thunders past. The surge of water rushes up the river channel so fast that it almost looks as if the river is flowing backward.

This thundering wall of water is an everyday event at Saint John. The town is located where the Saint John River enters the Bay of Fundy, an arm of the Atlantic Ocean. The Bay of Fundy is famous for its dramatic daily tides. When the tide comes in, fishing boats float on the water near the piers, as shown in Figure 1A. But once the tide goes out, so much water flows back to sea that the boats are stranded on the muddy harbor bottom (Figure 1B).

Figure 1 The Bay of Fundy in Canada is noted for its great differences in water level at high and low tide. **A.** Near the mouth of the bay, boats float in the Saint John River at high tide. **B.** At low tide, the boats are grounded.

What Causes Tides?

The daily rise and fall of Earth's waters on its coastlines are called **tides**. As the tide comes in, the level of the water on the beach rises gradually. When the water reaches its highest point, it is high tide. Then the tide goes out, flowing back toward the sea. When the water reaches its lowest point, it is low tide. **Tides are caused by the interaction of Earth, the moon, and the sun.**

Figure 2 shows the effect of the moon's gravity on the water on Earth's surface. The moon pulls on the water on the side closest to it (point A) more strongly than it pulls on the center of the Earth. This pull creates a bulge of water, called a tidal bulge, on the side of Earth facing the moon. The water at point C is pulled toward the moon less strongly than is Earth as a whole. This water is "left behind," forming a second bulge.

In the places in Figure 2 where there are tidal bulges (points A and C), high tide is occurring along the coastlines. In the places between the bulges (points B and D), low tide is occurring. As Earth rotates, different places on the planet's surface pass through the areas of the tidal bulges and experience the change in water levels.

Figure 2
The moon's pull on Earth's water causes tidal bulges to form on the side closest to the moon and the side farthest from the moon.

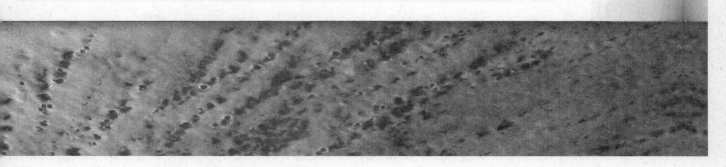

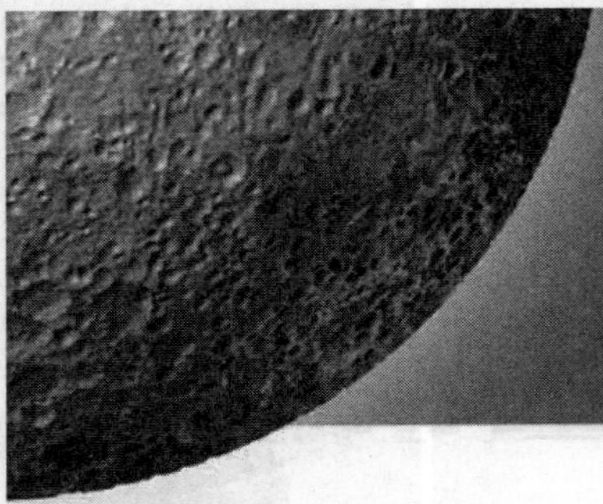

Day	Highest High Tide (m)	Lowest Low Tide (m)
1	1.9	0.2
2	2.1	0.1
3	2.3	0.0
4	2.4	-0.2
5	2.5	-0.2
6	2.6	-0.3
7	1.9	0.3

Figure 3
This table lists the highest high tides and lowest low tides at the mouth of the Savannah River at the Atlantic Ocean in Georgia for one week.

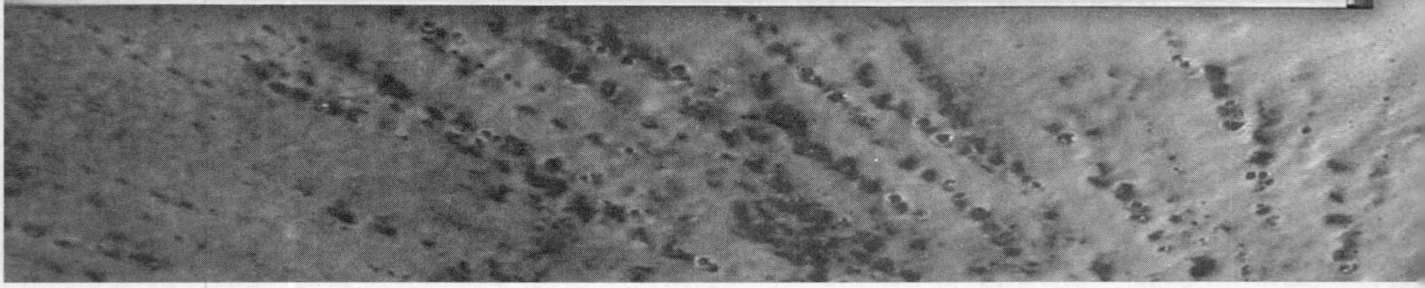

The Daily Tide Cycle

As Earth turns completely around once each day, people on or near the shore observe the rise and fall of the tides as they reach the area of each tidal bulge. The high tides occur about 12 hours and 25 minutes apart in each location. As Earth rotates, eastern-most points pass through the area of the tidal bulge before points farther to the west. Therefore, high tide occurs later the farther west you go along a coastline.

The Monthly Tide Cycle

Even though the sun is 150 million kilometers from Earth, it is so massive that its gravity also affects the tides. The sun pulls the water on Earth's surface toward it. In Figure 4 (next page), you can follow the positions of the Earth, moon, and sun at different times during a month.

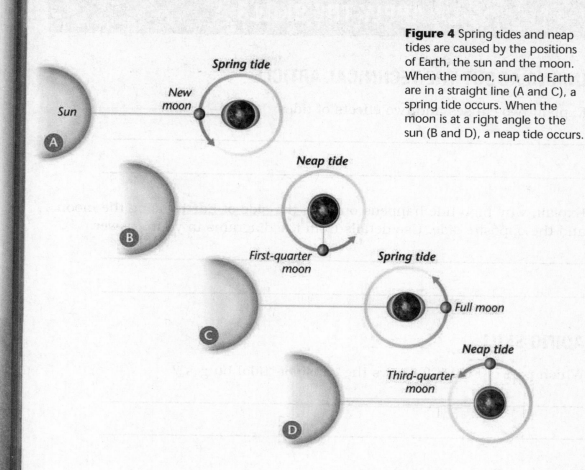

Figure 4 Spring tides and neap tides are caused by the positions of Earth, the sun and the moon. When the moon, sun, and Earth are in a straight line (A and C), a spring tide occurs. When the moon is at a right angle to the sun (B and D), a neap tide occurs.

Spring Tides Twice a month, at the new moon and the full moon, the sun and moon are lined up. Their combined gravitational pull produces the greatest range between high and low tide, called a **spring tide.** These tides get their name not because they occur during the spring season, but from an Old English word, *springen,* which means "to jump."

Neap Tides In between spring tides, at the first and third quarters of the moon, the sun and moon pull at right angles to each other. This line-up produces a **neap tide,** a tide with the least difference between low and high tide. During a neap tide, the sun's gravity pulls some of the water away from the tidal bulge facing the moon. This acts to "even out" the water level over Earth's surface, reducing the difference between high and low tides.

THINKING ABOUT THE TECHNICAL ARTICLE

1. Explain two causes and two effects of tides.

   _____

   _____

2. Explain why high tide happens on both the side of Earth facing the moon and the opposite side. Use details from the diagrams in your answer.

   _____

   _____

READING SKILL

3. Which part of Figure 2 shows the cause of "tidal bulges"?

   _____

   _____

4. What does Figure 3 show?

   _____

   _____

TIMED WRITING: EXPOSITION (20 minutes)

Summarize the main ideas of the article "Tides." Start with an overview of the subject. Before you begin, make a few notes about each of the five headings in this article.

1. _____

2. _____

3. _____

4. _____

5. _____

The Threads of Time

A **short story** is a brief work of fiction. It is intended to be read in one sitting. The writer must limit the number of characters and settings. The writer also limits the amount of action.

The following are some of the key elements of a short story.

Plot

The short story's **plot** is the sequence of events that makes up the action. These events build to a **climax**, or high point. The events are then resolved, or sorted out, during the **resolution**.

Conflict

Most plots are built around a **conflict**. The conflict is a problem or struggle. In traditional stories, the conflict ends at the resolution. In modern stories, characters may experience an **epiphany**. This sudden insight changes their feelings about the conflict without necessarily resolving it. The chart below shows the two main types of conflict in literature.

Types of Conflict	
Internal Conflict: struggle within the mind of one character **Example:** A character has to overcome fear in order to perform a dangerous task.	**External Conflict:** a struggle between two characters, between a person and a group, or between a character and nature or fate **Example:** A character battles a hurricane to save the family home.

Character

The **characters** in a story are the people who participate in the action. The **protagonist** is the main character. The **hero**, a person with positive traits, is often the protagonist. The **antagonist** is the enemy or opponent of the main character.

Characterization

Characterization is the writer's way of revealing a character's personality to the reader. The process of showing different sides of a character's personality or showing how a character changes is called **character development**. Writers use these two methods of characterization:

- **Direct characterization:** Writers make direct statements about a character's personality, appearance, habits, goals, values, or beliefs.
- **Indirect characterization:** Writers report a character's words, thoughts, actions, and interactions with other characters. Readers then use clues from the story to draw conclusions about the characters.

Setting

The **setting** of a story is the backdrop of the action. It establishes the time and place. It can also include the social, economic, or cultural circumstances that affect the characters and their location. Setting can add complications to the plot. It can also contribute to the mood of the story.

- The setting can be past, present, or future. It can also include a specific year, season, or hour of day.
- The setting can include the social, economic, or cultural circumstances that affect the characters. It can also be the country, town, or community in which the characters live.

Theme

The **theme** of a short story is its central message or insight about life. The theme is not a summary about "what happens" in a story. Instead, it tells you the overall meaning of the events. Themes may be stated or implied.

Types of Themes	Definition
Stated Theme	• expressed directly by author
Implied Theme	• suggested indirectly through the experiences of the characters • can also be suggested through events and the setting of the story

The Threads of Time

C. J. Cherryh

Summary The qhal have been able to travel through time for over 5,000 years. They are able to slip from one future age to another. This means that they have lost such things as memory and death. Agent Harrh is a time-mender. He is one of the few who can go back in time. He makes small adjustments to reality. However, even he cannot escape the dangers of time travel.

Note-taking Guide

Use this diagram to write details about how Harrh thinks and feels.

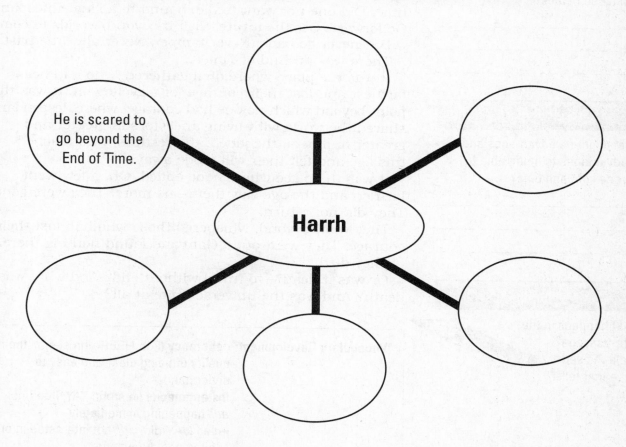

He is scared to go beyond the End of Time.

Harrh

The Threads of Time

C. J. Cherryh

Would you rather travel to the past or travel to the future? Explain your reasons.

_____

_____

_____

The **setting** of a story is its time and place. Circle the words in the bracketed passage that tell you about the story's setting. What can you conclude about the setting from these details?

_____

_____

_____

What might be advantages and disadvantages to being able to outrace light and time?

_____

_____

_____

What happens in the Gate-passage? Circle the sentence that tells you.

It was possible that the Gates were killing the qhal. They were everywhere, on every world, had been a fact of life for five thousand years, and linked the whole net of qhalur civilization into one present-tense coherency.

They had not, to be sure, invented the Gates. Chance gave them that gift . . . on a dead world of their own sun. One Gate stood—made by unknown hands.

And the qhal made others, imitating what they found. The Gates were instantaneous transfer, not alone from place to place, but, because of the motion of worlds and suns and the traveling galaxies—involving time.

There was an end of time. Ah, qhal *could* venture anything. If one supposed, if one believed, if one were very *sure,* one could step through a Gate to a Gate that would/might exist on some other distant world.

And if one were wrong?

If it did not exist?

If it never had?

Time warped in the Gate-passage. One could step across light-years, unaged; so it was possible to outrace light and time. Did one not want to die, bound to a single lifespan? Go forward. See the future. Visit the world/worlds to come.

But never go back. Never tamper. Never alter the past.

There was an End of Time.

It was the place where qhal gathered, who had been farthest and lost their courage for traveling on. It was the point beyond which no one had courage, where descendants shared the world with living ancestors in greater and greater numbers, the jaded, the restless, who reached this age and felt their will erode away.

It was the place where hope ended. Oh, a few went farther, and the age saw them—no more. They were gone. They did not return.

They went beyond, whispered those who had lost their courage. They went out a Gate and found nothing there.

They died.

Or was it death—to travel without end? And what was death? And was the universe finite at all?

Vocabulary Development: coherency (koh HEER uhn see) *n.* the quality of being clear and easy to understand
instantaneous (in stuhn TAYN ee uhs) *adj.* happening immediately
jaded (JAY did) *adj.* not interested in or excited about anything

Some went, and vanished, and the age knew nothing more of them.

Those who were left were in agony—of desire to go; of fear to go farther.

Of changes.

This age—did change. It rippled with possibilities. Memories deceived. One remembered, or remembered that one had remembered, and the fact grew strange and dim, contradicting what obviously *was*. People remembered things that never had been true.

And one must never go back to see. Backtiming—had direst possibilities. It made paradox.[1]

But some tried, seeking a time as close to their original exit point as possible. Some came too close, and involved themselves in time-loops, a particularly distressing kind of accident and unfortunate equally for those involved as bystanders.

Among qhal, between the finding of the first Gate and the End of Time, a new kind of specialist evolved: time-menders, who in most extreme cases of disturbance policed the Gates and carefully researched afflicted areas. They alone were licensed to violate the back-time barrier, passing back and forth under strict non-involvement regulations, exchanging intelligence only with each other, to minutely adjust reality.

Evolved.

Agents recruited other agents at need—but at whose instance? There might be some who knew. It might have come from the far end of time—in that last (or was it last?) age beyond which nothing seemed certain, when the years since the First Gate were more than five thousand, and the Now in which all Gates existed was—very distant. Or it might have come from those who had found the Gate, overseeing their invention. Someone knew, somewhen, somewhere along the course of the stars toward the end of time.

But no one said.

It was hazardous business, this time-mending, in all senses. Precisely *what* was done was something virtually unknowable after it was done, for alterations in the past produced (one believed) changes in future reality. Whole time-fields, whose events could be wiped and redone, with effects which widened the farther down the timeline they proceeded. Detection of time-tampering was almost impossible.

A stranger wanted something to eat, a long time ago.
He shot himself his dinner.

---

1. **paradox** (PAR uh dahks) *n.* a statement or situation that seems strange or impossible because it contains two opposing ideas.

TAKE NOTES

Short Story

Why did the qhal need time-menders? Circle the answer. How does the introduction of these characters affect the **plot**?

_____

_____

Short Story

The **conflict** is a problem or struggle in a story. There may be more than one conflict in a short story. Describe the conflict in the bracketed passage.

_____

_____

_____

Stop to Reflect

What might it be like to be a time-mender?

_____

_____

_____

_____

The main character is introduced late in the story. Why might the author have chosen to delay the introduction of the character?

_____

_____

_____

_____

What is the only thing Harrh had ever run from? Underline the text that tells you.

What details do you learn about Agent Harrh's **character**? Underline words and phrases that tell you what kind of man he is.

A small creature was not where it had been, when it had been.

A predator missed a meal and took another . . . likewise small.

A child lost a pet.

And found another.

And a friend she would not have had. She was happier for it.

She met many people she had never/would never meet.

A man in a different age had breakfast in a house on a hill.

Agent Harrh had acquired a sense about disruptions, a kind of extrasensory queasiness about a just-completed timewarp. He was not alone in this. But the time-menders (Harrh knew three others of his own age) never reported such experiences outside their own special group. Such reports would have been meaningless to his own time, involving a past which (as a result of the warp) was neither real nor valid nor perceptible to those in Time Present. Some time-menders would reach the verge of insanity because of this. This was future fact. Harrh knew this.

He had been there.

And he refused to go again to Now, that Now to which time had advanced since the discovery of the Gate—let alone to the End of Time, which was the farthest that anyone imagined. He was one of a few, a very few, licensed to do so, but he refused.

He lived scattered lives in ages to come, and remembered the future with increasing melancholy.

He had visited the End of Time, and left it in the most profound despair. He had seen what was there, and when he had contemplated going beyond, that most natural step out the Gate which stood and beckoned—

He fled. He had never run from anything but that. It remained, a recollection of shame at his fear.

A sense of a limit which he had never had before.

And this in itself was terrible, to a man who had thought time infinite and himself immortal.

In his own present of 1003 since the First Gate, Harrh had breakfast, a quiet meal. The children were off to the beach. His wife shared tea with him and thought it would be a fine morning.

"Yes," he said. "Shall we take the boat out? We can fish a little, take the sun."

"Marvelous," she said. Her gray eyes shone. He loved her—for herself, for her patience. He caught her hand on the crystal table, held slender fingers, not speaking his thoughts, which were far too somber for the morning.

They spent their mornings and their days together. He came back to her, time after shifting time. He might be gone a month; and home a week; and gone two months next time. He never dared cut it too close. They lost a great deal of each other's lives, and so much—so much he could not share with her.

"The island," he said. "Mhreihrrinn, I'd like to see it again."

"I'll pack," she said.

And went away.

He came back to her never aged; and she bore their two sons; and reared them; and managed the accounts: and explained his absences to relatives and the world. *He travels,* she would say, with that right amount of secrecy that protected secrets.

And even to her he could never confide what he knew.

"I trust you," she would say—knowing what he was, but never what he did.

He let her go. She went off to the hall and out the door—He imagined happy faces, holiday, the boys making haste to run the boat out and put on the bright colored sail. She would keep them busy carrying this and that, fetching food and clothes—things happened in shortest order when Mhreihrrinn set her hand to them.

He wanted that, wanted the familiar, the orderly, the homely. He was, if he let his mind dwell on things—afraid. He had the notion never to leave again.

He had been to the Now most recently—5045, and his flesh crawled at the memory. There was recklessness there. There was disquiet. The Now had traveled two decades and more since he had first begun, and he felt it more and more. The whole decade of the 5040's had a queasiness about it, ripples of instability as if the whole fabric of the Now were shifting like a kaleidoscope.

And it headed for the End of Time. It had become more and more like that age, confirming it by its very collapse.

People had illusions in the Now. They perceived what had not been true.

And yet it *was* when he came home.

It had grown to be so—while he was gone.

A university stood in Morurir, which he did not remember.

A hedge of trees grew where a building had been in Morurir.

A man was in the Council who had died.

He would not go back to Now. He had resolved that this morning.

Vocabulary Development: somber (SAHM ber) *adj.* dark and gloomy

Short Story

What do you learn about the **character** of Mhreihrrinn?

_____

_____

_____

Short Story

What details do you learn about the **setting** of Now? Underline words and groups of words in the text that tell you what it is like.

Reading Check

Where had Harrh been most recently? Underline the sentence that contains the answer.

Which **character** is the **protagonist**, or main character, of this story?

_____

Which character could be the **antagonist**, or enemy of the main character, in this story?

_____

Underline details in the story that help you decide who the antagonist is.

How is **conflict** introduced when Alhir mentions the potsherd?

_____
_____
_____

Is the conflict **internal** or **external**?

_____

Why does Alhir use his Master Key to visit Harrh? Underline the text that tells you why.

He had children, begotten before his first time-traveling. He had so very much to keep him—this place, this home, this stability—He was very well to do. He had invested well—his own small tampering. He had no lack, no need. He was mad to go on and on. He was done.

But a light distracted him, an opal shimmering beyond his breakfast nook, arrival in that receptor which his fine home afforded, linked to the master gate at Pyvrrhn.

A young man materialized there, opal and light and then solidity, a distraught young man.

"Harrh," the youth said, disregarding the decencies of meeting, and strode forward unasked. "Harrh, is everything all right here?"

Harrh arose from the crystal table even before the shimmer died, beset by that old queasiness of things out of joint. This was Alhir from 390 Since the Gate, an experienced man in the force: he had used a Master Key to come here—had such access, being what he was.

"Alhir," Harrh said, perplexed. "What's wrong?"

"You don't know." Alhir came as far as the door.

"A cup of tea?" Harrh said. Alhir had been here before. They were friends. There were oases along the course of suns, friendly years, places where houses served as rest-stops. In this too Mhreihrrinn was patient. "I've got to tell you— No, don't tell me. I don't want to know. I'm through. I've made up my mind. You can carry that where you're going. —But if you want the breakfast—"

"There's been an accident."

"I don't want to hear."

"He got past us."

"I don't want to know." He walked over to the cupboard, took another cup. "Mhreihrrinn's with the boys down at the beach. You just caught us." He set the cup down and poured the tea, where Mhreihrrinn had sat. "Won't you? You're always welcome here. Mhreihrrinn has no idea what you are. My young friend, she calls you. She doesn't know. Or she suspects. She'd never say.—Sit _down._"

Alhir had strayed aside, where a display case sat along the wall, a lighted case of <u>mementoes</u> of treasures, of crystal. "Harrh, there was a potsherd here."

"No," Harrh said, less and less comfortable. "Just the glasses. I'm quite sure."

"Harrh, it was very old."

"No," he said. "—I promised Mhreihrrinn and the boys— I mean it. I'm through. I don't want to know."

Vocabulary Development: mementoes (muh MEN tohz) _n._ souvenirs; objects that serve as reminders

"It came from Silen. From the digs at the First Gate, Harrh. It was a very valuable piece. You valued it very highly.—You don't remember."

"No," Harrh said, feeling fear thick about him, like a change in atmosphere. "I don't know of such a piece. I never had such a thing. Check your memory, Alhir."

"It was from the ruins by the *First Gate*, don't you understand?"

And then Alhir did not exist.

Harrh blinked, remembered pouring a cup of tea. But he was sitting in the chair, his breakfast before him.

He poured the tea and drank.

He was sitting on rock, amid the grasses blowing gently in the wind, on a clifftop by the sea.

He was standing there. "Mhreihrrinn," he said, in the first chill touch of fear.

But that memory faded. He had never had a wife, nor children. He forgot the house as well.

Trees grew and faded.

Rocks moved at random.

The time-menders were in most instances the only ones who survived even a little while.

Wrenched loose from time and with lives rooted in many parts of it, they felt it first and lived it longest, and not a few were trapped in backtime and did not die, but survived the horror of it and begot children who further confounded the time-line.

Time, stretched thin in possibilities, adjusted itself.

He was Harrh.

But he was many possibilities and many names.

In time none of them mattered.

He was many names; he lived. He had many bodies; and the souls stained his own.

In the end he remembered nothing at all, except the drive to live.

And the dreams.

And none of the dreams were true.

Vocabulary Development: confounded (kuhn FOWN did) *v.* confused; mixed up

---

Reader's Response: How do you feel about time travel after reading this short story? Explain your reasons.

_____

_____

_____

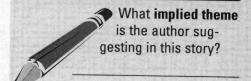

Short Story

What **implied theme** is the author suggesting in this story?

_____

_____

Circle details that support this theme.

Stop to Reflect

Why do you think Cherryh chooses to take the memories away from Harrh in this order?

_____

_____

_____

Short Story

How is Harrh's **conflict** resolved?

_____

_____

_____

The Short Story

1. **Draw Conclusions:** Harrh notices some changes in his own present of 1003. Then, Alhir notices the disappearance of the potsherd. Why are these changes important?

   _____

   _____

   _____

2. **Speculate:** What is the "accident" that Alhir reports to Harrh?

   _____

   _____

3. **Short Story:** Use the chart below to analyze key terms from the story.

Term	What It Means	Why It Is Important
the qhal		
Gate		
time-mender		
the Now		
End of Time		

4. **Short Story:** Does Cherryh emphasize **plot**, **character**, or **setting** in this short story? Explain your answer.

   _____

   _____

   _____

RESEARCH THE AUTHOR

Report

Investigate one of the science-fiction worlds that C. J. Cherryh has created. Present your findings to the class.

- Use the Internet or library resources to find one of the several science-fiction worlds that C. J. Cherryh has created. List the series and the novels you have chosen here.

  _____

  _____

  _____

- Take notes on the imagined universe, the beings that live there, and the conflicts they face.

  _____

  _____

  _____

  _____

  _____

  _____

- Decide on the main point you want to make about the world C. J. Cherryh has created. Write the topic sentence of your report here.

  _____

  _____

- Watch the video interview with C. J. Cherryh. How do C. J. Cherryh's writing techniques help her create such vivid science-fiction worlds?

  _____

  _____

Use your notes to support your main idea.

A Visit to Grandmother • A Problem

LITERARY ANALYSIS

Characters are the people, animals, or even objects that perform the actions and experience the events of a story. Writers use two main types of **characterization** to bring characters to life:

- **Direct characterization:** The writer tells readers exactly what a character is like.
- **Indirect characterization:** The writer reveals a character's traits through **dialogue** (the character's words), the character's actions and thoughts, and the effect the character has on others.

To better understand characters and gain insight into the message of a story, notice the **character development**—changes the character undergoes or new aspects of the character the writer reveals.

READING SKILL

An **inference** is an insight you reach that is based on stated details about information that is not stated directly. To make inferences, **relate characters and events to your own experience**.

For instance, when reading the story of a space captain on her first voyage, you might compare the captain with leaders whom you have known. Use this chart to relate your reading to your experiences.

Story Detail		Your Experience		Inference
The new captain's palms are sweating as she addresses the crew.	+	New camp counselors are nervous about whether campers will obey them.	→	The new captain is unsure of herself.

A Visit to Grandmother

William Melvin Kelley

Summary Charles and his son Chig pay an unexpected visit to Chig's grandmother. Charles is normally kind and caring. However, he treats his mother coldly. The family tells stories during dinner about Charles's brother. Charles does not find the stories funny. He confesses a secret he has believed since he was a child.

Reading/Writing Connection

Complete the paragraph to describe reasons for misunderstandings between people.

One person can <u>agitate</u> another by _____. Often,

the first person does not <u>comprehend</u> _____. In

some cases, a misunderstanding may cause two people to <u>dissolve</u>

_____.

Note-taking Guide

Use this diagram to summarize the major events of the story.

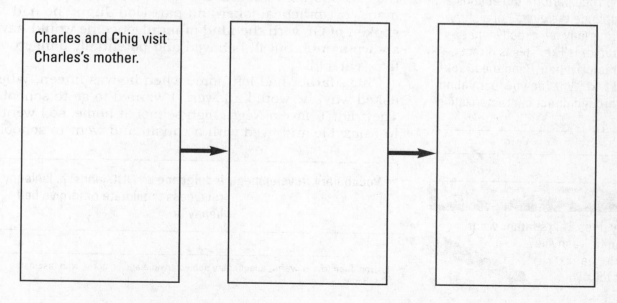

Charles and Chig visit Charles's mother.

Describe a relationship you have with a family member. When there is a conflict between the two of you, what do you do to resolve it?

_____

_____

An **inference** is a conclusion you reach that is based on stated details about information that is not stated directly. **Relate characters and events to your own experience** to make inferences. What can you infer about Charles's relationship with his mother from the way Chig describes him kissing her?

_____

_____

The **characters** are the people, animals, and even objects in a story. They perform the actions and experience the events of a story. A writer may tell exactly what a character is like. This is **direct characterization**. Read the bracketed text. What do you learn about GL through direct characterization?

_____

_____

Why does Chig's father want to go to Nashville? Circle the text that tells you.

A Visit to Grandmother

William Melvin Kelley

Chig knew something was wrong the instant his father kissed her. He had always known his father to be the warmest of men, a man so kind that when people ventured timidly into his office, it took only a few words from him to make them relax, and even laugh. Doctor Charles Dunford cared about people.

But when he had bent to kiss the old lady's black face, something new and almost ugly had come into his eyes: fear, uncertainty, sadness, and perhaps even hatred.

Ten days before in New York, Chig's father had decided suddenly he wanted to go to Nashville to attend his college class reunion, twenty years out. Both Chig's brother and sister, Peter and Connie, were packing for camp and besides were too young for such an affair. But Chig was seventeen, had nothing to do that summer, and his father asked if he would like to go along. His father had given him additional reasons: "All my running buddies got their diplomas and were snapped up by them crafty young gals, and had kids within a year—now all those kids, some of them gals, are your age."

The reunion had lasted a week. As they packed for home, his father, in a far too offhand way, had suggested they visit Chig's grandmother. "We this close. We might as well drop in on her and my brothers."

So, instead of going north, they had gone farther south, had just entered her house. And Chig had a suspicion now that the reunion had been only an excuse to drive south, that his father had been heading to this house all the time.

His father had never talked much about his family, with the exception of his brother, GL, who seemed part con man, part practical joker and part Don Juan;[1] he had spoken of GL with the kind of <u>indulgence</u> he would have shown a cute, but ill-behaved and potentially dangerous, five-year-old.

Chig's father had left home when he was fifteen. When asked why, he would answer: "I wanted to go to school. They didn't have a Negro high school at home, so I went up to Knoxville and lived with a cousin and went to school."

Vocabulary Development: indulgence (in DUL juhns) *n.* leniency; readiness to tolerate or forgive bad behavior

---

1. **Don Juan** (dahn wahn) a legendary nobleman, idle and immoral, who fascinates women.

They had been met at the door by Aunt Rose, GL's wife, and ushered into the living room. The old lady had looked up from her seat by the window. Aunt Rose stood between the visitors.

The old lady eyed his father. "Rose, who that? Rose?" She squinted. She looked like a doll, made of black straw, the wrinkles in her face running in one direction like the head of a broom. Her hair was white and coarse and grew out straight from her head. Her eyes were brown—the whites, too, seemed light brown—and were hidden behind thick glasses, which remained somehow on a tiny nose. "That Hiram?" That was another of his father's brothers. "No, it ain't Hiram; too big for Hiram." She turned then to Chig. "Now that man, he look like Eleanor, Charles's wife, but Charles wouldn't never send my grandson to see me. I never even hear from Charles." She stopped again.

"It Charles, Mama. That who it is." Aunt Rose, between them, led them closer. "It Charles come all the way from New York to see you, and brung little Charles with him."

The old lady stared up at them. "Charles? Rose, that really Charles?" She turned away, and reached for a handkerchief in the pocket of her clean, ironed, flowered housecoat, and wiped her eyes. "God have mercy, Charles." She spread her arms up to him, and he bent down and kissed her cheek. That was when Chig saw his face, grimacing. She hugged him; Chig watched the muscles in her arms as they tightened around his father's neck. She half rose out of her chair. "How are you, son?"

Chig could not hear his father's answer.

She let him go, and fell back into her chair, grabbing the arms. Her hands were as dark as the wood, and seemed to become part of it. "Now, who that standing there? Who that man?"

"That's one of your grandsons, Mama." His father's voice cracked. "Charles Dunford, junior. You saw him once, when he was a baby, in Chicago. He's grown now."

"I can see that, boy!" She looked at Chig squarely. "Come here, son, and kiss me once." He did. "What they call you? Charles too?"

"No, ma'am, they call me Chig."

She smiled. She had all her teeth, but they were too perfect to be her own. "That's good. Can't have two boys answering to Charles in the same house. Won't nobody at all come. So you that little boy. You don't remember me, do you. I used to take you to church in Chicago, and you'd get up and hop in time to the music. You studying to be a preacher?"

Vocabulary Development: grimacing (GRIM uhs ing) *v.* making a twisted face showing disgust or pain

---

TAKE NOTES

Literary Analysis

A writer may also reveal a character's traits through **dialogue**, or the character's words. This is **indirect characterization**. What is revealed about the grandmother's vision in the underlined text?

_____

_____

_____

_____

Reading Skill

What can you **infer** about the grandmother's feelings when she sees her son? Circle the details that support your inference.

_____

_____

_____

_____

_____

Reading Check

When was the last time the grandmother saw Chig? Underline the sentence that answers the question.

Literary Analysis

Read the bracketed **dialogue**. Name one trait of the grandmother that is suggested in the dialogue. Circle the line or lines of dialogue that support your conclusion.

_____

_____

Reading Skill

What can you **infer** about Chig's upbringing by how he treats his grandmother?

_____

_____

_____

Literary Analysis

Notice the **character development**, or the changes the character goes through. This may include new things about the character that the writer reveals. What does the writer reveal about Charles in the bracketed paragraph?

_____

_____

Reading Check

By how many years is GL older than Chig's father? Underline the text that tells you.

"No, ma'am. I don't think so. I might be a lawyer."

"You'll be an honest one, won't you?"

"I'll try."

"Trying ain't enough! You be honest, you hear? Promise me. You be honest like your daddy."

"All right. I promise."

"Good. Rose, where's GL at? Where's that thief? He gone again?"

"I don't know, Mama." Aunt Rose looked embarrassed. "He say he was going by the store. He'll be back."

"Well, then where's Hiram? You call up those boys, and get them over here—now! You got enough to eat? Let me go see." She started to get up. Chig reached out his hand. She shook him off. "What they tell you about me, Chig? They tell you I'm all laid up? Don't believe it. They don't know nothing about old ladies. When I want help, I'll let you know. Only time I'll need help getting anywheres is when I dies and they lift me into the ground."

She was standing now, her back and shoulders straight. She came only to Chig's chest. She squinted up at him. "You eat much? Your daddy ate like two men."

"Yes, ma'am."

"That's good. That means you ain't nervous. Your mama, she ain't nervous. I remember that. In Chicago, she'd sit down by a window all afternoon and never say nothing, just knit." She smiled. "Let me see what we got to eat."

"I'll do that, Mama." Aunt Rose spoke softly. "You haven't seen Charles in a long time. You sit and talk."

The old lady squinted at her. "You can do the cooking if you promise it ain't because you think I can't."

Aunt Rose chuckled. "I know you can do it, Mama."

"All right. I'll just sit and talk a spell." She sat again and arranged her skirt around her short legs.

Chig did most of the talking, told all about himself before she asked. His father spoke only when he was spoken to, and then, only one word at a time, as if by coming back home, he had become a small boy again, sitting in the parlor while his mother spoke with her guests.

When Uncle Hiram and Mae, his wife, came they sat down to eat. Chig did not have to ask about Uncle GL's absence; Aunt Rose volunteered an explanation: "Can't never tell where the man is at. One Thursday morning he left here and next thing we knew, he was calling from Chicago, saying he went up to see Joe Louis[2] fight. He'll be here though; he ain't as young and footloose as he used to be." Chig's father had mentioned driving down that GL was about five years older than he was, nearly fifty.

Uncle Hiram was somewhat smaller than Chig's father; his short-cropped kinky hair was half gray, half black.

---

2. **Joe Louis** (1914–1981) U.S. boxer and the world heavyweight champion from 1937 to 1949.

One spot, just off his forehead, was totally white. Later, Chig found out it had been that way since he was twenty. Mae (Chig could not bring himself to call her Aunt) was a good deal younger than Hiram, pretty enough so that Chig would have looked at her twice on the street. She was a honey-colored woman, with long eyelashes. She was wearing a white sheath.

At dinner, Chig and his father sat on one side, opposite Uncle Hiram and Mae; his grandmother and Aunt Rose sat at the ends. The food was good; there was a lot and Chig ate a lot. All through the meal, they talked about the family as it had been thirty years before, and particularly about the young GL. Mae and Chig asked questions; the old lady answered; Aunt Rose directed the discussion, steering the old lady onto the best stories; Chig's father laughed from time to time; Uncle Hiram ate.

"Why don't you tell them about the horse, Mama?" Aunt Rose, over Chig's weak protest, was spooning mashed potatoes onto his plate. "There now, Chig."

"I'm trying to think." The old lady was holding her fork halfway to her mouth, looking at them over her glasses. "Oh, you talking about that crazy horse GL brung home that time."

"That's right, Mama." Aunt Rose nodded and slid another slice of white meat on Chig's plate.

Mae started to giggle. "Oh, I've heard this. This is funny, Chig."

The old lady put down her fork and began: Well, GL went out of the house one day with an old, no-good chair I wanted him to take over to the church for a bazaar, and he met up with this man who'd just brung in some horses from out West. Now, I reckon you can expect one swindler[3] to be in every town, but you don't rightly think there'll be two, and God forbid they should ever meet—but they did, GL and his chair, this man and his horses. Well, I wished I'd-a been there; there must-a been some mighty high-powered talking going on. That man with his horses, he told GL them horses was half-Arab, half-Indian, and GL told that man the chair was an antique he'd stole from some rich white folks. So they swapped. Well, I was a-looking out the window and seen GL dragging this animal to the house. It looked pretty gentle and its eyes was most closed and its feet was shuffling.

"GL, where'd you get that thing?" I says.

"I swapped him for that old chair, Mama," he says. "And made myself a bargain. This is even better than Papa's horse."

---

3. **swindler** (SWIND ler) *n.* a cheater; a person who takes the money or property of others using deception.

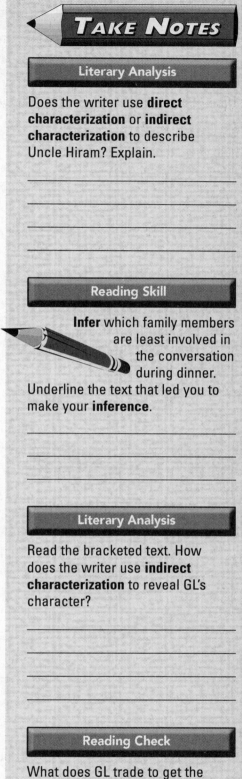

TAKE NOTES

Literary Analysis

Does the writer use **direct characterization** or **indirect characterization** to describe Uncle Hiram? Explain.

_____
_____
_____
_____

Reading Skill

Infer which family members are least involved in the conversation during dinner. Underline the text that led you to make your **inference**.

_____
_____
_____

Literary Analysis

Read the bracketed text. How does the writer use **indirect characterization** to reveal GL's character?

_____
_____
_____
_____

Reading Check

What does GL trade to get the horse? Circle the text that tells you.

Think of a person you know who likes to get attention. How does **relating your own experiences** help you understand GL's trying to get his mother to go for a ride?

_____

_____

_____

The grandmother decides to go with GL against her better judgment. What does this reveal about her **character**?

_____

_____

_____

Read the underlined sentence. What can you **infer** about why the grandmother felt good when GL did these things?

_____

_____

_____

Well, I'm a-looking at this horse and noticing how he be looking more and more wide awake every minute, sort of warming up like a teakettle until, I swears to you, that horse is blowing steam out its nose.

"Come on, Mama," GL says, "come on and I'll take you for a ride." Now George, my husband, God rest his tired soul, he'd brung home this white folks' buggy which had a busted wheel and fixed it and was to take it back that day and GL says: "Come on, Mama, we'll use this fine buggy and take us a ride."

"GL," I says, "no, we ain't. Them white folks'll burn us alive if we use their buggy. You just take that horse right on back." You see, I was sure that boy'd come by that animal ungainly.

"Mama, I can't take him back," GL says.

"Why not?" I says.

"Because I don't rightly know where that man is at," GL says.

"Oh," I says. "Well, then I reckon we stuck with it." And I turned around to go back into the house because it was getting late, near dinner time, and I was cooking for ten.

"Mama," GL says to my back. "Mama, ain't you coming for a ride with me?"

"Go on, boy. You ain't getting me inside kicking range of that animal." I was eying that beast and it was boiling hotter all the time. I reckon maybe that man had drugged it. "That horse is wild, GL," I says.

"No, he ain't. He ain't. That man say he is buggy and saddle broke⁴ and as sweet as the inside of a apple."

My oldest girl, Essie, had-a come out on the porch and she says: "Go on, Mama. I'll cook. You ain't been out the house in weeks."

"Sure, come on, Mama," GL says. "There ain't nothing to be fidgety about. This horse is gentle as a rose petal." And just then that animal snorts so hard it sets up a little dust storm around its feet.

"Yes, Mama," Essie says, "you can see he gentle." Well, I looked at Essie and then at that horse because I didn't think we could be looking at the same animal. I should-a figured how Essie's eyes ain't never been so good.

"Come on, Mama," GL says.

"All right," I says. So I stood on the porch and watched GL hitching that horse up to the white folks' buggy. For a while there, the animal was pretty quiet, pawing a little, but not much. And I was feeling a little better about riding with GL behind that crazy-looking horse. I could see how GL was happy I was going with him. He was scurrying around that animal buckling buckles and strapping straps, all the time smiling, and that made me feel good.

---

4. **buggy and saddle broke** trained to carry a mounted rider or to pull a carriage.

Then he was finished, and I must say, that horse looked mighty fine hitched to that buggy and I knew anybody what climbed up there would look pretty good too. GL came around and stood at the bottom of the steps, and took off his hat and bowed and said: "Madam," and reached out his hand to me and I was feeling real elegant like a fine lady. He helped me up to the seat and then got up beside me and we moved out down our alley. And I remember how colored folks come out on their porches and shook their heads, saying: "Lord now, will you look at Eva Dunford, the fine lady! Don't she look good sitting up there!" And I pretended not to hear and sat up straight and proud.

We rode on through the center of town, up Market Street, and all the way out where Hiram is living now, which in them days was all woods, there not being even a farm in sight and that's when that horse must-a first realized he weren't at all broke or tame or maybe thought he was back out West again, and started to gallop.

"GL," I says, "now you ain't joking with your mama, is you? Because if you is, I'll strap you purple if I live through this."

Well, GL was pulling on the reins with all his meager strength, and yelling, "Whoa, you. Say now, whoa!" He turned to me just long enough to say, "I ain't fooling with you, Mama. Honest!"

I reckon that animal weren't too satisfied with the road, because it made a sharp right turn just then, down into a gulley and struck out across a hilly meadow. "Mama," GL yells. "Mama, do something!"

I didn't know what to do, but I figured I had to do something so I stood up, hopped down onto the horse's back and pulled it to a stop. Don't ask me how I did that; I reckon it was that I was a mother and my baby asked me to do something, is all.

"Well, we walked that animal all the way home; sometimes I had to club it over the nose with my fist to make it come, but we made it, GL and me. You remember how tired we was, Charles?"

"I wasn't here at the time." Chig turned to his father and found his face completely blank, without even a trace of a smile or a laugh.

"Well, of course you was, son. That happened in . . . in . . . it was a hot summer that year and—"

"I left here in June of that year. You wrote me about it."

The old lady stared past Chig at him. They all turned to him; Uncle Hiram looked up from his plate.

Vocabulary Development: trace (trays) *n.* tiny amount; hint

How does Charles respond to the grandmother's story about GL? What **inference** can you make about Charles from his response? Underline details that support your answer.

_____

_____

_____

_____

_____

What new information is revealed about Charles's **character**?

_____

_____

_____

_____

When was the last time Charles cried? Underline the text that tells you.

"Then you don't remember how we all laughed?"

"No, I don't, Mama. And I probably wouldn't have laughed. I don't think it was funny." They were staring into each other's eyes.

"Why not, Charles?"

"Because in the first place, the horse was gained by fraud. And in the second place, both of you might have been seriously injured or even killed." He broke off their stare and spoke to himself more than to any of them: "And if I'd done it, you would've beaten me good for it."

"Pardon?" The old lady had not heard him; only Chig had heard.

Chig's father sat up straight as if preparing to debate. "I said that if I had done it, if I had done just exactly what GL did, you would have beaten me good for it, Mama." He was looking at her again.

"Why you say that, son?" She was leaning toward him.

"Don't you know? Tell the truth. It can't hurt me now." His voice cracked, but only once. "If GL and I did something wrong, you'd beat me first and then be too tired to beat him. At dinner, he'd always get seconds and I wouldn't. You'd do things with him, like ride in that buggy, but if I wanted you to do something with me, you were always too busy." He paused and considered whether to say what he finally did say: "I cried when I left here. Nobody loved me, Mama. I cried all the way up to Knoxville. That was the last time I ever cried in my life."

"Oh, Charles." She started to get up, to come around the table to him.

He stopped her. "It's too late."

"But you don't understand."

"What don't I understand? I understood then; I understand now."

Tears now traveled down the lines in her face, but when she spoke, her voice was clear. "I thought you knew. I had ten children. I had to give all of them what they needed most." She nodded. "I paid more mind to GL. I had to. GL could-a ended up swinging if I hadn't. But you was smarter. You was more growed up than GL when you was five and he was ten, and I tried to show you that by letting you do what you wanted to do."

"That's not true, Mama. You know it. GL was light-skinned and had good hair and looked almost white and you loved him for that."

"Charles, no. No, son. I didn't love any one of you more than any other."

"That can't be true." His father was standing now, his fists clenched tight. "Admit it, Mama . . . please!" Chig looked at him, shocked; the man was actually crying.

"It may not-a been right what I done, but I ain't no liar." Chig knew she did not really understand what had happened, what he wanted of her. "I'm not lying to you, Charles."

Chig's father had gone pale. He spoke very softly. "You're about thirty years too late, Mama." He bolted from the table. Silverware and dishes rang and jumped. Chig heard him hurrying up to their room.

They sat in silence for a while and then heard a key in the front door. A man with a new, lacquered[5] straw hat came in. He was wearing brown and white two-tone shoes with very pointed toes and a white summer suit. "Say now! Man! I heard my brother was in town. Where he at? Where that rascal?"

He stood in the doorway, smiling broadly, an engaging, open, friendly smile, the innocent smile of a five-year-old.

---

5. **lacquered** (LAK erd) *adj.* coated with a hardened protective layer of resinous material, which gives a shine.

Reader's Response: Do you believe Charles's mother? Why or why not?

_____

_____

_____

_____

TAKE NOTES

Reading Skill

What can you **infer** about GL's feelings toward Charles?

_____

_____

_____

_____

Reading Check

Does Charles forgive his mother? Underline the text that tells you.

A Visit to Grandmother

1. **Hypothesize:** Charles says that he left home because there was no high school for African Americans. What other reasons might Charles have had for leaving home?

   _____

   _____

2. **Speculate:** What do you think Charles's relationship with his mother might be like in the future? Explain.

   _____

   _____

3. **Literary Analysis:** Use the chart to show two examples of **indirect characterization** of Charles.

What He Says	What He Does	What Others Say About Him
"We this close. We might as well drop in on her and my brothers."		

4. **Reading Skill:** Make an **inference** about Charles's feelings toward GL. Explain which details from the story you used to make your inference.

   _____

   _____

SUPPORT FOR WRITING AND EXTEND YOUR LEARNING

Writing: Retellings

Write two brief **retellings** of the events in "A Visit to Grandmother." First, retell the story as Mama would tell it. Then, retell the story from GL's viewpoint. List the main events of the story. Identify details that will show the difference from the characters' perspectives. Use your notes to write your retellings.

1. Event: _____
   1. Mama's view: _____
   2. GL's view: _____

2. Event: _____
   1. Mama's view: _____
   2. GL's view: _____

Listening and Speaking: Overview of Speech Patterns

Prepare an **overview of speech patterns** of the characters in the story. List the major characters, examples of their speech, and social and regional factors for their speech. Complete the following to help you organize your analysis.

First Example: _____

Character: _____

Social and Regional Factors: _____

Second Example: _____

Character: _____

Social and Regional Factors: _____

Third Example: _____

Character: _____

Social and Regional Factors: _____

A Problem

Anton Chekhov

Summary Three uncles must decide what to do with their young nephew Sasha. Sasha has cashed a false promissory note. His uncles debate Sasha's crime. They can quietly pay the debt and save the family honor. Or, they can let him stand trial to accept public punishment.

Reading/Writing Connection

Complete this paragraph to describe how media attention may affect someone.

The way that the media reports information about someone causes people to <u>define</u> _____. A media report may <u>injure</u> _____. A media report may also <u>isolate</u> _____.

Note-taking Guide

Use this chart to record how each character views Sasha's crime.

Character	How the Character Views the Problem	Character's Desired Solution
Sasha Uskov	Does not think he has committed a crime; feels indifferent to the consequences	Wants uncles to pay the note
The Colonel		
The Treasury official		
Ivan Markovitch		

A Problem

1. **Infer:** How does Ivan Markovitch change the Colonel's mind?

_____

_____

_____

2. **Take a Position:** What should Ivan Markovitch have done when Sasha asked him for money after the meeting? Explain.

_____

_____

_____

3. **Literary Analysis:** Identify three examples of the author's use of **indirect characterization** to portray Sasha. Use a chart such as the one shown here.

What He Says	What He Does	What Others Say About Him

4. **Reading Skill:** How does Ivan Markovitch feel at the end of the story? Use story details and your own experience to make an **inference**.

_____

_____

_____

SUPPORT FOR WRITING AND EXTEND YOUR LEARNING

Writing: Retellings

Write two short **retellings** of the events in "A Problem." First, retell the story as one of the uncles would tell it. Then, retell it as Sasha would tell it.

- Look at the events in the story as the uncle would see them. List four events the uncle would consider the main events.

_____

_____

- Choose words that express the uncle's thoughts and feelings. List five words you think this character would use to tell the story.

_____

_____

Repeat this process to retell the story as Sasha would tell it.

Research and Technology: Report on Sources

Write a **report on sources** for a research project about the social status in Russia during the nineteenth century. Use the library or the Internet to find three to four sources. Consider whether each source is accurate and reliable. Use this chart to help you write your report.

	Title	Author/ Credentials	Date Published	Reliability/ Accuracy
Source 1				
Source 2				
Source 3				
Source 4				

The Street of the Cañon •
There Will Come Soft Rains

LITERARY ANALYSIS

All stories have a **setting**—the time and the place of the story's events. Writers use **description**, or word-pictures appealing to the senses, to establish a setting. Settings shape stories in different ways:

- Setting may determine plot. In a story set in the Arctic wilderness, characters will face challenges not found in a Caribbean resort hotel.

- Setting may shape a character's concerns and values. A character from the days of knights may be concerned with honor. A character from the Stone Age may be concerned only with survival.

Use this chart to identify the setting of the story and the details that describe it.

When		Where
	+	
Descriptive Details		**Descriptive Details**

READING SKILL

An **inference** is an insight, based on stated details, about information that is not stated directly. Drawing inferences helps you make connections between facts or events. For instance, if a writer does not name a setting but describes extreme cold, hunters huddled in igloos, and a night that will last all winter, you can make the inference that the story is set in the Arctic.

Read on to find additional support after you make an inference. Modify your inference if new details contradict the inference.

The Street of the Cañon

Josephina Niggli

Summary A stranger comes to Sarita Calderón's eighteenth birthday celebration. He carries a mysterious package with him. He dances with Sarita. They talk about the quarrel between their villages. The mysterious package is opened. Sarita realizes that she may know who the stranger is.

Reading/Writing Connection

Complete these sentences. Describe reasons that people sometimes use humor during a disagreement.

1. A person might <u>provoke</u> someone _____.

2. Sometimes humor can <u>diminish</u> _____.

3. Humor is one way to <u>mediate</u> _____.

Note-taking Guide

Use this diagram to record details about the story.

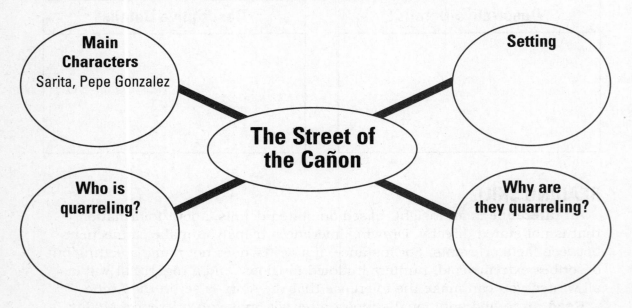

The Street of the Cañon
Josephina Niggli

It was May, the flowering thorn was sweet in the air, and the village of San Juan Iglesias in the Valley of the Three Marys was celebrating. The long dark streets were empty because all of the people, from the lowest-paid cowboy to the mayor, were helping Don Roméo Calderón celebrate his daughter's eighteenth birthday.

On the other side of the town, where the Cañon Road led across the mountains to the Sabinas Valley, a tall slender man, a package clutched tightly against his side, slipped from shadow to shadow. Once a dog barked, and the man's black suit merged into the blackness of a wall. But no voice called out, and after a moment he slid into the narrow, dirt-packed street again.

The moonlight touched his shoulder and spilled across his narrow hips. He was young, no more than twenty-five, and his black curly head was bare. He walked swiftly along, heading always for the distant sound of guitar and flute. If he met anyone now, who could say from which direction he had come? He might be a trader from Monterrey, or a buyer of cow's milk from farther north in the Valley of the Three Marys. Who would guess that an Hidalgo man dared to walk alone in the moonlit streets of San Juan Iglesias?

Carefully adjusting his flat package so that it was not too prominent, he squared his shoulders and walked jauntily across the street to the laughter-filled house. Little boys packed in the doorway made way for him, smiling and nodding to him. The long, narrow room with the orchestra at one end was filled with whirling dancers. Rigid-backed chaperones[1] were gossiping together, seated in their straight chairs against the plaster walls. Over the scene was the yellow glow of kerosene lanterns, and the air was hot with the too-sweet perfume of gardenias, tuberoses,[2] and the pungent scent of close-packed humanity.

The man in the doorway, while trying to appear at ease, was carefully examining every smiling face. If just one person recognized him, the room would turn on him like a den of snarling mountain cats, but so far all the laughter-dancing eyes were friendly.

1. **chaperones** (SHAP uh rohnz) older or married women who accompany and supervise the behavior of a young person in public.
2. **gardenias** (gahr DEEN yuhz), **tuberoses** (TOOB rohz iz) two types of plant with especially sweet-smelling flowers.

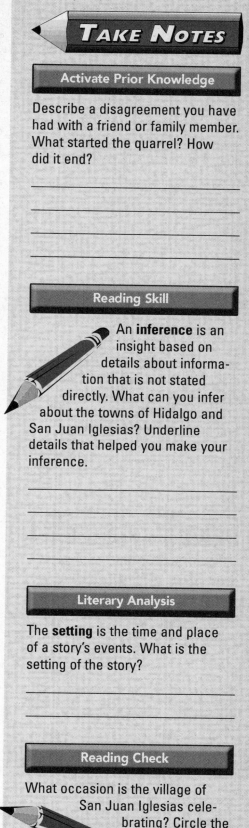

TAKE NOTES

Activate Prior Knowledge

Describe a disagreement you have had with a friend or family member. What started the quarrel? How did it end?

_____

_____

_____

Reading Skill

An **inference** is an insight based on details about information that is not stated directly. What can you infer about the towns of Hidalgo and San Juan Iglesias? Underline details that helped you make your inference.

_____

_____

_____

Literary Analysis

The **setting** is the time and place of a story's events. What is the setting of the story?

_____

_____

Reading Check

What occasion is the village of San Juan Iglesias celebrating? Circle the sentence that tells you.

Reading Skill

What **inference** can you make about the stranger? Why does he not want to be recognized by the people of San Juan Iglesias?

_____

_____

_____

_____

Literary Analysis

Writers use **description**, or word-pictures appealing to the senses, to help create a setting. Underline details about the setting in the first bracketed passage. What sense does the description of the setting most appeal to?

_____

_____

Reading Skill

Read the second bracketed passage. Make an **inference** about the age at which women in San Juan Iglesias usually marry.

_____

_____

Reading Check

Who welcomed the stranger to the party? Circle the text that tells you.

Suddenly a plump, officious little man, his round cheeks glistening with perspiration, pushed his way through the crowd. His voice, many times too large for his small body, boomed at the man in the doorway. "Welcome, stranger, welcome to our house." Thrusting his arm through the stranger's, and almost dislodging the package, he started to lead the way through the maze of dancers. "Come and drink a toast to my daughter—to my beautiful Sarita. She is eighteen this night."

In the square patio the gentle breeze ruffled the pink and white oleander bushes. A long table set up on sawhorses held loaves of flaky crusted French bread, stacks of thin, delicate tortillas, plates of barbecued beef, and long red rolls of spicy sausages. But most of all there were cheeses, for the Three Marys was a cheese-eating valley. There were yellow cheese and white cheese and curded cheese from cow's milk. There was even a flat white cake of goat cheese from distant Linares, a delicacy too expensive for any but feast days.

To set off this feast were bottles of beer floating in ice-filled tin tubs, and another table was covered with bottles of mescal, of tequila, of maguey wine.

Don Roméo Calderón thrust a glass of tequila into the stranger's hand. "Drink, friend, to the prettiest girl in San Juan. As pretty as my fine fighting cocks, she is. On her wedding day she takes to her man, and may she find him soon, the best fighter in my flock. Drink deep, friend. Even the rivers flow with wine."

The Hidalgo man laughed and raised his glass high. "May the earth be always fertile beneath her feet."

Someone called to Don Roméo that more guests were arriving, and with a final delighted pat on the stranger's shoulder, the little man scurried away. As the young fellow smiled after his retreating host, his eyes caught and held another pair of eyes—laughing black eyes set in a young girl's face. The last time he had seen that face it had been white and tense with rage, and the lips clenched tight to prevent an outgushing stream of angry words. That had been in February, and she had worn a white lace shawl over her hair. Now it was May, and a gardenia was a splash of white in the glossy dark braids. The moonlight had mottled his face that February night, and he knew that she did not recognize him. He grinned impudently[3] back at her, and her eyes widened, then slid sideways to one of the chaperones. The fan in her small hand snapped shut. She tapped its parchment tip against her mouth and slipped away to join the dancing couples in the front room. The gestures of a fan translate into a

---

3. **impudently** (IM pyuh duhnt lee) *adv.* in a shamelessly bold or provocative way.

coded language on the frontier. The stranger raised one eyebrow as he interpreted the signal.

But he did not move toward her at once. Instead, he inched slowly back against the table. No one was behind him, and his hands quickly unfastened the package he had been guarding so long. Then he <u>nonchalantly</u> walked into the front room.

The girl was sitting close to a chaperone. As he came up to her he swerved slightly toward the bushy-browed old lady.

"Your servant, señora. I kiss your hands and feet."

The chaperone stared at him in astonishment. Such fine manners were not common to the town of San Juan Iglesias.

"Eh, you're a stranger," she said. "I thought so."

"But a stranger no longer, señora, now that I have met you." He bent over her, so close she could smell the faint fragrance of talcum on his freshly shaven cheek.

"Will you dance the *parada* with me?"

This request startled her eyes into popping open beneath the heavy brows. "So, my young rooster, would you flirt with me, and I old enough to be your grandmother?"

"Can you show me a prettier woman to flirt with in the Valley of the Three Marys?" he asked audaciously.

She grinned at him and turned toward the girl at her side. "This young fool wants to meet you, my child."

The girl blushed to the roots of her hair and shyly lowered her white lids. The old woman laughed aloud.

"Go out and dance, the two of you. A man clever enough to pat the sheep has a right to play with the lamb."

The next moment they had joined the circle of dancers and Sarita was trying to control her laughter.

"She is the worst dragon in San Juan. And how easily you won her!"

"What is a dragon," he asked <u>imperiously</u>, "when I longed to dance with you?"

"Ay," she retorted, "you have a quick tongue. I think you are a dangerous man."

In answer he drew her closer to him, and turned her toward the orchestra. As he reached the chief violinist he called out, "Play the *Virgencita*, 'The Shy Young Maiden.'"

The violinist's mouth opened in soundless surprise. The girl in his arms said sharply, "You heard him, the Borachita, 'The Little Drunken Girl.'"

Vocabulary Development: nonchalantly (nahn shuh LAHNT lee) *adv.* casually; indifferently
imperiously (im PEER ee uhs lee) *adv.* arrogantly

TAKE NOTES

Stop to Reflect

What do you think the stranger's intentions are?

_____

_____

_____

_____

Reading Skill

Read the bracketed passage. What inference can you make about the two towns?

_____

_____

Reading Check

What did the men from Hidalgo try to do three months earlier? Underline details in the story that answer the question.

Literary Analysis

How does the **setting** of the dance floor help the stranger to keep his identity secret?

_____

_____

_____

With a relieved grin, the violinist tapped his music stand with his bow, and the music swung into the sad farewell of a man to his sweetheart:

Farewell, my little drunken one,
I must go to the capital
To serve the master
Who makes me weep for my return.

The stranger frowned down at her. "Is this a joke, señorita?" he asked coldly.

"No," she whispered, looking about her quickly to see if the incident had been observed. "But the *Virgencita* is the favorite song of Hidalgo, a village on the other side of the mountains in the next valley. The people of Hidalgo and San Juan Iglesias do not speak."

"That is a stupid thing," said the man from Hidalgo as he swung her around in a large turn. "Is not music free as air? Why should one town own the rights to a song?"

The girl shuddered slightly. "Those people from Hidalgo—they are wicked monsters. Can you guess what they did not six months since?"

The man started to point out that the space of time from February to May was three months, but he thought it better not to appear too wise. "Did these Hidalgo monsters frighten you, señorita? If they did, I personally will kill them all."

She moved closer against him and tilted her face until her mouth was close to his ear. "They attempted to steal the bones of Don Rómolo Balderas."

"Is it possible?" He made his eyes grow round and his lips purse up in disdain. "Surely not that! Why, all the world knows that Don Rómolo Balderas was the greatest historian in the entire Republic. Every school child reads his books. Wise men from Quintana Roo to the Río Bravo bow their heads in admiration to his name. What a wicked thing to do!" He hoped his virtuous tone was not too virtuous for plausibility, but she did not seem to notice.

"It is true! In the night they came. Three devils!"

"Young devils, I hope."

"Young or old, who cares? They were devils. The blacksmith surprised them even as they were opening the grave. He raised such a shout that all of San Juan rushed to his aid, for they were fighting, I can tell you. Especially one of them—their leader."

Vocabulary Development: plausibility (plaw zuh BIL uh tee) *n.* believability; seeming truth

"And who was he?"

"You have heard of him doubtless. A proper wild one named Pepe Gonzalez."

"And what happened to them?"

"They had horses and got away, but one, I think, was hurt."

The Hidalgo man twisted his mouth remembering how Rubén the candymaker had ridden across the whitewashed line high on the Cañon trail that marked the division between the Three Marys' and the Sabinas' sides of the mountains, and then had fallen in a faint from his saddle because his left arm was broken. There was no candy in Hidalgo for six weeks, and the entire Sabinas Valley resented that broken arm as fiercely as did Rubén.

The stranger tightened his arm in reflexed anger about Sarita's waist as she said, "All the world knows that the men of Hidalgo are sons of the mountain witches."

"But even devils are shy of disturbing the honored dead," he said gravely.

"'Don Rómolo was born in our village,' Hidalgo says. 'His bones belong to us.' Well, anyone in the valley can tell you he died in San Juan Iglesias, and here his bones will stay! Is that not proper? Is that not right?"

To keep from answering, he guided her through an intricate dance pattern that led them past the patio door. Over her head he could see two men and a woman staring with amazement at the open package on the table.

His eyes on the patio, he asked blandly, "You say the leader was one Pepe Gonzalez? The name seems to have a familiar sound."

"But naturally. He has a talent." She tossed her head and stepped away from him as the music stopped. It was a dance of two *paradas*. He slipped his hand through her arm and guided her into place in the large oval of parading couples. Twice around the room and the orchestra would play again.

"A talent?" he prompted.

"For doing the impossible. When all the world says a thing cannot be done, he does it to prove the world wrong. Why, he climbed to the top of the Prow, and not even the long vanished Joaquín Castillo had ever climbed that mountain before. And this same Pepe caught a mountain lion with nothing to aid him but a rope and his two bare hands."

"He doesn't sound such a bad friend," protested the stranger, slipping his arm around her waist as the music began to play the merry song of the soap bubbles:

Reading Skill

Make an **inference** about the stranger's connection to the men who tried to raid the grave.

_____

_____

_____

_____

Literary Analysis

Read the bracketed text. What is the **setting** for Pepe Gonzalez's adventures?

_____

_____

_____

_____

Reading Skill

Make an **inference** about the package the man brought with him. What do you think is in it?

_____

_____

Reading Check

Why do the people of Hidalgo say Don Romolo's bones should stay in their village? Underline the sentence that tells you.

Read the underlined sentence. Make an **inference** about why the stranger thinks this is his last moment of peace with Sarita.

_____

_____

_____

_____

Why do you think the stranger asked Sarita to walk around the plaza with him?

_____

_____

_____

What is Sarita's response to the stranger when he asks whether she will walk around the plaza with him? Circle the answer in the text. How does the time and place of the **setting** affect the way she responds to him?

_____

_____

_____

Why did the stranger not tell Sarita his name? Underline the sentence that tells you.

_____

_____

_____

Pretty bubbles of a thousand colors
That ride on the wind
And break as swiftly
As a lover's heart.

The events in the patio were claiming his attention. Little by little he edged her closer to the door. The group at the table had considerably enlarged. There was a low murmur of excitement from the crowd.

"What has happened?" asked Sarita, attracted by the noise.

"There seems to be something wrong at the table," he answered, while trying to peer over the heads of the people in front of him. Realizing that this might be the last moment of peace he would have that evening, he bent toward her.

"If I come back on Sunday, will you walk around the plaza with me?"

She was startled into exclaiming, "Ay, no!"

"Please. Just once around."

"And you think I'd walk more than once with you, señor, even if you were no stranger? In San Juan Iglesias, to walk around the plaza with a girl means a wedding."

"Ha, and you think that is common to San Juan alone? Even the devils of Hidalgo respect that law," he added hastily at her puzzled upward glance. "And so they do in all the villages." To cover his lapse[4] he said softly, "I don't even know your name."

A mischievous grin crinkled the corners of her eyes. "Nor do I know yours, señor. Strangers do not often walk the streets of San Juan."

Before he could answer, the chattering in the patio swelled to louder proportions. Don Roméo's voice lay on top, like thick cream on milk. "I tell you it is a jewel of a cheese. Such flavor, such texture, such whiteness. It is a jewel of a cheese."

"What has happened?" Sarita asked of a woman at her elbow.

"A fine goat's cheese appeared as if by magic on the table. No one knows where it came from."

"Probably an extra one from Linares," snorted a fat bald man on the right.

"Linares never made such a cheese as this," said the woman decisively.

"Silence!" roared Don Roméo. "Old Tío Daniel would speak a word to us."

A great hand of silence closed down over the mouths of the people. The girl was standing on tiptoe trying vainly to

_____

4. **lapse** (laps) *n.* slip; error.

see what was happening. She was hardly aware of the stranger's whispering voice although she remembered the words that he said. "Sunday night—once around the plaza."

She did not realize that he had moved away, leaving a gap that was quickly filled by the blacksmith.

Old Tío Daniel's voice was a shrill squeak, and his thin, stringy neck jutted forth from his body like a turtle's from its shell. "This is no cheese from Linares," he said with authority, his mouth sucking in over his toothless gums between his sentences. "Years ago, when the great Don Rómolo Balderas was still alive, we had such cheese as this—ay, in those days we had it. But after he died and was buried in our own sainted ground, as was right and proper . . ."

"Yes, yes," muttered voices in the crowd. He glared at the interruption. As soon as there was silence again, he continued:

"After he died, we had it no more. Shall I tell you why?"

"Tell us, Tío Daniel," said the voices humbly.

"Because it is made in Hidalgo!"

The sound of a waterfall, the sound of a wind in a narrow cañon, and the sound of an angry crowd are much the same. There were no distinct words, but the sound was enough.

"Are you certain, Tío?" boomed Don Roméo.

"As certain as I am that a donkey has long ears. The people of Hidalgo have been famous for generations for making cheese like this—especially that wicked one, that owner of a cheese factory, Timotéo Gonzalez, father to Pepe, the wild one, whom we have good cause to remember."

"We do, we do," came the sigh of assurance.

"But on the whole northern frontier there are no vats like his to produce so fine a product. Ask the people of Chihuahua, of Sonora. Ask the man on the bridge at Laredo, or the man in his boat at Tampico, 'Hola, friend, who makes the finest goat cheese?' And the answer will always be the same, 'Don Timotéo of Hidalgo.'"

It was the blacksmith who asked the great question. "Then where did that cheese come from, and we haters of Hidalgo these ten long years?"

No voice said, "The stranger," but with one fluid movement every head in the patio turned toward the girl in the doorway. She also turned, her eyes wide with something that she realized to her own amazement was more apprehension[5] than anger.

But the stranger was not in the room. When the angry, muttering men pushed through to the street, the stranger

---

5. **apprehension** (ap ri HEN shuhn) *n.* anxious feeling; fear.

TAKE NOTES

Literary Analysis

Setting may shape the values and concerns of characters. Underline details about Tío Daniel. How do the people of San Juan Iglesias treat him? What does this tell you about the setting?

_____

_____

_____

_____

Reading Skill

What was in the package the stranger brought to the party? Was your **inference** correct?

_____

_____

Reading Check

Where does Uncle Tío say that the cheese must have come from? Circle the sentence that tells you.

Literary Analysis

Make an **inference** about the reason the people of San Juan Iglesias are unable to get this kind of cheese.

_____

_____

_____

Literary Analysis

What features of the **setting** make it easy for the stranger to escape?

_____

_____

Reading Check

Who does Sarita think the stranger was? Underline the text that tells you.

was not on the plaza. He was not anywhere in sight. A few of the more religious crossed themselves for fear that the Devil had walked in their midst. "Who was he?" one voice asked another. But Sarita, who was meekly listening to a lecture from Don Roméo on the propriety of dancing with strangers, did not have to ask. She had a strong suspicion that she had danced that night within the circling arm of Pepe Gonzalez.

Reader's Response: When did you realize the stranger was Pepe Gonzalez? What led you to your conclusion?

_____

_____

_____

_____

The Street of the Cañon

1. **Hypothesize:** What might the villagers have done to the stranger if they had known who he was? Use details from the story to support your answer.

_____

_____

2. **Interpret:** Why does the young man risk danger to dance with Sarita and leave the gift of cheese?

_____

_____

3. **Literary Analysis:** Think about the specific dangers the man from Hidalgo faces in San Juan Iglesias. If the **setting** of the story were a different time or place, would he still face these dangers? Explain.

_____

_____

4. **Reading Skill:** Reread the first three paragraphs of the story. What **inferences** could you make about the stranger's plans? Record your inferences in the chart. Then, list details that appear later in the story that either prove or disprove your inferences.

Inferences	Confirming Details	Disproving Details

SUPPORT FOR WRITING AND EXTEND YOUR LEARNING

Writing: Letter to a Friend and Book Review

Write a **letter to a friend** summarizing this story. Then, rewrite the summary as part of a **book review** for newspaper readers. After you have written the letter, use the chart below to help you change the language. Write important phrases from the letter in the left column. Then, rewrite them using formal language in the right column. Use your notes to help you write your book review.

Letter	Book Review

Research and Technology: Visual Art Presentation

Prepare a **visual art presentation** for the story. Find at least two works of art that reflect the setting and spirit of the story. Use the chart below to help you evaluate the works of art you choose. Use your notes to prepare your visual art presentation.

Work of Art	Visual References to the Setting	Feelings That Fit the Mood of the Story

There Will Come Soft Rains

Ray Bradbury

Summary It is the year 2026. Houses can operate on their own. In the story, a fully automated house works to take care of its owners. The owners, however, are mysteriously absent.

Reading/Writing Connection

Complete the sentences to describe the positive and negative effects of machines such as car alarms and ATMs.

1. Machines such as ATMs can <u>minimize</u> _____.

2. They help people <u>maintain</u> _____.

3. They also <u>challenge</u> people to _____.

Note-taking Guide

Use this timeline to record what the automated house tells its owners to do at different times of the day.

7:00 A.M. _____	3:00 P.M. _____
8:00 A.M. _____	4:00 P.M. _____
9:00 A.M. _____	5:00 P.M. _____
10:00 A.M. _____	6:00 P.M. _____
11:00 A.M. _____	7:00 P.M. _____
12:00 P.M. _____	8:00 P.M. _____
1:00 P.M. _____	9:00 P.M. _____
2:00 P.M. _____	10:00 P.M. _____

There Will Come Soft Rains

1. **Infer:** Why does the house continue its activity even when it no longer makes sense?

   _____

2. **Analyze:** What does this fact indicate about the human qualities the house does not have?

   _____

   _____

3. **Literary Analysis:** Explain why, in this story, the **setting** might also be called the main character.

   _____

   _____

4. **Reading Skill:** From the information in the first two pages of the story, what two **inferences** can you make about events that occurred before the story opens? Record your answers in the first column of the chart below. For each inference, note at least one detail later in the story that either proves or disproves it.

Inferences	Confirming Details	Disproving Details

SUPPORT FOR WRITING AND EXTEND YOUR LEARNING

Writing: Letter to a Friend and Book Review

Write a **letter to a friend** summarizing the story. Then, rewrite the summary as part of a **book review** for newspaper readers. After you have written the letter, use the chart to help you change the language. Write important phrases from the letter in the left column. Then, rewrite them using formal language in the right column.

Letter	Book Review

Listening and Speaking: Oral Reading

Give an **oral reading** of "There Will Come Soft Rains." Use the following questions to prepare for your reading.

- Where will you vary your tone to show meaning in the story? Write down different tones you might use and the paragraphs you will use them in.

_____

_____

_____

- What hand gestures would be appropriate for your reading? When will you use them in the story?

_____

_____

_____

Use your notes to prepare your oral reading of the story.

Web Sites

ABOUT WEB SITES AS SOURCES

Search engines are sites that help you find information on the Web. You use a search engine by typing in words called search terms. Putting in search terms will give you a list of sites called "hits." These sites have information about the search terms and sites with related information. A Web site can be found directly by typing its address, or URL, in the browser window.

READING SKILL

Not all Web sites have correct information. You must be careful about which sites you use. For example, a Web site about Napoleon made by a sixth grader might have incorrect dates. Make sure that the Web site has information you can trust. You must **make inferences** about the Web site. Inferences are guesses about something that are based on the information in a text. **Evaluate the credibility of Web sources** before you use information from the Web. Follow this checklist to make decisions about Web sources:

CHECKLIST FOR EVALUATING WEB SITES
❑ Check the ending of the URL. • Educational institutions (URL ending ".edu") and government agencies (URL ending ".gov") generally provide reliable information. • Nonprofit organizations (URL ending ".org") may be unbiased, or they may have an agenda. • Businesses and individuals (URL ending ".com") may provide information of varying quality.
❑ Consider the credentials of the Web site's sponsor.
❑ Check information against a reliable print source.
❑ Check the "last updated" field on the page.

http://www.newton.cam.ac.uk/egypt/

Egyptology Resources

Popular local items

News & Gossip

Announcements

Bulletin Board

E-mail Addresses

Tomb of Sennefen

Beinlich Wordlist

Wilbour Library Acquisitions

Online Publications

Commercial Items

Server statistics

The first Egyptology site on the Web

This page is set up with the kind assistance of the Newton Institute in the University of Cambridge to provide a World Wide Web resource for Egyptological information. The pages are not a publication of the Newton Institute, and all matters concerning them (e.g., comments, criticisms, and suggestions for items to include) should be sent to Nigel Strudwick.

Click here for guidelines on the format of material.

Click here for site history.

Main pages

Essential Resources

Institutions

Museums

Digs

Publishers, Booksellers

Journals, Magazines

Organizations, Societies

Interesting Egypt Pages

Personal Egypt Pages

Other Resources of Interest

http://www.newton.cam.ac.uk/egypt/

Museums Online with Egyptian Collections

Many museums, of course, have WWW pages now. I have tried to select some of those which have more specific information on their Egyptian Collections, but I do also include the general Web presences of major museums with relevant material. Some of these links often go directly to the Egypt pages and bypass the home page. A more general set of links will be found in the ABZU indexes.

Egypt
- The Egyptian Museum, Cairo
- The Coptic Museum, Cairo

North America
- Museum of Fine Arts, Boston
- Metropolitan Museum, New York
- Michael C. Carlos Museum, Emory University, Atlanta
- Brooklyn Museum
- Oriental Institute, University of Chicago

Europe
- The British Museum, London COMPASS Project
- The Louvre, Paris
- Musées royaux d'art et d'art historie, Brussels
- Museo Egizio, Torino
- Agyptisches Museum und Papyrussammlung Berlin-Charlottenburg
- Allard Pierson Museum
- Carsten Niebuhr Institute, University of Copenhagen, Papyrus Collection

Back to Egyptology Resources home page

THINKING ABOUT THE WEB SITE

1. Which links would you click on to learn more about new developments in the study of ancient Egypt? Explain.

   _____

   _____

2. What kind of student or researcher would learn the most from this site? Explain your answer.

   _____

   _____

READING SKILL

3. A university helps set up this Web site. What does this fact tell you about the site?

   _____

4. How would a list of facts about Nigel Strudwick's experience help you evaluate the credibility of this site? Explain.

   _____

TIMED WRITING: PERSUASION (20 minutes)

   Write a letter to the person who made the Egyptology Resources Web site. Suggest improvements for the site. Make suggestions about pictures on the site, the design of the site, and instructions on the site.

   Make notes about each of the three areas for improvement listed above.

   _____

   _____

   _____

   _____

How Much Land Does a Man Need? •
Civil Peace

LITERARY ANALYSIS

The **theme** of a literary work is the central message it communicates. For example, a simple story might have the theme, "Honesty is the best policy." A more complex work might show that "Human suffering cannot be justified or explained." To express a theme, a writer may take one of these approaches:

- Directly state the theme of the work, or have a character directly state it.
- Create patterns of story elements to suggest a larger meaning—for instance, by contrasting a generous man and his selfish brother to say something about generosity.

In many cases, a theme reflects a **philosophical assumption**—the writer's basic beliefs about life. For instance, a writer may make the assumption that being generous leads to happiness. The writer's literary work may reflect this belief.

READING SKILL

When you **draw a conclusion**, you reach a decision or form an opinion based on information in a text. To draw a conclusion identifying the theme of a work, **recognize key details**, combining later details with earlier ones. Use this chart to draw conclusions.

Story Detail		Story Detail		Pattern
Greedy Joe invests in a crooked scheme. He loses all of his money.	+	Generous John tricks the crooks and saves Joe.	→	Being greedy causes harm. Being generous leads to solutions.

How Much Land Does a Man Need?

Leo Tolstoy

Summary A peasant named Pahom wants to acquire his own land. He buys land. But he finds fault with it and decides he needs more land. He continues to acquire land. However, he is still not satisfied. Far from home, he meets tragedy in his last desperate grab for more land.

Reading/Writing Connection

Complete the paragraph to describe material possessions that people desire today.

People today like to <u>accumulate</u> _____. They believe

that if they work hard, they can <u>justify</u> _____. Then,

they <u>display</u> their possessions for _____.

Note-taking Guide

Use this chart to summarize what happens in the story.

What does Pahom want at the beginning of the story?	What happens next?	What happens next?	What happens to Pahom at the end of the story?
Pahom desires more land.			

How Much Land Does a Man Need?
Leo Tolstoy

Think of a material possession you want to have. How would you feel if you had it? How would it change your life?

_____

_____

When you **draw a conclusion,** you reach a decision or form an opinion. A conclusion is based on information in a text. From the information in the first bracketed paragraph, draw a conclusion about the kind of person the older sister is.

_____

_____

Circle the text that supports your conclusion.

The **theme** of a story is its central message. What theme does the younger sister directly state in the second bracketed paragraph?

_____

_____

For what does Pahom wish? Underline the text that tells you.

1

An elder sister came to visit her younger sister in the country. The elder was married to a shopkeeper in town, the younger to a peasant in the village. As the sisters sat over their tea talking, the elder began to boast of the advantages of town life, saying how comfortably they lived there, how well they dressed, what fine clothes her children wore, what good things they ate and drank, and how she went to the theater, promenades, and entertainments.

The younger sister was <u>piqued</u>, and in turn disparaged the life of a shopkeeper, and stood up for that of a peasant.

"I wouldn't change my way of life for yours," said she. "We may live roughly, but at least we're free from worry. You live in better style than we do, but though you often earn more than you need, you're very likely to lose all you have. You know the proverb, 'Loss and gain are brothers twain.' It often happens that people who're wealthy one day are begging their bread the next. Our way is safer. Though a peasant's life is not a rich one, it's long. We'll never grow rich, but we'll always have enough to eat."

The elder sister said sneeringly:

"Enough? Yes, if you like to share with the pigs and the calves! What do you know of elegance or manners! However much your good man may slave, you'll die as you live—in a dung heap—and your children the same."

"Well, what of that?" replied the younger sister. "Of course our work is rough and hard. But on the other hand, it's sure, and we need not bow to anyone. But you, in your towns, are surrounded by temptations; today all may be right, but tomorrow the Evil One may tempt your husband with cards, wine, or women, and all will go to ruin. Don't such things happen often enough?"

Pahom, the master of the house, was lying on the top of the stove and he listened to the women's chatter.

"It is perfectly true," thought he. "Busy as we are from childhood tilling mother earth, we peasants have no time to let any nonsense settle in our heads. Our only trouble is that we haven't land enough. If I had plenty of land, I shouldn't fear the Devil himself!"

The women finished their tea, chatted a while about dress, and then cleared away the tea things and lay down to sleep.

> **Vocabulary Development: piqued** (peekt) *adj.* irritated; offended, and so resentful

But the Devil had been sitting behind the stove and had heard all that had been said. He was pleased that the peasant's wife had led her husband into boasting and that he had said that if he had plenty of land he would not fear the Devil himself.

"All right," thought the Devil. "We'll have a tussle. I'll give you land enough; and by means of the land I'll get you into my power."

2

Close to the village there lived a lady, a small landowner who had an estate of about three hundred acres. She had always lived on good terms with the peasants until she engaged as her manager an old soldier, who took to burdening the people with fines. However careful Pahom tried to be, it happened again and again that now a horse of his got among the lady's oats, now a cow strayed into her garden, now his calves found their way into her meadows—and he always had to pay a fine.

Pahom paid up, but grumbled, and, going home in a temper, was rough with his family. All through that summer Pahom had much trouble because of this manager, and he was actually glad when winter came and the cattle had to be stabled. Though he grudged the fodder when they could no longer graze on the pasture land, at least he was free from anxiety about them.

In the winter the news got about that the lady was going to sell her land and that the keeper of the inn on the high road was bargaining for it. When the peasants heard this they were very much alarmed.

"Well," thought they, "if the innkeeper gets the land, he'll worry us with fines worse than the lady's manager. We all depend on that estate."

So the peasants went on behalf of their village council and asked the lady not to sell the land to the innkeeper, offering her a better price for it themselves. The lady agreed to let them have it. Then the peasants tried to arrange for the village council to buy the whole estate, so that it might be held by them all in common. They met twice to discuss it, but could not settle the matter; the Evil One sowed discord among them and they could not agree. So they decided to buy the land individually, each according to his means; and the lady agreed to this plan as she had to the other.

Presently Pahom heard that a neighbor of his was buying fifty acres, and that the lady had consented to accept one half in cash and to wait a year for the other half. Pahom felt envious.

"Look at that," thought he, "the land is all being sold, and I'll get none of it." So he spoke to his wife.

Literary Analysis

Underline **details** in the first bracketed paragraph that show how the Devil reacts to Pahom's desire for more land. How does the Devil's reaction reinforce the **theme** that the younger sister suggested on the previous page?

_____

_____

_____

Reading Skill

To **draw conclusions** about a **theme, recognize key details.** Combine later details with earlier ones. In the second bracketed passage, what details suggest that the Devil's plan is becoming a reality?

_____

_____

_____

_____

_____

Stop to Reflect

Which would you rather live in, the city or the country? Explain.

_____

_____

_____

_____

Draw a conclusion about what could happen if Pahom is not successful on his new land.

_____

_____

Underline details from the first bracketed passage that support your conclusion.

Imagine that the story was finished at the end of section 2. What could a **theme** of the story be?

_____

_____

_____

How does Pahom feel at first after gaining his own land? Circle the text that tells you.

"Other people are buying," said he, "and we must also buy twenty acres or so. Life is becoming impossible. That manager is simply crushing us with his fines."

So they put their heads together and considered how they could manage to buy it. They had one hundred rubles[1] laid by. They sold a colt and one half of their bees, hired out one of their sons as a farmhand and took his wages in advance, borrowed the rest from a brother-in-law, and so scraped together half the purchase money.

Having done this, Pahom chose a farm of forty acres, some of it wooded, and went to the lady to bargain for it. They came to an agreement, and he shook hands with her upon it and paid her a deposit in advance. Then they went to town and signed the deeds, he paying half the price down, and undertaking to pay the remainder within two years.

So now Pahom had land of his own. He borrowed seed and sowed it on the land he had bought. The harvest was a good one, and within a year he had managed to pay off his debts both to the lady and to his brother-in-law. So he became a landowner, plowing and sowing his own land, making hay on his own land, cutting his own trees, and feeding his cattle on his own pasture. When he went out to plow his fields, or to look at his growing corn, or at his grass meadows, his heart would fill with joy. The grass that grew and the flowers that bloomed there seemed to him unlike any that grew elsewhere. Formerly, when he had passed by that land, it had appeared the same as any other land, but now it seemed quite different.

3

So Pahom was well contented, and everything would have been right if the neighboring peasants would only not have trespassed on his wheatfields and meadows. He appealed to them most civilly, but they still went on: now the herdsmen would let the village cows stray into his meadows, then horses from the night pasture would get among his corn. Pahom turned them out again and again, and forgave their owners, and for a long time he forbore to prosecute anyone. But at last he lost patience and complained to the District Court. He knew it was the peasants' want of land, and no evil intent on their part, that caused the trouble, but he thought:

Vocabulary Development: forbore (fawr BAWR) *v.* prevented oneself from doing something; refrained from

---

1. **rubles** (ROO buhlz) *n.* A ruble is the basic unit of Russian currency.

"I can't go on overlooking it, or they'll destroy all I have. They must be taught a lesson."

So he had them up, gave them one lesson, and then another, and two or three of the peasants were fined. After a time Pahom's neighbors began to bear him a grudge for this, and would now and then let their cattle onto his land on purpose. One peasant even got into Pahom's wood at night and cut down five young lime trees for their bark. Pahom, passing through the wood one day, noticed something white. He came nearer and saw the stripped trunks lying on the ground, and close by stood the stumps where the trees had been. Pahom was furious.

"If he'd only cut one here and there it would have been bad enough," thought Pahom, "but the rascal has actually cut down a whole clump. If I could only find out who did this, I'd get even with him."

He racked his brains as to who it could be. Finally he decided: "It must be Simon—no one else could have done it." So he went to Simon's homestead to have a look around, but he found nothing and only had an angry scene. However, he now felt more certain than ever that Simon had done it, and he lodged a complaint. Simon was summoned. The case was tried, and retried, and at the end of it all Simon was acquitted, there being no evidence against him. Pahom felt still more aggrieved, and let his anger loose upon the Elders and the Judges.

"You let thieves grease your palms," said he. "If you were honest folk yourselves you wouldn't let a thief go free."

So Pahom quarreled with the judges and with his neighbors. Threats to burn his hut began to be uttered. So though Pahom had more land, his place in the community was much worse than before.

About this time a rumor got about that many people were moving to new parts.

"There's no need for me to leave my land," thought Pahom. "But some of the others may leave our village and then there'd be more room for us. I'd take over their land myself and make my estates somewhat bigger. I could then live more at ease. As it is, I'm still too cramped to be comfortable."

One day Pahom was sitting at home when a peasant, passing through the village, happened to drop in. He was allowed to stay the night, and supper was given him. Pahom had a talk with this peasant and asked him where he came from. The stranger answered that he came from

Vocabulary Development: aggrieved (uh GREEVD) *adj.* injured or wronged

TAKE NOTES

Stop to Reflect

Read the first bracketed passage. What would you do if you were a peasant living in the community with Pahom? What would you say to him?

_____

_____

_____

Reading Skill

Underline **key details** in the second bracketed passage about how Pahom and the peasants treat each other. What do these key details show about the effects of Pahom's desire for land?

_____

_____

Literary Analysis

What detail in the second bracketed passage reinforces the **theme** of the story? Explain.

_____

_____

Reading Check

Is Pahom happy with the amount of land he has? Circle the text that tells you.

© Pearson Education, Inc., publishing as Pearson Prentice Hall.
How Much Land Does a Man Need? **149**

Readers need to have enough information to successfully **draw conclusions**. Circle **key details** on this page that support the conclusion that the new land Pahom is going to is good land.

What does Pahom decide to do after he fights with his neighbors? Underline the text that tells you.

Do you think that Pahom will be satisfied at his new settlement? Explain your answer.

_____

_____

_____

_____

beyond the Volga,[2] where he had been working. One word led to another, and the man went on to say that many people were settling in those parts. He told how some people from his village had settled there. They had joined the community there and had had twenty-five acres per man granted them. The land was so good, he said, that the rye sown on it grew as high as a horse, and so thick that five cuts of a sickle made a sheaf.[3] One peasant, he said, had brought nothing with him but his bare hands, and now he had six horses and two cows of his own.

Pahom's heart kindled with desire.

"Why should I suffer in this narrow hole, if one can live so well elsewhere?" he thought. "I'll sell my land and my homestead here, and with the money I'll start afresh over there and get everything new. In this crowded place one is always having trouble. But I must first go and find out all about it myself."

Toward summer he got ready and started out. He went down the Volga on a steamer to Samara, then walked another three hundred miles on foot, and at last reached the place. It was just as the stranger had said. The peasants had plenty of land: every man had twenty-five acres of communal land given him for his use, and anyone who had money could buy, besides, at a ruble and a half an acre, as much good freehold land[4] as he wanted.

Having found out all he wished to know, Pahom returned home as autumn came on, and began selling off his belongings. He sold his land at a profit, sold his homestead and all his cattle, and withdrew from membership in the village. He only waited till the spring, and then started with his family for the new settlement.

4

As soon as Pahom and his family reached their new abode, he applied for admission into the council of a large village. He stood treat to the Elders and obtained the necessary documents. Five shares of communal land were given him for his own and his sons' use: that is to say— 125 acres (not all together, but in different fields) besides the use of the communal pasture. Pahom put up the buildings he needed and bought cattle. Of the communal land alone he had three times as much as at his former home, and the land was good wheat land. He was ten times better off than he had been. He had plenty of arable[5] land and pasturage, and could keep as many head of cattle as he liked.

---

2. **Volga** (VAHL guh) the major river in western Russia.
3. **sheaf** (sheef) *n.* bundle of grain.
4. **freehold land** privately owned land that the owner can lease to others for a fee.
5. **arable** (AR uh buhl) *adj.* suitable for growing crops.

At first, in the bustle of building and settling down, Pahom was pleased with it all, but when he got used to it he began to think that even here he hadn't enough land. The first year he sowed wheat on his share of the communal land and had a good crop. He wanted to go on sowing wheat, but had not enough communal land for the purpose, and what he had already used was not available, for in those parts wheat is sown only on virgin soil or on fallow land. It is sown for one or two years, and then the land lies fallow till it is again overgrown with steppe grass. There were many who wanted such land, and there was not enough for all, so that people quarreled about it. Those who were better off wanted it for growing wheat, and those who were poor wanted it to let to dealers, so that they might raise money to pay their taxes. Pahom wanted to sow more wheat, so he rented land from a dealer for a year. He sowed much wheat and had a fine crop, but the land was too far from the village—the wheat had to be carted more than ten miles. After a time Pahom noticed that some peasant dealers were living on separate farms and were growing wealthy, and he thought:

"If I were to buy some freehold land and have a homestead on it, it would be a different thing altogether. Then it would all be fine and close together."

The question of buying freehold land recurred to him again and again.

He went on in the same way for three years, renting land and sowing wheat. The seasons turned out well and the crops were good, so that he began to lay by money. He might have gone on living contentedly, but he grew tired of having to rent other people's land every year and having to scramble for it. Wherever there was good land to be had, the peasants would rush for it and it was taken up at once, so that unless you were sharp about it, you got none. It happened in the third year that he and a dealer together rented a piece of pasture land from some peasants, and they had already plowed it up, when there was some dispute and the peasants went to law about it, and things fell out so that the labor was all lost.

"If it were my own land," thought Pahom, "I should be independent, and there wouldn't be all this unpleasantness."

So Pahom began looking out for land which he could buy, and he came across a peasant who had bought thirteen hundred acres, but having got into difficulties was willing to sell again cheap. Pahom bargained and haggled with him, and at last they settled the price at fifteen hundred rubles, part in cash and part to be paid later. They had all but clinched the matter when a passing dealer happened to stop at Pahom's one day to get feed for his horses. He drank tea with Pahom, and they had a

Literary Analysis

Underline key details that show how Pahom's view of his land has changed since he bought it. How does this detail support the **theme** of the story?

_____

_____

_____

_____

_____

_____

Reading Skill

Think about the land Pahom has acquired so far. **Draw a conclusion** about the amount of land Pahom will need before he is satisfied.

_____

_____

_____

_____

Stop to Reflect

How does the way wheat is grown contribute to more problems between people?

_____

_____

_____

Draw a conclusion about how Pahom will treat the Bashkirs.

_____

_____

Circle details that support your conclusion.

Where does Pahom decide to go next? Underline the text that tells you.

Authors sometimes create patterns of story elements to help reveal the story's **theme**. What pattern do you see developing for Pahom and his land purchases?

_____

_____

_____

talk. The dealer said that he was just returning from the land of the Bashkirs,[6] far away, where he had bought thirteen thousand acres of land, all for a thousand rubles. Pahom questioned him further, and the dealer said:

"All one has to do is to make friends with the chiefs. I gave away about one hundred rubles' worth of silk robes and carpets, besides a case of tea, and I gave wine to those who would drink it; and I got the land for less than three kopecks[7] an acre." And he showed Pahom the title deed, saying:

"The land lies near a river, and the whole steppe[8] is virgin soil."

Pahom plied him with questions, and the dealer said:

"There's more land there than you could cover if you walked a year, and it all belongs to the Bashkirs. They're as simple as sheep, and land can be got almost for nothing."

"There, now," thought Pahom, "with my one thousand rubles, why should I get only thirteen hundred acres, and saddle myself with a debt besides? If I take it out there, I can get more than ten times as much for my money."

5

Pahom inquired how to get to the place, and as soon as the grain dealer had left him, he prepared to go there himself. He left his wife to look after the homestead, and started on his journey, taking his hired man with him. They stopped at a town on their way and bought a case of tea, some wine, and other presents, as the grain dealer had advised.

On and on they went until they had gone more than three hundred miles, and on the seventh day they came to a place where the Bashkirs had pitched their round tents. It was all just as the dealer had said. The people lived on the steppe, by a river, in felt-covered tents. They neither tilled the ground nor ate bread. Their cattle and horses grazed in herds on the steppe. The colts were tethered behind the tents, and the mares were driven to them twice a day. The mares were milked, and from the milk kumiss[9] was made. It was the women who prepared the kumiss, and they also made cheese. As far as the men were concerned, drinking kumiss and tea, eating mutton, and playing on their pipes was all they cared about. They were all stout and merry, and all the summer long they

---

6. **Bashkirs** (bash KEERZ) *n.* originally nomadic people who live in the plains of southwestern Russia.
7. **kopecks** (KOH peks) *n.* A kopeck is a unit of Russian money, equal to one hundredth of a ruble.
8. **steppe** (step) *n.* high grassland plains stretching from Hungary through Russia into central Asia.
9. **kumiss** (KOO mis) *n.* fermented mare's or camel's milk that is used as a drink.

never thought of doing any work. They were quite ignorant, and knew no Russian, but were good-natured enough.

As soon as they saw Pahom, they came out of their tents and gathered around the visitor. An interpreter was found, and Pahom told them he had come about some land. The Bashkirs seemed very glad; they took Pahom and led him into one of the best tents, where they made him sit on some down cushions placed on a carpet, while they sat around him. They gave him some tea and kumiss, and had a sheep killed, and gave him mutton to eat. Pahom took presents out of his cart and distributed them among the Bashkirs, and divided the tea amongst them. The Bashkirs were delighted. They talked a great deal among themselves and then told the interpreter what to say.

"They wish to tell you," said the interpreter, "that they like you and that it's our custom to do all we can to please a guest and to repay him for his gifts. You have given us presents, now tell us which of the things we possess please you best, that we may present them to you."

"What pleases me best here," answered Pahom, "is your land. Our land is crowded and the soil is worn out, but you have plenty of land, and it is good land. I never saw the likes of it."

The interpreter told the Bashkirs what Pahom had said. They talked among themselves for a while. Pahom could not understand what they were saying, but saw that they were much amused and heard them shout and laugh. Then they were silent and looked at Pahom while the interpreter said:

"They wish me to tell you that in return for your presents they will gladly give you as much land as you want. You have only to point it out with your hand and it is yours."

The Bashkirs talked again for a while and began to dispute. Pahom asked what they were disputing about, and the interpreter told him that some of them thought they ought to ask their chief about the land and not act in his absence, while others thought there was no need to wait for his return.

6

While the Bashkirs were disputing, a man in a large fox-fur cap appeared on the scene. They all became silent and rose to their feet. The interpreter said: "This is our chief himself."

Pahom immediately fetched the best dressing gown and five pounds of tea, and offered these to the chief. The chief accepted them and seated himself in the place of honor. The Bashkirs at once began telling him something. The chief listened for a while, then made a sign with his head for them to be silent, and addressing himself to Pahom, said in Russian:

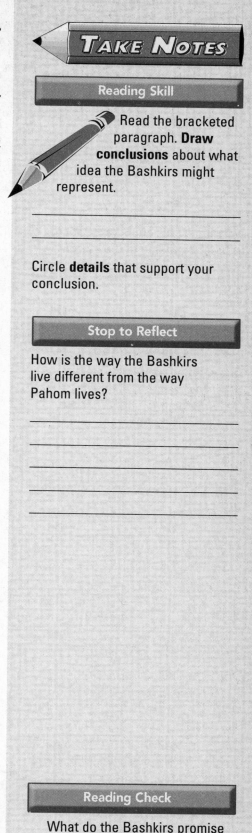

TAKE NOTES

Reading Skill

Read the bracketed paragraph. **Draw conclusions** about what idea the Bashkirs might represent.

_____

_____

Circle **details** that support your conclusion.

Stop to Reflect

How is the way the Bashkirs live different from the way Pahom lives?

_____

_____

_____

_____

Reading Check

What do the Bashkirs promise to give Pahom? Underline the text that tells you.

What do Pahom's thoughts in the bracketed text tell about the person he has become?

_____

_____

How does this change in Pahom add to the **theme** of the story?

_____

_____

Draw a conclusion about the Bashkirs' values from their attitude toward land. What are two **details** that support your conclusion?

_____

_____

_____

What is the one condition that could cause Pahom to lose all of his land and money? Underline the text that tells you.

"Well, so be it. Choose whatever piece of land you like; we have plenty of it."

"How can I take as much as I like?" thought Pahom. "I must get a deed to make it secure, or else they may say: 'It is yours,' and afterward may take it away again."

"Thank you for your kind words," he said aloud. "You have much land, and I only want a little. But I should like to be sure which portion is mine. Could it not be measured and made over to me? Life and death are in God's hands. You good people give it to me, but your children might wish to take it back again."

"You are quite right," said the chief. "We will make it over to you."

"I heard that a dealer had been here," continued Pahom, "and that you gave him a little land, too, and signed title deeds to that effect. I should like to have it done in the same way."

The chief understood.

"Yes," replied he, "that can be done quite easily. We have a scribe, and we will go to town with you and have the deed properly sealed."

"And what will be the price?" asked Pahom.

"Our price is always the same: one thousand rubles a day."

Pahom did not understand.

"A day? What measure is that? How many acres would that be?"

"We do not know how to reckon it out," said the chief. "We sell it by the day. As much as you can go around on your feet in a day is yours, and the price is one thousand rubles a day."

Pahom was surprised.

"But in a day you can get around a large tract of land," he said.

The chief laughed.

"It will all be yours!" said he. "But there is one condition: If you don't return on the same day to the spot whence you started, your money is lost."

"But how am I to mark the way that I have gone?"

"Why, we shall go to any spot you like and stay there. You must start from that spot and make your round, taking a spade with you. Wherever you think necessary, make a mark. At every turning, dig a hole and pile up the turf; then afterward we will go around with a plow from hole to hole. You may make as large a circuit as you please, but before the sun sets you must return to the place you started from. All the land you cover will be yours."

Pahom was delighted. It was decided to start early next morning. They talked a while, and after drinking some more kumiss and eating some more mutton, they had tea again, and then the night came on. They gave Pahom a featherbed to sleep on, and the Bashkirs dispersed for the night, promising to assemble the next morning at daybreak and ride out before sunrise to the appointed spot.

7

Pahom lay on the featherbed, but could not sleep. He kept thinking about the land.

"What a large tract I'll mark off!" thought he. "I can easily do thirty-five miles in a day. The days are long now, and within a circuit of thirty-five miles what a lot of land there will be! I'll sell the poorer land or let it to peasants, but I'll pick out the best and farm it myself. I'll buy two ox teams and hire two more laborers. About a hundred and fifty acres shall be plowland, and I'll pasture cattle on the rest."

Pahom lay awake all night and dozed off only just before dawn. Hardly were his eyes closed when he had a dream. He thought he was lying in that same tent and heard somebody chuckling outside. He wondered who it could be, and rose and went out, and he saw the Bashkir chief sitting in front of the tent holding his sides and rolling about with laughter. Going nearer to the chief, Pahom asked: "What are you laughing at?" But he saw that it was no longer the chief but the grain dealer who had recently stopped at his house and had told him about the land. Just as Pahom was going to ask: "Have you been here long?" he saw that it was not the dealer, but the peasant who had come up from the Volga long ago, to Pahom's old home. Then he saw that it was not the peasant either, but the Devil himself with hoofs and horns, sitting there and chuckling, and before him lay a man, prostrate on the ground, barefooted, with only trousers and a shirt on. And Pahom dreamed that he looked more attentively to see what sort of man it was lying there, and he saw that the man was dead, and that it was himself. Horror-struck, he awoke.

"What things one dreams about!" thought he.

Looking around he saw through the open door that the dawn was breaking.

"It's time to wake them up," thought he. "We ought to be starting."

He got up, roused his man (who was sleeping in his cart), bade him harness, and went to call the Bashkirs.

"It's time to go to the steppe to measure the land," he said.

The Bashkirs rose and assembled, and the chief came, too. Then they began drinking kumiss again, and offered Pahom some tea, but he would not wait.

"If we are to go, let's go. It's high time," said he.

Reading Skill

Which **key details** in the bracketed text suggest that the Devil is responsible for all of Pahom's land deals?

_____

_____

_____

_____

Literary Analysis

What key detail of Pahom's dream supports the **theme** that greed leads to destruction? Underline the text that tells you.

Reading Check

How large a tract of land does Pahom decide he will mark off? Circle the text that tells you.

8

TAKE NOTES

Literary Analysis

Philosophical assumptions are a writer's basic beliefs about life. A **theme** often reflects a writer's philosophical assumptions. A philosophical assumption of this writer is that material things are not important. What details about the Bashkirs' plan for giving out land support this philosophical assumption?

_____

_____

_____

_____

Stop to Reflect

What is dangerous about the conditions set up by the Bashkirs for Pahom to get his land?

_____

_____

_____

_____

Reading Check

At what sort of pace does Pahom set out? Underline the text that tells you.

The Bashkirs got ready and they all started; some mounted on horses and some in carts. Pahom drove in his own small cart with his servant and took a spade with him. When they reached the steppe, the red dawn was beginning to kindle. They ascended a hillock (called by the Bashkirs a *shikhan*) and, dismounting from their carts and their horses, gathered in one spot. The chief came up to Pahom and, stretching out his arm toward the plain:

"See," said he, "all this, as far as your eye can reach, is ours. You may have any part of it you like."

Pahom's eyes glistened: it was all virgin soil, as flat as the palm of your hand, as black as the seed of a poppy, and in the hollows different kinds of grasses grew breast-high.

The chief took off his fox-fur cap, placed it on the ground, and said:

"This will be the mark. Start from here, and return here again. All the land you go around shall be yours."

Pahom took out his money and put it on the cap. Then he took off his outer coat, remaining in his sleeveless undercoat. He unfastened his girdle[10] and tied it tight below his stomach, put a little bag of bread into the breast of his coat, and, tying a flask of water to his girdle, he drew up the tops of his boots, took the spade from his man, and stood ready to start. He considered for some moments which way he had better go—it was tempting everywhere.

"No matter," he concluded, "I'll go toward the rising sun."

He turned his face to the east, stretched himself, and waited for the sun to appear above the rim.

"I must lose no time," he thought, "and it's easier walking while it's still cool."

The sun's rays had hardly flashed above the horizon when Pahom, carrying the spade over his shoulder, went down into the steppe.

Pahom started walking neither slowly nor quickly. After having gone a thousand yards he stopped, dug a hole, and placed pieces of turf one on another to make it more visible. Then he went on; and now that he had walked off his stiffness he quickened his pace. After a while he dug another hole.

Pahom looked back. The hillock could be distinctly seen in the sunlight, with the people on it, and the glittering iron rims of the cartwheels. At a rough guess Pahom concluded that he had walked three miles. It was growing warmer; he took off his undercoat, slung it across his shoulder, and went on again. It had grown quite warm now; he looked at the sun—it was time to think of breakfast.

---

10. **girdle** (GERD duhl) *n.* belt or sash for the waist.

"The first shift is done, but there are four in a day, and it's too soon yet to turn. But I'll just take off my boots," said he to himself.

He sat down, took off his boots, stuck them into his girdle, and went on. It was easy walking now.

"I'll go on for another three miles," thought he, "and then turn to the left. This spot is so fine that it would be a pity to lose it. The further one goes, the better the land seems."

He went straight on for a while, and when he looked around, the hillock was scarcely visible and the people on it looked like black ants, and he could just see something glistening there in the sun.

"Ah," thought Pahom, "I have gone far enough in this direction; it's time to turn. Besides, I'm in a regular sweat, and very thirsty."

He stopped, dug a large hole, and heaped up pieces of turf. Next he untied his flask, had a drink, and then turned sharply to the left. He went on and on; the grass was high, and it was very hot.

Pahom began to grow tired: he looked at the sun and saw that it was noon.

"Well," he thought, "I must have a rest."

He sat down, and ate some bread and drank some water; but he did not lie down, thinking that if he did he might fall asleep. After sitting a little while, he went on again. At first he walked easily; the food had strengthened him; but it had become terribly hot and he felt sleepy. Still he went on, thinking: "An hour to suffer, a lifetime to live."

He went a long way in this direction also, and was about to turn to the left again, when he perceived a damp hollow: "It would be a pity to leave that out," he thought. "Flax would do well there." So he went on past the hollow and dug a hole on the other side of it before he made a sharp turn. Pahom looked toward the hillock. The heat made the air hazy: it seemed to be quivering, and through the haze the people on the hillock could scarcely be seen.

"Ah," thought Pahom, "I have made the sides too long; I must make this one shorter." And he went along the third side, stepping faster. He looked at the sun: it was nearly halfway to the horizon, and he had not yet done two miles of the third side of the square. He was still ten miles from the goal.

"No," he thought, "though it will make my land lopsided, I must hurry back in a straight line now. I might go too far, and as it is I have a great deal of land."

So Pahom hurriedly dug a hole and turned straight toward the hillock.

Literary Analysis

How do Pahom's thoughts and actions in the first bracketed passage reflect his earlier attitude toward acquiring land?

_____

_____

_____

How do these thoughts and actions add to the **theme** of the story?

_____

_____

_____

Reading Skill

Underline the **details** on this page about the weather. What **conclusion** can you **draw** about the role the weather may play in Pahom's attempt to get land?

_____

_____

_____

Stop to Reflect

Read the second bracketed text. Do you think Pahom has learned a lesson about his greed?

_____

_____

_____

9

Reading Skill

Based on details here and earlier, what **conclusion** can you **draw** about the chances for Pahom's success?

_____

_____

_____

_____

Literary Analysis

Read the underlined text. Rephrase Pahom's statement to make it apply to the **theme** in the story.

_____

_____

_____

_____

Stop to Reflect

Imagine you are one of the Bashkirs waiting on the hillock. Describe the action on this page and what Pahom looks like to you.

_____

_____

_____

_____

_____

_____

Pahom went straight toward the hillock, but he now walked with difficulty. He was exhausted from the heat, his bare feet were cut and bruised, and his legs began to fail. He longed to rest, but it was impossible if he meant to get back before sunset. The sun waits for no man, and it was sinking lower and lower.

"Oh, Lord," he thought, "if only I have not blundered trying for too much! What if I am too late?"

He looked toward the hillock and at the sun. He was still far from his goal, and the sun was already near the rim of the sky.

Pahom walked on and on; it was very hard walking, but he went quicker and quicker. He pressed on, but was still far from the place. He began running, threw away his coat, his boots, his flask, and his cap, and kept only the spade which he used as a support.

"What am I to do?" he thought again. "I've grasped too much and ruined the whole affair. I can't get there before the sun sets."

And this fear made him still more breathless. Pahom kept on running; his soaking shirt and trousers stuck to him, and his mouth was parched. His breast was working like a blacksmith's bellows, his heart was beating like a hammer, and his legs were giving way as if they did not belong to him. Pahom was seized with terror lest he should die of the strain.

Though afraid of death, he could not stop.

"After having run all that way they will call me a fool if I stop now," thought he.

And he ran on and on, and drew near and heard the Bashkirs yelling and shouting to him, and their cries inflamed his heart still more. He gathered his last strength and ran on.

The sun was close to the rim of the sky and, cloaked in mist, looked large, and red as blood. Now, yes, now, it was about to set! The sun was quite low, but he was also quite near his goal. Pahom could already see the people on the hillock waving their arms to make him hurry. He could see the fox-fur cap on the ground and the money in it, and the chief sitting on the ground holding his sides. And Pahom remembered his dream.

"There's plenty of land," thought he, "but will God let me live on it? I have lost my life, I have lost my life! Never will I reach that spot!"

Pahom looked at the sun, which had reached the earth: one side of it had already disappeared. With all his remaining strength he rushed on, bending his body forward so that his legs could hardly follow fast enough to keep him from falling. Just as he reached the hillock it suddenly grew dark. He looked up—the sun had

He gave a cry: "All my labor has been in vain," thought he, and was about to stop, but he heard the Bashkirs still shouting and remembered that though to him, from below, the sun seemed to have set, they on the hillock could still see it. He took a long breath and ran up the hillock. It was still light there. He reached the top and saw the cap. Before it sat the chief, laughing and holding his sides. Again Pahom remembered his dream, and he uttered a cry: his legs gave way beneath him, he fell forward and reached the cap with his hands.

"Ah, that's a fine fellow!" exclaimed the chief. "He has gained much land!"

Pahom's servant came running up and tried to raise him, but he saw that blood was flowing from his mouth. Pahom was dead.

The Bashkirs clicked their tongues to show their pity.

His servant picked up the spade and dug a grave long enough for Pahom to lie in, and buried him in it.

Six feet from his head to his toes was all he needed.

Reader's Response: How has Pahom's experience affected the way you feel about material things?

_____

_____

_____

_____

Reading Skill

Underline a **key detail** on this page that would support the **conclusion** that the Devil is to blame for Pahom's troubles.

Literary Analysis

Recall the title of this story. Reread the final sentence of this story. How do the final sentence and the title clarify the **theme** of this story?

_____

_____

_____

_____

Reading Check

As Pahom nears the hillock, what encourages him to keep moving? Underline the text that tells you.

How Much Land Does a Man Need?

1. **Analyze Cause and Effect:** What effect does owning land have on Pahom's life?

_____

_____

2. **Summarize:** What events take place on the last day of Pahom's life?

_____

_____

_____

3. **Reading Skill: Draw a conclusion** about Pahom's dream. Explain how it helps readers grasp the theme of the story.

_____

_____

_____

4. **Literary Analysis:** Analyze each time Pahom is given the chance to acquire land. Describe the chance, how Pahom responded, reasons why he responded this way, and the result. Use this chart.

Episode	Pahom's Response	Reasons for the Response	Result: Peace of Mind/Problems

5. **Literary Analysis:** State the **theme** of this story. How do the events in the chart above show the theme to the reader?

_____

_____

SUPPORT FOR WRITING AND EXTEND YOUR LEARNING

Writing: Character Analysis

Write a brief **character analysis** of Pahom.

- Make a list of Pahom's character traits. List as many as you can.

  _____

  _____

  _____

- Trim your list to three traits that best describe Pahom's character.

  _____

  _____

- Rank the three traits in order of importance: first, second, third.

  _____

  _____

Use your notes to write your character analysis.

Listening and Speaking: Group Discussion

Prepare for a **group discussion** on the theme of "How Much Land Does a Man Need?"

- What is the author's theme or main message in this story?

  _____

  _____

- How do Pahom's words and actions reveal the theme? List two examples.

  _____

  _____

- Do you think the theme applies to life today? Explain.

  _____

  _____

Use your notes to prepare for the group discussion.

Civil Peace

Chinua Achebe

Summary Jonathan Iwegbu survives the Nigerian Civil War. He is grateful that his family also survives the war. Jonathan is flexible. He begins one business to make money. He starts another business when the first one fails. Thieves threaten his family, and Jonathan must decide how to get out of the situation.

Reading/Writing Connection

Complete the sentences to show how a positive outlook can help people manage problems.

1. Having a positive attitude can <u>maximize</u> _____.

2. It often helps <u>minimize</u> _____.

3. A positive attitude helps people <u>perceive</u> _____.

Note-taking Guide

Fill in this character wheel to describe Jonathan's character.

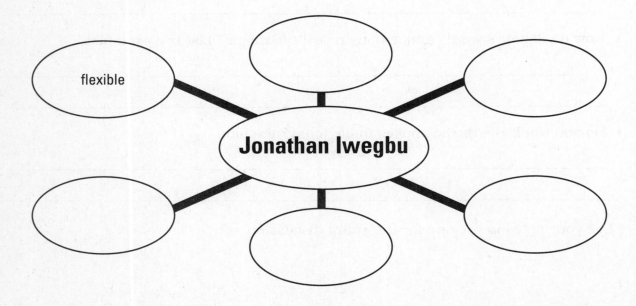

Civil Peace

1. **Infer:** In what sense has the war enhanced Jonathan's appreciation of his life?

   _____

   _____

2. **Compare:** In what ways is the period the thieves call "Civil Peace" like a civil war?

   _____

   _____

3. **Literary Analysis:** Use this chart to describe two episodes that spark a response in Jonathan.

Episode	Jonathan's Response	Reasons for the Response	Result: Peace of Mind/Problems

   Explain how the episodes described in your chart help develop the **theme** of the story.

   _____

   _____

5. **Reading Skill: Draw a conclusion** about the thieves' response to the losses of war. What do the thieves say and do that tells you?

   _____

   _____

SUPPORT FOR WRITING AND EXTEND YOUR LEARNING

Writing: Character Analysis

Write a brief **character analysis** of Jonathan.

- Make a list of Jonathan's character traits. List as many as you can.

_____

_____

_____

- Trim your list to three traits that best describe Jonathan's character.

_____

_____

- Rank the three traits in order of importance: first, second, third.

_____

_____

Use your notes to write your character analysis.

Listening and Speaking: Group Discussion

Prepare for a **group discussion** on the theme of "Civil Peace."

- What is the author's theme or main message in this story?

_____

_____

- How do Jonathan's words and actions reveal the theme? List two examples.

_____

_____

- Do you think the theme applies to life today? Explain.

_____

_____

Use your notes to prepare for the group discussion.

The Masque of the Red Death •
The Garden of Stubborn Cats

LITERARY ANALYSIS

Symbolism is a writer's use of symbols. A **symbol** is a character, a place, a thing, or an event in a literary work that stands for a larger idea. For example, a dog in a story may stand for loyalty. To make something into a symbol, a writer may use these common strategies:

- Call on traditional associations—a dog is a symbol of loyalty because dogs are often praised for that virtue.
- Create new associations—if the dog in the story runs away when its owner betrays a friend, a connection is made because both loyalty and the dog "disappear" at the same time.

A story in which all characters, settings, and events are clearly symbolic is called an **allegory**.

As you read, use the diagram below to identify details that show that an object or a character symbolizes a larger meaning.

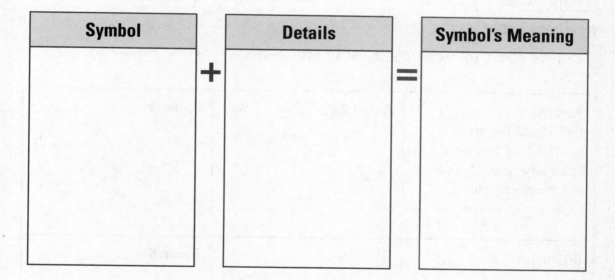

READING SKILL

When you **draw a conclusion**, you make a decision or form an opinion on the basis of facts and details in a text. To draw a conclusion about the meaning of a symbol, **identify patterns** that suggest its larger meaning.

- Consider the repeated actions, qualities, and other details that the work associates with the symbol.
- Make a logical guess about the meaning of the symbol—the meaning that best explains its role in the work.

The Masque of the Red Death

Edgar Allan Poe

Summary Prince Prospero believes that he can escape a deadly plague. He locks himself and his friends in his palace and throws a party. They learn that they cannot escape death.

Reading/Writing Connection

Complete this paragraph about the dangers of hiding from problems.

To ignore problems will _____. It is not a good idea to

withdraw _____. It is better to resolve _____.

Note-taking Guide

Use this chart to recall the setting of the story.

Room 1 Gothic, stained-glass window looking out on closed corridor; blue décor; window vividly blue	**Room 2**	**Room 3**
Room 4	**Room 5**	**Room 6**
	Room 7	

The Masque of the Red Death

1. **Evaluate:** What does the prince's response to the Red Death suggest about the kind of person he is? Explain.

   _____

   _____

2. **Analyze:** What message do you think Poe conveys in this story? Support your answer with details from the story.

   _____

   _____

   _____

3. **Literary Analysis:** In the story, the uninvited guest might be thought of as a symbol of death. Describe two responses the partygoers have to the stranger. Are these responses similar to possible responses to death? Explain.

   _____

   _____

   _____

   _____

4. **Reading Skill:** In the chart below, identify the pattern of details that shows the importance of the clock.

Detail	Conclusion	Detail

SUPPORT FOR WRITING AND EXTEND YOUR LEARNING

Writing: Narrative

Write a brief **narrative**, using an object as a symbol. Use the following list to help you write your narrative.

- Choose an object, and decide what the object stands for.

_____

_____

- What is the object's purpose in your narrative?

_____

- How does the object affect events in your narrative?

_____

- What words or phrases can describe what the object stands for?

_____

_____

Research and Technology: Research Summary

Research Poe's influence on mysteries and detective stories. Use the chart below to record your findings. Present your findings in a **research summary**.

Poe's Influence on Mysteries and Detective Stories		
Encyclopedia	**Internet site** *.edu*	**Second Internet site** *.edu*
Notes:	Notes:	Notes:

The Garden of Stubborn Cats

Italo Calvino

Summary An Italian worker named Marcovaldo befriends a cat. He follows the cat and discovers an old villa where cats in the city gather. The city tries to build a huge building there. The cats and other creatures will not leave.

Reading/Writing Connection

Complete the sentences to describe a place in your neighborhood that you have just discovered.

1. Sometimes, a place can <u>emerge</u> when _____.

2. It can <u>capture</u> one's _____.

3. The <u>appeal</u> of this place is _____.

Note-taking Guide

Use this diagram to record the six main events of the story.

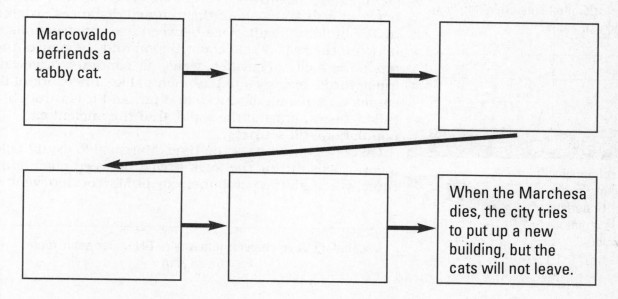

Marcovaldo befriends a tabby cat.

When the Marchesa dies, the city tries to put up a new building, but the cats will not leave.

Is the community you live in grow-ing and changing? Describe how.

_____

_____

_____

Symbolism is a writer's use of symbols. A **symbol** is a character, a place, a thing, or an event in a story that stands for a larger idea. Read the first paragraph. What association with cats is the writer making?

_____

_____

When you **draw a conclusion**, you make a decision or form an opinion that is based on facts and details in a text. Which details support the conclusion that cats are not fully at home in the city?

_____

_____

_____

What happened to the gardens in the city? Underline the text that tells you.

The Garden of Stubborn Cats
Italo Calvino

The city of cats and the city of men exist one inside the other, but they are not the same city. Few cats recall the time when there was no distinction: the streets and squares of men were also streets and squares of cats, and the lawns, courtyards, balconies, and fountains: you lived in a broad and various space. But for several generations now domestic felines have been prisoners of an uninhabitable city: the streets are uninterruptedly overrun by the mortal traffic of cat-crushing automobiles; in every square foot of terrain where once a garden extended or a vacant lot or the ruins of an old demolition, now condominiums loom up, welfare housing, brand-new skyscrapers; every entrance is crammed with parked cars; the courtyards, one by one, have been roofed by reinforced concrete and transformed into garages or movie houses or storerooms or workshops. And where a rolling plateau of low roofs once extended, copings, terraces, water tanks, balconies, skylights, corrugated-iron sheds, now one general superstructure rises wherever structures can rise; the intermediate differences in height, between the low ground of the street and the supernal[1] heaven of the penthouses, disappear; the cat of a recent litter seeks in vain the itinerary of its fathers, the point from which to make the soft leap from balustrade to cornice to drainpipe, or for the quick climb on the roof-tiles.

But in this vertical city, in this compressed city where all voids tend to fill up and every block of cement tends to mingle with other blocks of cement, a kind of counter-city opens, a negative city, that consists of empty slices between wall and wall, of the minimal distances ordained by the building regulations between two constructions, between the rear of one construction and the rear of the next; it is a city of cavities, wells, air conduits, driveways, inner yards, accesses to basements, like a network of dry canals on a planet of stucco and tar, and it is through this network, grazing the walls, that the ancient cat population still scurries.

On occasion, to pass the time, Marcovaldo would follow a cat. It was during the work-break, between noon and three, when all the personnel except Marcovaldo went

Vocabulary Development: itinerary (y TIN uh rer ee) *n.* route; travel plan

1. **supernal** (soo PER nuhl) *adj.* from the heavens

home to eat, and he—who brought his lunch in his bag—laid his place among the packing-cases in the warehouse, chewed his snack, smoked a half-cigar, and wandered around, alone and idle, waiting for work to resume. In those hours, a cat that peeped in at a window was always welcome company, and a guide for new explorations. He had made friends with a tabby, well fed, a blue ribbon around its neck, surely living with some well-to-do family. This tabby shared with Marcovaldo the habit of an afternoon stroll right after lunch; and naturally a friendship sprang up.

Following his tabby friend, Marcovaldo had started looking at places as if through the round eyes of a cat and even if these places were the usual environs of his firm he saw them in a different light, as settings for cattish stories, with connections practicable only by light, velvety paws. Though from the outside the neighborhood seemed poor in cats, every day on his rounds Marcovaldo made the acquaintance of some new face, and a miau, a hiss, a stiffening of fur on an arched back was enough for him to sense ties and <u>intrigues</u> and rivalries among them. At those moments he thought he had already penetrated the secrecy of the felines' society: and then he felt himself scrutinized by pupils that became slits, under the surveillance of the antennae of taut whiskers, and all the cats around him sat impassive as sphinxes, the pink triangles of their noses convergent on the black triangles of their lips, and the only things that moved were the tips of the ears, with a vibrant jerk like radar. They reached the end of a narrow passage, between squalid blank walls; and, looking around, Marcovaldo saw that the cats that had led him this far had vanished, all of them together, no telling in which direction, even his tabby friend, and they had left him alone. Their realm had territories, ceremonies, customs that it was not yet granted to him to discover.

On the other hand, from the cat city there opened unsuspected peepholes onto the city of men: and one day the same tabby led him to discover the great Biarritz Restaurant.

Anyone wishing to see the Biarritz Restaurant had only to assume the posture of a cat, that is, proceed on all fours. Cat and man, in this fashion, walked around a kind of dome, at whose foot some low, rectangular little windows opened. Following the tabby's example, Marcovaldo looked down. They were transoms through which the luxurious hall received air and light. To the sound of gypsy violins, partridges and quails swirled by on silver dishes balanced by the white-gloved fingers of waiters in tailcoats. Or,

---

Vocabulary Development: intrigues (IN treegz) *n.* plots; schemes

© Pearson Education, Inc., publishing as Pearson Prentice Hall.

The Garden of Stubborn Cats 171

TAKE NOTES

Stop to Reflect

Do you feel sorry for Marcovaldo? Explain your answer.

_____

_____

_____

_____

Reading Skill

Draw a conclusion about why "from the outside the neighborhood seemed poor in cats."

_____

_____

_____

_____

_____

Reading Check

What happens when Marcovaldo and the cats reach the end of a narrow passage? Circle the answer in the text.

_____

_____

_____

Read the first bracketed passage. What details support the **conclusion** that the cat intends to find food at the restaurant?

_____

_____

_____

_____

Read the second bracketed passage. How are the cats different from the people at the restaurant? What do you think each **symbolizes**?

_____

_____

_____

_____

What captures Marcovaldo's interest in the restaurant? Circle the answer in the text.

more precisely, above the partridges and quails the dishes whirled, and above the dishes the white gloves, and poised on the waiters' patent-leather shoes, the gleaming parquet floor, from which hung dwarf potted palms and tablecloths and crystal and buckets like bells with the champagne bottle for their clapper: everything was turned upside-down because Marcovaldo, for fear of being seen, wouldn't stick his head inside the window and confined himself to looking at the reversed reflection of the room in the tilted pane.

But it was not so much the windows of the dining-room as those of the kitchens that interested the cat: looking through the former you saw, distant and somehow transfigured, what in the kitchens presented itself—quite concrete and within paw's reach—as a plucked bird or a fresh fish. And it was toward the kitchens, in fact, that the tabby wanted to lead Marcovaldo, either through a gesture of altruistic friendship or else because it counted on the man's help for one of its raids. Marcovaldo, however, was reluctant to leave his belvedere over the main room: first as he was fascinated by the luxury of the place, and then because something down there had riveted his attention. To such an extent that, overcoming his fear of being seen, he kept peeking in, with his head in the transom.

In the midst of the room, directly under that pane, there was a little glass fish tank, a kind of aquarium, where some fat trout were swimming. A special customer approached, a man with a shiny bald pate, black suit, black beard. An old waiter in tailcoat followed him, carrying a little net as if he were going to catch butterflies. The gentleman in black looked at the trout with a grave, intent air; then he raised one hand and with a slow, solemn gesture singled out a fish. The waiter dipped the net into the tank, pursued the appointed trout, captured it, headed for the kitchens, holding out in front of him, like a lance, the net in which the fish wriggled. The gentleman in black, solemn as a magistrate[2] who has handed down a capital sentence, went to take his seat and wait for the return of the trout, sautéed "à la meunière."[3]

If I found a way to drop a line from up here and make one of those trout bite, Marcovaldo thought, I couldn't be accused of theft; at worst, of fishing in an unauthorized place. And ignoring the miaus that called him toward the kitchens, he went to collect his fishing tackle.

Nobody in the crowded dining room of the Biarritz saw the long, fine line, armed with hook and bait, as it slowly dropped into the tank. The fish saw the bait, and flung

2. **magistrate** (MAJ i strayt) *n.* judge.
3. **sautéed "à la meunière"** (saw TAYD ah lah muh nee ER) rolled in flour, fried in butter, and sprinkled with lemon juice and chopped parsley.

themselves on it. In the fray one trout managed to bite the worm: and immediately it began to rise, rise, emerge from the water, a silvery flash, it darted up high, over the laid tables and the trolleys of hors d'oeuvres, over the blue flames of the crêpes Suzette, until it vanished into the heavens of the transom.

Marcovaldo had yanked the rod with the brisk snap of the expert fisherman, so the fish landed behind his back. The trout had barely touched the ground when the cat sprang. What little life the trout still had was lost between the tabby's teeth. Marcovaldo, who had abandoned his line at that moment to run and grab the fish, saw it snatched from under his nose, hook and all. He was quick to put one foot on the rod, but the snatch had been so strong that the rod was all the man had left, while the tabby ran off with the fish, pulling the line after it. Treacherous kitty! It had vanished.

But this time it wouldn't escape him: there was that long line trailing after him and showing the way he had taken. Though he had lost sight of the cat, Marcovaldo followed the end of the line: there it was, running along a wall; it climbed a parapet, wound through a doorway, was swallowed up by a basement . . . Marcovaldo, venturing into more and more cattish places, climbed roofs, straddled railings, always managed to catch a glimpse—perhaps only a second before it disappeared—of that moving trace that indicated the thief's path.

Now the line played out down a sidewalk, in the midst of the traffic, and Marcovaldo, running after it, almost managed to grab it. He flung himself down on his belly: there, he grabbed it! He managed to seize one end of the line before it slipped between the bars of a gate.

Beyond a half-rusted gate and two bits of wall buried under climbing plants, there was a little rank[4] garden, with a small, abandoned-looking building at the far end of it. A carpet of dry leaves covered the path, and dry leaves lay everywhere under the boughs of the two plane-trees, forming actually some little mounds in the yard. A layer of leaves was yellowing in the green water of a pool. Enormous buildings rose all around, skyscrapers with thousands of windows, like so many eyes trained disapprovingly on that little square patch with two trees, a few tiles, and all those yellow leaves, surviving right in the middle of an area of great traffic.

And in this garden, perched on the capitals and balustrades, lying on the dry leaves of the flowerbeds, climbing on the trunks of the trees or on the drainpipes, motionless on their four paws, their tails making a question-mark, seated to wash their faces, there were

---

4. **rank** (rangk) *adj.* growing vigorously and coarsely.

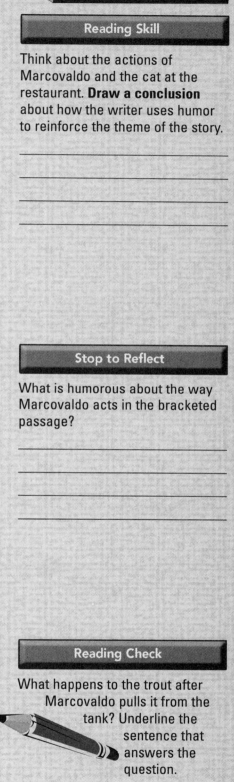

TAKE NOTES

Reading Skill

Think about the actions of Marcovaldo and the cat at the restaurant. **Draw a conclusion** about how the writer uses humor to reinforce the theme of the story.

_____

_____

_____

Stop to Reflect

What is humorous about the way Marcovaldo acts in the bracketed passage?

_____

_____

_____

Reading Check

What happens to the trout after Marcovaldo pulls it from the tank? Underline the sentence that answers the question.

Several cats have made this garden their home. Why do you think they have chosen this garden? **Draw a conclusion** about the garden to answer the question.

_____

_____

_____

_____

_____

What do you think the garden **symbolizes**? Explain your answer.

_____

_____

_____

_____

What place does Marcovaldo realize that he has found? Circle the text that answers the question.

tiger cats, black cats, white cats, calico cats, tabbies, angoras, Persians, house cats and stray cats, perfumed cats and mangy cats. Marcovaldo realized he had finally reached the heart of the cats' realm, their secret island. And, in his emotion, he almost forgot his fish.

It had remained, that fish, hanging by the line from the branch of a tree, out of reach of the cats' leaps; it must have dropped from its kidnapper's mouth at some clumsy movement, perhaps as it was defended from the others, or perhaps displayed as an extraordinary prize. The line had got tangled, and Marcovaldo, tug as he would, couldn't manage to yank it loose. A furious battle had meanwhile been joined among the cats, to reach that unreachable fish, or rather, to win the right to try and reach it. Each wanted to prevent the others from leaping: they hurled themselves on one another, they tangled in midair, they rolled around clutching each other, and finally a general war broke out in a whirl of dry, crackling leaves.

After many futile yanks, Marcovaldo now felt the line was free, but he took care not to pull it: the trout would have fallen right in the midst of that infuriated scrimmage of felines.

It was at this moment that, from the top of the walls of the gardens, a strange rain began to fall: fish-bones, heads, tails, even bits of lung and lights.[5] Immediately the cats' attention was distracted from the suspended trout and they flung themselves on the new delicacies. To Marcovaldo, this seemed the right moment to pull the line and regain his fish. But, before he had time to act, from a blind of the little villa, two yellow, skinny hands darted out: one was brandishing scissors; the other, a frying pan. The hand with the scissors was raised above the trout, the hand with the frying pan was thrust under it. The scissors cut the line, the trout fell into the pan; hands, scissors and pan withdrew, the blind closed: all in the space of a second. Marcovaldo was totally bewildered.

"Are you also a cat lover?" A voice at his back made him turn round. He was surrounded by little old women, some of them ancient, wearing old-fashioned hats on their heads; others, younger, but with the look of spinsters; and all were carrying in their hands or their bags packages of leftover meat or fish, and some even had little pans of milk. "Will you help me throw this package over the fence, for those poor creatures?"

All the ladies, cat lovers, gathered at this hour around the garden of dry leaves to take the food to their protégés.[6]

"Can you tell me why they are all here, these cats?" Marcovaldo inquired.

---

5. **lights** term for animal organs used for catfood.
6. **protégés** (PROHT uh zhayz) *n.* those guided and helped by another.

"Where else could they go? This garden is all they have left! Cats come here from other neighborhoods, too, from miles and miles around . . ."

"And birds, as well," another lady added. "They're forced to live by the hundreds and hundreds on these few trees . . ."

"And the frogs, they're all in that pool, and at night they never stop croaking . . . You can hear them even on the eighth floor of the buildings around here."

"Who does this villa belong to anyway?" Marcovaldo asked. Now, outside the gate, there weren't just the cat-loving ladies but also other people: the man from the gas pump opposite, the apprentices from a mechanic's shop, the postman, the grocer, some passers-by. And none of them, men and women, had to be asked twice: all wanted to have their say, as always when a mysterious and controversial subject comes up.

"It belongs to a Marchesa.[7] She lives there, but you never see her . . ."

"She's been offered millions and millions, by developers, for this little patch of land, but she won't sell . . ."

"What would she do with millions, an old woman all alone in the world? She wants to hold on to her house, even if it's falling to pieces, rather than be forced to move . . ."

"It's the only undeveloped bit of land in the downtown area . . . Its value goes up every year . . . They've made her offers—"

"Offers! That's not all. Threats, intimidation, persecution . . . You don't know the half of it! Those contractors!"

"But she holds out. She's held out for years . . ."

"She's a saint. Without her, where would those poor animals go?"

"A lot she cares about the animals, the old miser! Have you ever seen her give them anything to eat?"

"How can she feed the cats when she doesn't have food for herself? She's the last descendant of a ruined family!"

"She hates cats. I've seen her chasing them and hitting them with an umbrella!"

"Because they were tearing up her flowerbeds!"

"What flowerbeds? I've never seen anything in this garden but a great crop of weeds!"

Marcovaldo realized that with regard to the old Marchesa opinions were sharply divided: some saw her as an angelic being, others as an egoist and a miser.

"It's the same with the birds; she never gives them a crumb!"

"She gives them hospitality. Isn't that plenty?"

---

7. **Marchesa** (mahr KAY zah) *n.* title of an Italian noblewoman.

TAKE NOTES

Literary Analysis

Underline details about the other creatures that can be found in the garden. What do the frogs and birds **symbolize**?

_____

_____

Stop to Reflect

Why do you think so many people care about what happens to this garden?

_____

_____

_____

_____

_____

Reading Check

Who owns the villa? Underline the sentence that answers the question.

Literary Analysis

A story in which all characters, settings, and events are symbolic is called an **allegory.** How is the argument outside the villa symbolic?

_____
_____
_____
_____

Reading Skill

Read the bracketed text. **Draw a conclusion** about why both sides want Marcovaldo to ask the Marchesa for an explanation.

_____
_____
_____
_____
_____

Reading Check

How does Marcovaldo end the argument? Circle the text that answers the question.

"Like she gives the mosquitoes, you mean. They all come from here, from that pool. In the summertime the mosquitoes eat us alive, and it's all the fault of that Marchesa!"

"And the mice? This villa is a mine of mice. Under the dead leaves they have their burrows, and at night they come out . . ."

"As far as the mice go, the cats take care of them . . ."

"Oh, you and your cats! If we had to rely on them . . ."

"Why? Have you got something to say against cats?"

Here the discussion degenerated into a general quarrel.

"The authorities should do something: confiscate the villa!" one man cried.

"What gives them the right?" another protested.

"In a modern neighborhood like ours, a mouse-nest like this . . . it should be forbidden . . ."

"Why, I picked my apartment precisely because it overlooked this little bit of green . . ."

"Green, hell! Think of the fine skyscraper they could build here!"

Marcovaldo would have liked to add something of his own, but he couldn't get a word in. Finally, all in one breath, he exclaimed: "The Marchesa stole a trout from me!"

The unexpected news supplied fresh ammunition to the old woman's enemies, but her defenders exploited it as proof of the <u>indigence</u> to which the unfortunate noblewoman was reduced. Both sides agreed that Marcovaldo should go and knock at her door to demand an explanation.

It wasn't clear whether the gate was locked or unlocked; in any case, it opened, after a push, with a mournful creak. Marcovaldo picked his way among the leaves and cats, climbed the steps to the porch, knocked hard at the entrance.

At a window (the very one where the frying pan had appeared), the blind was raised slightly and in one corner a round, pale blue eye was seen, and a clump of hair dyed an undefinable color, and a dry skinny hand. A voice was heard, asking: "Who is it? Who's at the door?", the words accompanied by a cloud smelling of fried oil.

"It's me, Marchesa. The trout man," Marcovaldo explained. "I don't mean to trouble you. I only wanted to tell you, in case you didn't know, that the trout was stolen from me, by that cat, and I'm the one who caught it. In fact the line . . ."

"Those cats! It's always those cats . . ." the Marchesa said, from behind the shutter, with a shrill, somewhat

Vocabulary Development: indigence (IN di juhns) *n.* poverty

nasal voice. "All my troubles come from the cats! Nobody knows what I go through! Prisoner night and day of those horrid beasts! And with all the refuse people throw over the walls, to spite me!"

"But my trout . . ."

"Your trout! What am I supposed to know about your trout!" The Marchesa's voice became almost a scream, as if she wanted to drown out the sizzle of oil in the pan, which came through the window along with the aroma of fried fish. "How can I make sense of anything, with all the stuff that rains into my house?"

"I understand, but did you take the trout or didn't you?"

"When I think of all the damage I suffer because of the cats! Ah, fine state of affairs! I'm not responsible for anything! I can't tell you what I've lost! Thanks to those cats, who've occupied house and garden for years! My life at the mercy of those animals! Go and find the owners! Make them pay damages! Damages? A whole life destroyed! A prisoner here, unable to move a step!"

"Excuse me for asking: but who's forcing you to stay?"

From the crack in the blind there appeared sometimes a round, pale blue eye, sometimes a mouth with two protruding teeth; for a moment the whole face was visible, and to Marcovaldo it seemed, bewilderingly, the face of a cat.

"They keep me prisoner, they do, those cats! Oh, I'd be glad to leave! What wouldn't I give for a little apartment all my own, in a nice clean modern building! But I can't go out . . . They follow me, they block my path, they trip me up!" The voice became a whisper, as if to confide a secret. "They're afraid I'll sell the lot . . . They won't leave me . . . won't allow me . . . When the builders come to offer me a contract, you should see them, those cats! They get in the way, pull out their claws; they even chased a lawyer off! Once I had the contract right here, I was about to sign it, and they dived in through the window, knocked over the inkwell, tore up all the pages . . ."

All of a sudden Marcovaldo remembered the time, the shipping department, the boss. He tiptoed off over the dried leaves, as the voice continued to come through the slats of the blind, enfolded in that cloud apparently from the oil of a frying pan. "They even scratched me . . . I still have the scar . . . All alone here at the mercy of these demons . . ."

Winter came. A blossoming of white flakes decked the branches and capitals and the cats' tails. Under the snow, the dry leaves dissolved into mush. The cats were rarely seen, the cat lovers even less; the packages of fish-bones were consigned only to cats who came to the door. Nobody, for quite a while, had seen anything of the Marchesa. No smoke came now from the chimneypot of the villa.

The Garden of Stubborn Cats **177**

TAKE NOTES

Reading Skill

To draw conclusions about the meaning of a symbol, **identify patterns** that suggest its larger meaning. What does the Marchesa represent in the story?

_____

_____

_____

_____

Literary Analysis

Which details from the story tell you that the Marchesa and the cats **symbolize** similar ideas?

_____

_____

_____

_____

_____

_____

Reading Check

Why does the Marchesa hate the cats? Underline the answers in the text.

Literary Analysis

Read the bracketed text. How do these details show that the cats **symbolize** the forces resisting the modern city?

_____

_____

_____

_____

Reading Check

What do the neighbors realize? Underline details that tell you.

One snowy day, the garden was again full of cats, who had returned as if it were spring, and they were miauing as if on a moonlight night. The neighbors realized that something had happened: they went and knocked at the Marchesa's door. She didn't answer: she was dead.

In the spring, instead of the garden, there was a huge building site that a contractor had set up. The steam shovels dug down to great depths to make room for the foundations, cement poured into the iron armatures, a very high crane passed beams to the workmen who were making the scaffoldings. But how could they get on with their work? Cats walked along all the planks, they made bricks fall and upset buckets of mortar, they fought in the midst of the piles of sand. When you started to raise an armature, you found a cat perched on top of it, hissing fiercely. More treacherous pusses climbed onto the masons' backs as if to purr, and there was no getting rid of them. And the birds continued making their nests in all the trestles, the cab of the crane looked like an aviary[8] . . . And you couldn't dip up a bucket of water that wasn't full of frogs, croaking and hopping . . .

8. **aviary** (AY vee er ee) *n.* building or large cage for housing many birds.

Reader's Response: Should the garden of cats remain as it is, or should developers be free to build over it? Support your opinion.

_____

_____

_____

_____

The Garden of Stubborn Cats

1. **Infer:** How have changes in the city changed the way cats live?

   _____

   _____

2. **Analyze:** When Marcovaldo finds the garden, the writer suggests that such a garden is rare in the city. What are two details that support this idea?

   _____

   _____

   _____

3. **Literary Analysis:** This story can be read as an **allegory**. Explain what the final conflict between cats and humans symbolizes.

   _____

   _____

   _____

4. **Reading Skill:** Use the chart below. List two details that show a pattern in the Marchesa's relationship to the other people in the city. Then, use those details to **draw a conclusion** about what she symbolizes.

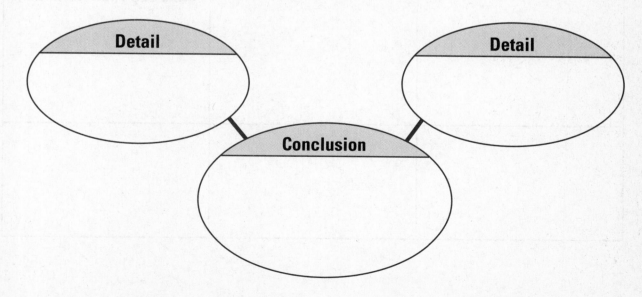

SUPPORT FOR WRITING AND EXTEND YOUR LEARNING

Writing: Narrative

Calvino turns cats into a symbol of mischief and mystery. Write a brief **narrative** using another animal as a symbol.

- Choose an animal, and decide what the animal stands for.

  _____

- What is the animal's purpose in your narrative?

  _____

  _____

- How does the animal affect events in your narrative?

  _____

- What words or phrases can describe what the animal stands for?

  _____

  _____

Use your notes to write your narrative.

Research and Technology: Research Summary

Write a **research summary** about the historic architecture of a European city. Use the chart below to record information about one or two famous structures in the city. Use your notes to prepare your research summary.

Famous Structure	Description	Important Architectural Terms and Their Definitions

Literary Reviews

ABOUT LITERARY REVIEWS

A **literary review** gives a writer's opinion about a work of literature. Most literary reviews include:

- a summary of the work being reviewed
- background information on the writer or developments in writing
- quotations or examples from the work that show its "flavor"
- the reviewer's opinion of the work

READING SKILL

Remember that a literary review is a critic's opinion. Draw conclusions to **evaluate the critic's judgments**.

- Think about how well the critic supports his or her judgments. For example, a critic might call a biography "boring." He or she should give examples, such as quotations, to explain why it is boring.
- Think about the critic's standards. For example, a critic who loves action might say that a story is excellent because it is action-packed.

Use the following checklist to evaluate a review.

CHECKLIST FOR EVALUATING A REVIEW
Does the critic
❏ provide sufficient background information?
❏ give an adequate overview or summary of the work?
❏ suggest the "flavor" of the work through descriptions or quotations?
❏ clearly state his or her opinions of the work?
❏ support opinions with specific examples or quotations?
❏ avoid unmerited praise or unjustified attacks?

The New York Times

Calvino's Urban Allegories

The New York Times, January 22, 1984

MARCOVALDO

Or The Seasons in the City. By Italo Calvino. Translated by William Weaver. 121 pp. San Diego: Helen & Kurt Wolff/Harcourt Brace Jovanovich. Cloth, $9.95. Paper, $3.95.

By Franco Ferrucci

A SENTENCE from Italo Calvino's introduction to his "Italian Folktales" reveals the secret behind the magic of the earlier stories in "Marcovaldo": "I believe that fables are true." Conversely, Mr. Calvino believes that reality is fabulous. When he began the stories of "Marcovaldo" in the 1950s and 60s he did not know he was creating a masterwork in the narrative trend labeled the nouveau roman[1] by French critics. He simply followed his instincts as a storyteller and achieved a durable balance between the heritage of 20th-century Italian neorealism and a fabulous vision of reality. [. . .]

"Marcovaldo," sensitively translated by William Weaver, is a series of ecological allegories[2] in the form of urban tales. Psychological insights are held back in favor of cartoons in which facts and people succeed one another with the geometrical smoothness of movie animation. Sharp definition and clarity are characteristics of Mr. Calvino's best prose in such books as "The Castle of Crossed Destinies," "The Nonexistent Knight and the Cloven Viscount" and "Cosmi-comics." Even early in his career, his rhetorical virtuosity disguised the subtlety and depth of his vision—especially in some of the stories in "Marcovaldo," like "The City Lost in the Snow," "A Saturday of Sun, Sand and Sleep" and "The Wrong Stop." He writes lightly and jauntily; any trace of effort is concealed. But what catches the reader goes beyond the unspotted perfection of the style; it is his uninhibited poetic sense of life.

Each story belongs to a season, and all of them together take their shape from the cycle of the seasons. Marcovaldo lives through the stories as the double of the writer, observing, reflecting and comparing in a perfectly detached way. He is a humble and romantic blue-collar worker lost in the big city, which perverts rhythms and obfuscates cycles. He is trapped in the unreality of this modern city (the setting is vividly evoked in "Marcovaldo at the Supermarket"), a place that even suffocates the life of the animals in the stories [. . .]

What is so much admired by the readers of Mr. Calvino's later "Invisible Cities" was already at work in "Marcovaldo" and with a more cogent narrative drive. "Invisible Cities" seems like a memory, while "Marcovaldo" conveys the sensuous, tangible qualities of life. The opening lines from "The Forest on the Super-highway," a story in "Marcovaldo," might serve as an invitation to readers to meet this tender and humorous Kafka of our days: "Cold has a thousand shapes and a thousand ways of moving in the world: on the sea it gallops like a troop of horses, on the countryside it falls like a swarm of locusts, in the cities like a knife-blade it slashes the streets and penetrates the chinks of unheated houses."

---

1. **nouveau roman** (noo VOH roh MAHN) French for "new novel"; term for works of the 1950s and 1960s in which writers rejected realistic representations of life.
2. **allegories** (AL uh gawr eez) *n.* stories in which characters stand for ideas and so tend to lack individual personalities.

Easy Ironies

The New York Times, November 9, 1983

MARCOVALDO

Or The Seasons in the City. By Italo Calvino.
Translated by William Weaver.

By Anatole Broyard

While Umberto Eco has been on the best-seller list for 20 weeks with "The Name of the Rose," Italo Calvino is the Italian writer who seems to cause the most excitement among American readers. With three books especially—"Cosmicomics," "Invisible cities" and "If on a winter's night a traveler"—Mr. Calvino has earned comparisons with Jorge Luis Borges and Gabriel García Márquez.[1] After decades of Italian neorealism in the works of authors like Alberto Moravia, Elio Vittorini and Cesare Pavese, Mr. Calvino's fictions appear to be closer to the fantastic Italy of a Fellini film or a painting by Giorgio de Chirico.

He is seen by some critics as an emancipation, as a writer who has brought back humor, lightness and freedom of invention to contemporary Italian fiction. Others find him too light, or all light and no shadow, no substance. He is clever and witty, they concede, but all surface. Italy, it seems, has grown used to taking itself very seriously and is resisting, in fiction at least, the anarchic pleasures of the international modern style.

"Marcovaldo" reads like an attempt to satisfy both schools of thought. The hero for whom the book is named is a Chaplinesque[2] figure posed against the background of a drab and nameless industrial city in the north of Italy. Marcovaldo is Mr. Calvino's Candide,[3] his image of an innocent who survives the 1950s and 60s in a modern metropolis by willfully misreading reality, as Chaplin did, by opposing his optimism to its negative influences.

Since all 20 of these very short stories feature the same character, "Marcovaldo" might just as easily be read as a novel. In fact, some of the stories are so slight that without the support of the others, they seem negligible. Taken together, they have a mild charm. [. . .]

An unskilled laborer with a wife and several children to feed, Marcovaldo is always searching his city for some sign of a relenting. In one story, he finds this relenting in the form of mushrooms springing up under the city's trees. As it turns out, the mushrooms are poisonous. Yet, because there are not enough of them, the poison is not fatal. Marcovaldo and his family enjoy the poisoned, metropolitan pleasure of eating the mushrooms and surviving them. In Mr. Calvino's work, irony too springs up underneath the city's trees. [. . .]

In another story, a herd of cattle passes through the streets in the middle of the night and the whole family wakes up to see it. The story is turned away from this promising epiphany, though, when the eldest boy runs off with the herd and returns, months later, disillusioned with the pastoral life. [. . .]

This may be the trouble with Marcovaldo and with Mr. Calvino's work in general: It leans almost entirely on irony, but of a rather bland or schematic kind. One feels, in reading the book, a sort of fatigue in regard to irony. [. . .]

---

1. **Jorge Luis Borges** (HAWR he loo EES BAWR hes) **and Gabriel García Márquez** (gah vree EL gahr SEE ah MAHR kes) Borges (1899–1986) and Márquez (b. 1928) are two Latin American writers noted for fantastical stories.
2. **Chaplinesque** (chap lin ESK) resembling the characters played by silent movie actor Charlie Chaplin (1889–1977); innocent and optimistic even in the midst of misfortune.
3. **Candide** (kahn DEED) hero of French thinker Voltaire's 1759 novel of the same name, whose inexperience helps emphasize the evil he encounters in his travels.

THINKING ABOUT THE LITERARY REVIEW

1. What is Ferrucci's opinion of Calvino's writing style? Give two examples from the review to support your answer.

   _____

   _____

2. Find a passage from each review that talks about the same feature of Calvino's writing. Compare the reviewers' opinions of that feature.

   _____

   _____

READING SKILL

3. What topic does each reviewer use as background information?

   _____

4. Why might Broyard's review seem more balanced than Ferrucci's?

   _____

TIMED WRITING: EXPOSITION (20 minutes)

Write a short essay comparing the standards of both reviewers. Use the list below to evaluate the critical reviews.

   • What reasons does the reviewer give for his opinions?

   _____

   _____

   • What do these reasons tell you about his standards?

   _____

   _____

Everest
from Touch the Top of the World

Essays are short works of nonfiction. Their authors are usually named and are always real people. An essay examines and discusses a topic. It may present a writer's personal viewpoints. Essays usually explore ideas and opinions.

Speeches present a topic as well. A speech is delivered by a speaker to an audience. A speech often marks a special occasion, such as a graduation or a building dedication. Speeches range from informal talks to formal lectures.

Essays and speeches offer more than ideas and facts. Both essays and speeches also express a writer's style, tone, perspective, and purpose.

- **Style** is the distinctive way the author uses language. Style reflects an author's individuality. It can be as unique as a fingerprint. Style may be formal or informal. It is determined by word choice and use of figurative language. Sentence structure and type of organization also characterize an author's style.

- **Tone** is the author's attitude toward both the subject and the audience. You can hear tone in an author's choice of words and details. Tone is often described with a single adjective, such as *formal, amused,* or *angry.*

- **Perspective** is the author's opinion or viewpoint about the subject. **Bias** occurs when a writer gives a one-sided view of the subject, distorts the facts, or uses emotional language to influence the audience unfairly.

- **Purpose** is the author's reason for writing or speaking. Common purposes are to inform, to entertain, to persuade, to praise, to celebrate, and to warn.

Essays are grouped by the author's purpose. The chart below will help you identify different types of essays.

Type of Essay	Definition	Example
Narrative essay	• tells the story of real events or a person's experiences	a famous movie star's story of how her career started
Descriptive essay	• creates an impression about a person, an object, or an experience	a first-hand account of surviving a storm at sea
Expository essay	• provides information, discusses ideas, or explains a process	an explanation of how to build a birdhouse
Persuasive essay	• attempts to influence readers to think or act in a certain way	an editorial about why a historical building should not be torn down
Reflective essay	• expresses the writer's thoughts and feelings about a personal experience or an idea	a travel writer's thoughts on the different displays of patriotism he has seen around the country and what these say about the United States

Speeches are grouped by their levels of formality. Formality is determined by the speaker, the occasion, and the purpose. This chart will help you identify different types of speeches.

Type of Speech	Definition	Occasion
Address	• a formal, prepared speech, usually delivered by someone of importance	a college graduation address
Talk	• an informal speech delivered in a conversational style	a student's report to the Spanish Club about a trip to Mexico
Oration	• an eloquent speech given on a formal occasion	Martin Luther King, Jr.'s "I Have a Dream" speech
Lecture	• a prepared speech that informs or instructs an audience	a history teacher's introduction to the Industrial Revolution

Everest from Touch the Top of the World

Erik Weihenmayer

Summary This excerpt follows Erik Weihenmayer as he makes the dangerous climb to the highest point on Earth. You will experience Everest's strong winds and steep slopes through Weihenmayer's words. You will also discover how thin the air is at high altitudes. You will get to know the author and what it took for him to be the first blind man to climb Mount Everest.

Note-taking Guide

Use this chart to record some problems that Eric Weihenmayer and his fellow climbers experience on their climb.

Problems
PV becomes exhausted and needs help.

Activate Prior Knowledge

British mountain climber George Mallory, who disappeared on Mount Everest in 1924, once answered the question, "Why do you climb mountains?" with this: "Because they are there." Is this a good explanation for why people take the risk?

_____

_____

_____

_____

What other reasons do you think people have for mountain climbing?

_____

_____

_____

_____

Essay

Tone reveals the author's attitude. What do the underlined sentences illustrate about Weihenmayer's attitude toward himself, his subject, and his audience?

_____

_____

_____

_____

Reading Check

What help does Weihenmayer get in climbing the mountain? Underline the part of the text that tells you.

Everest
from Touch the Top of the World
Erik Weihenmayer

Background

The dangers of high-altitude climbing are severe. Many climbers fall sick and even die from illnesses caused by reduced oxygen. Others freeze or plummet to their deaths. Despite these risks, Erik Weihenmayer had successfully reached the summits of five of the world's highest peaks by 1999. In that year, when Pasquale "PV" Scaturro, a geophysicist and expert climber, suggested an expedition to the top of Mount Everest, Weihenmayer readily agreed. He arranged sponsorship from the National Federation of the Blind and, with Scaturro, organized the expedition. The other members of the team included Sherm Bull and his son Brad; Ang Pasang, a Sherpa who had climbed Everest twice; and Weihenmayer's long-time mountaineering buddies Eric "Erie" Alexander, Jeff Evans, Chris Morris, and Mike O'Donnell. On May 25, 2001, Weihenmayer and many of his teammates reached the top of Mount Everest. This excerpt describes the final leg of that adventure.

We left our tents a little before 9:00 P.M. on May 24. Because of our twenty-four-hour delay and the apprehension of other expeditions to share a summit day with me, we moved across the South Col with only one other team behind us. We had no worries of the typical horde clogging the fixed lines but could direct our full focus toward the mountain. The wind was blowing so loudly through the col that I couldn't hear the bells jingling from Chris's ice axe. Chris and I expected this, so for the first two hours he clanked his metal axe against rocks he passed. Finally, we worked our way around to the mountain's leeward[1] side, where Everest itself protected us from the wind. Chris had lost his voice, so his verbal directions were sparse. At each anchor, he'd hold the new line with his hand, so I could locate it and clip in. Chris was moving in front of me at his usual rock-solid pace, and I was right on his heels. We were making unbelievable time.

Vocabulary Development: apprehension (ap ree HEN shuhn) *n.* nervousness; anxiety
sparse (spars) *adj.* thinly spread; not plentiful

---

1. **leeward** (LEE werd) *adj.* away from the wind.

As we got higher up the mountain, four distinct changes had begun to work in my favor. Earlier, in the icefall, each step was very specific, but the terrain above the South Col consisted of steep forty-five-degree snow faces a hundred yards wide, intermingled with ten-to-fifty-foot crumbly rock steps. I could stay in the kicked boot holes of Chris or kick my own steps. Where I stepped had become less important than maintaining internal balance. I could breathe, scan my ice axe, and count on the next step. The slope was often so steep that I could lean forward and feel the rock or snow steps with my gloved hands, and I had trained myself long ago to save energy by landing my feet in the same holds my hands had just left. Finally, when I needed it most, the mountain had given me a pattern.

The thin oxygen of extreme altitude reduced us to a crawl. It was like moving through a bizarre atmosphere of syrup mixed with a narcotic. My team, struggling just to put one foot in front of the other, moved so slowly, it gave me more time to scan my axe across the snow and feel my way forward. The third equalizer was the darkness. With just a trickle of light produced by headlamps, my sighted team could only see a few feet in front of them. Bulky goggles blocked their side vision, and oxygen masks covered much of their visual field. Also, the pure oxygen trickling through their masks would flow up and freeze the lenses of their goggles so that they constantly had to remove them to wipe the lenses clean. Those brief moments when eyes are exposed to the elements, corneas will freeze, and the intense rays of the sun reflecting off the snow cause instant snow blindness. Not once did I ever have to worry about these complications.

In addition, my teammates had chosen smaller masks that rode low and tight across their cheeks and hung mostly below their chins. This allowed climbers to see better and prevented pure oxygen from seeping into their lenses, but also allowed plenty of pure oxygen to escape into the wind. I, on the other hand, had the luxury of choosing the largest mask I could find and wore it high on my face, getting the most benefit from the oxygen flow and the <u>ambient</u> air around the mask. I'm sure I made a

Stop to Reflect

Weihenmayer writes about ways in which his lack of sight gives him an advantage over the other climbers. Why do you think he makes this point?

_____

_____

_____

_____

_____

Essay

What is the author's **tone** in the bracketed paragraph?

_____

Circle two details that support your answer.

Reading Check

What did the mountain give the author when he needed it the most? Underline the sentence that tells you.

Vocabulary Development: ambient (AM bee uhnt) *adj.*
surrounding; on all sides

Essay

Purpose is the author's reason for writing. Mark the places in the text that give you clues about why Weihenmayer may have included the story about PV. What do you think is his purpose for including this story?

_____

_____

_____

_____

_____

Essay

Style is the way an author uses language. Why does Weihenmayer use dialogue in his account of what happened to PV? How does this use affect his style of writing so far?

_____

_____

_____

_____

Reading Check

Who helps PV to the tents? Underline the text that tells you.

freakish sight with my gigantic mask covering my goggles, like a day long ago in wrestling practice when I had put my sweatshirt on backward, with the hood covering my face, and chased the terrified freshmen around the mat. The consistent terrain, the altitude, the mask, and the darkness were great equalizers. I wouldn't go so far as to claim these gave me an advantage, but it was a matter of perspective. The mountain had gotten desperately harder for everyone else, while it had gotten slightly easier for me.

For two and a half months, all the decisions, the logistics, the backup safety plans had been implemented and executed by PV, and now, somewhere below the Balcony, the exhausting burden of leadership finally took its toll. Suddenly feeling listless and unable to catch his breath even with his oxygen bottle at full flow, PV had arduously turned back. He managed to convince Brad and Sherm, next to him, that he was strong enough to descend alone, in retrospect, a ploy that might have turned deadly, but PV's weary brain had never stopped calculating the big picture. He had refused to divert any energy from the team's summit effort. Through periodic radio checks as PV dropped altitude, I could hear his characteristically hyper voice growing flat, and just below a steep ice bulge, only an hour from Camp Four, PV sat down in the snow. "I'm very tired," he said. "I don't know if I can make it. I might need some assistance." PV's one warning before we left the tent was "If you sit down, you'll stay there." So, beginning to panic, I ripped my radio out of my pocket. "Is anyone near PV who can help him down?" I asked. "Is anyone reading me?" I repeated myself several times to empty static.

A few weeks earlier, Dr. Gipe had received the sad news that a close family friend had been killed in a skiing accident; a three-thousand-foot day in the Death Zone just didn't seem fair to his family, so that night, he had never left his tent. His decision was a tough one to make, but extremely fortunate for PV's sake. "This is Gipe at the South Col," finally came over the radio. "I'm strapping on my crampons right now. I'm going out to get PV." Dr. Gipe met PV about a half an hour from camp, up again and staggering slowly toward the tents.

Vocabulary Development: arduously (AHR joo uhs lee) *adv.* with great difficulty; laboriously

With the first crisis of the night averted, Chris and I plodded up a steep gully, which led us to the Balcony, a flat snow platform, ten feet wide. Michael Brown arrived first at about 2:00 A.M., with Chris and me right behind. All night, the weather had remained clear, with high clouds to the southeast and distant lightning flashes illuminating the sky, but at the Balcony, our luck suddenly ran out. <u>We walked into a blasting storm. Wind and horizontal snow raked our down suits and covered us with a layer of ice. The lightning strikes were now on top of us, exploding like a pyrotechnic[2] show.</u> Chris later said he couldn't see his feet through the blowing snow, which stopped us short, since the southeast ridge above narrowed to fifteen feet wide. Mike O.'s and Didrik's headlamps had simultaneously flickered out, and one of Didrik's crampons had popped off. "Someone come and help us," Mike yelled over the radio. Charley headed back and found them sitting in the snow only twenty feet away.

Chris and I huddled together in the wind, waiting for the others to arrive. "What do you think, Big E?" he asked. "It's lookin' pretty grim." When the others trickled in, Sherm wanted to go on; Charley wanted to turn back, and Erie thought we should wait. For forty-five minutes, we waited, periodic arguments breaking out whether to go on or descend. I was beginning to shiver and forced myself to bounce up and down, and to windmill my arms. We were so close, and I was feeling strong. Turning back was a crushing proposition, but I also wasn't willing to go bullheadedly forward and throw my life away. My mind was starting to settle on the possibility of turning back, when Kevin's voice from Base Camp crackled over my radio. Throughout the expedition, Kevin had been learning to read the satellite weather reports we received every few days over the Internet. From the weather map, it appeared the storm was moving rapidly to the northeast toward Bhutan, and where we stood on the Balcony, we were directly northeast of Base Camp. "Hey you guys, don't quit yet," his voice sounded urgent. "The storm's cleared down here. It just might pass over you."

"Weather is also clearing here," Kami said from Camp Two below.

Chris glanced over at me. Beyond my right hip, shining through the storm clouds, he could see a star. "Let's see if this thing breaks up," he said. Sherm must have felt good tidings, too, because he pushed on. Chris and I followed. Following the narrow exposed southeast shoulder, I felt the first warmth of the sun about 4:00 A.M.; so high up, no other mountain blocked the sunrise. The weather had thankfully turned spectacular.

---

2. **pyrotechnic** (py roh TEK nik) *adj.* of or pertaining to fireworks; here, brilliant; dazzling.

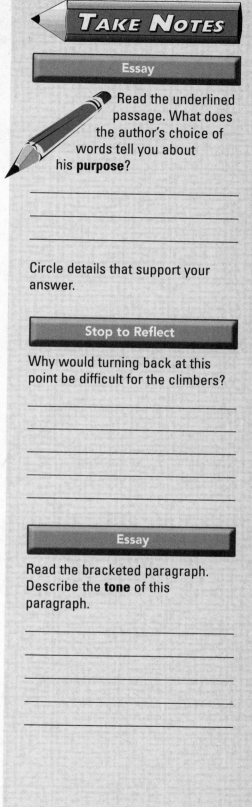

TAKE NOTES

Essay

Read the underlined passage. What does the author's choice of words tell you about his **purpose**?

_____

_____

_____

Circle details that support your answer.

Stop to Reflect

Why would turning back at this point be difficult for the climbers?

_____

_____

_____

_____

_____

Essay

Read the bracketed paragraph. Describe the **tone** of this paragraph.

_____

_____

_____

_____

_____

Perspective is the author's opinion or viewpoint about the subject. What do the details about the other climbers show about the author's perspective?

_____

_____

_____

_____

_____

_____

What impression do you get of Weihenmayer's relationship with Jeff in this **essay**? Underline the words and groups of words in the text that tell you.

Why do you think that the author supports Jeff's decision to turn back?

_____

_____

_____

_____

Still hours below the South Summit, we were stalled out again. The fixed lines, running up the steepest slope yet, had been frozen over by a hard windswept crust of snow. Jeff and Brad moved ahead, pulling the lines free, an exhausting job at twenty-eight thousand feet. The job was quickly wearing Jeff down, but he said later that with each gasping breath as he heaved the rope free, he envisioned the two of us standing on top together. Soon he was beginning to feel faint and dizzy. As he knelt in the snow, Brad, behind him, examined his oxygen equipment and assessed that his regulator, connecting the long tube of his mask to his bottle, had malfunctioned. The internal valves responsible for regulating flow were notoriously prone to freezing shut. "Who's got an extra regulator?" Brad called out over the radio, but tired bodies and brains could not recall who had thrown in the extras in the pre-summit shuffle. "My day's finished if I can't find the extra," Jeff yelled testily.

It may not have been PV's time to summit, but he wasn't through benefiting the team. "Calm down," he advised, lying weakly on his back in his tent. "Everyone take a deep breath. Ang Pasang and Sherm are carrying the extra regulators." Luckily, Ang Pasang was only a hundred feet behind. Together, Brad and Ang Pasang screwed on Jeff's new regulator.

By 8:00 A.M., we had struggled on to the South Summit, 28,700 feet. After a short rest, Chris took off for the summit, cranking it into "Morris gear," and Luis took over in front of me. From the South Summit, the true summit is still at least two hours away across the three hundred-foot-long knife-edge ridge, up the fifty-foot vertical Hillary Step, and finally traversing up a long slightly broader ridge to the summit.

Jeff, exhausted from his two-hour struggle pulling lines, stopped short in front of me. "I'm wasted. I've gotta go down," he said reluctantly. "This'll have to be my summit."

For a moment I wanted to goad him on the way we had done each other on winter training climbs of Colorado fourteeners. "If you wanna turn back, just say the word," we'd jab. "Of course, I'll have to tell everyone you were a whiney little crybaby." But 28,700 feet above sea level wasn't the place to motivate with bravado or ego, so assessing that he was strong enough to get down, I rested a hand on Jeff's shoulder and wished him a safe descent.

Jeff had been with me from the beginning, practically introducing me to the mountains. He had shown extraordinary patience as I stumbled along experimenting with brand-new trekking poles. We had even stood together on the summit of Denali[3] and El Capitana,[4] so I knew that reaching the summit of Mt. Everest without him wouldn't feel complete. Suddenly, a wave of heavy exhaustion passed over me, and I felt weary and crumpled. "Maybe I'll go down too," I readied my lips to say, but then Luis was crunching through the snow in front of me, and I forced myself to revive.

Down-climbing the twenty-foot vertical snow face on the backside of the South Summit leading onto the knife-edge ridge went against my survival instinct. The ridge is the width of a picnic table and always heavily corniced[5] with snow. To the left is an eight- thousand-foot drop into Nepal, and on the right, a twelve-thousand-foot drop into Tibet. PV had told me that while crossing the ridge on his 1998 attempt, he had driven his ice axe into the snow and, after withdrawing it, had stared through the small hole into the early morning light of Tibet. In 1995, on Brad's second attempt, a climber in front of him had taken his first step onto the ridge just before the entire right half of it dropped away. The climber jumped back to safety, but a second later he would have ridden the cornice into Tibet. This year, the ridge was drier and more stable. Frozen boot steps traversed along the lefthand side. I'd scan my pole until it dropped into a boot mark, then cautiously lower my foot. I knew I couldn't make a mistake here: six hard steady breaths, another solid step, and a relaxed, focused mind like clear water.

Climbing the Hillary Step, I felt I was in my element, feeling the rock under my gloves. I stuck the crampon points of my right foot tenuously into a tiny crack and the left points into a cornice of snow, slid my ascender as high as it would go on the rope, and stood up and quickly reached for the next knob of rock. At the top, I awkwardly belly-flopped onto a flat ledge, slowly pulled myself to my feet, and began traversing the last slope to the summit. For forty minutes I trudged upward. My heavy sluggish muscles felt as if they were pushing through wet cement. With each step closer, the real possibility of standing on

TAKE NOTES

Stop to Reflect

Why does Weihenmayer mention the difficulties experienced by climbers in 1995 and 1998?

_____

_____

_____

Essay

How does the author's **tone** change throughout this page?

_____

_____

_____

_____

_____

Reading Check

What other mountains has Erik Weihenmayer climbed? Underline the text that tells you.

---

3. **Denali** (di NAH lee) name of the National Park in which Mt. McKinley is located.
4. **El Capitana** peak in the Sierra Nevada mountain range in the Yosemite Valley of central California.
5. **corniced** (KAWR nist) *adj.* in architecture, a projecting decorative strip atop a wall or building; here, characterized by overhanging masses of snow or ice.

Essay

Read the bracketed passage. What does this passage show about the author's **perspective**?

_____

_____

_____

_____

_____

Stop to Reflect

Why does Weihenmayer include the achievements of others in his autobiographical essay?

_____

_____

_____

_____

_____

_____

Reading Check

Who surprises Erik Weihenmayer by showing up on the summit of Everest? Underline the text that tells you.

top began to trickle through my focused brain. I had speculated success in a conceptual way and as a way to motivate myself when I was down, but it was dangerous to believe it as a fact. A team could be turned back for so many reasons at any time. Just keep moving, I thought. You're not there yet.

Then a body moved down the slope toward me and I felt thin wiry arms beneath a puffy down suit wrapping around me. "Big E!" The voice rasped, so hollow and wispy, I had trouble recognizing it as Chris. His voice tried to say more, but his quaking words dissipated in the wind. Then he leaned in against my ear. "Big E"—his voice gave way to tears, then struggled out in an immense effort—"you're about to stand on top of the world." Then he quickly let go and hurriedly moved down the slope.

Luis and I linked our arms, and in a few steps, the earth flattened and the massive sky closed around me on all sides. "This is Erik, Luis, and Ang Pasang," I said over the radio. "We're on the top. I can't believe it; we're on the top."

"You're the best, Big E!" Kevin yelled from Base Camp. "I love you guys." I could hear the entire Base Camp crew cheering behind him.

"You're the strongest man in the world," PV said.

I turned around, surprised to hear more crampons moving up behind me. "I wasn't gonna let you stand on top and hear about it the rest of my life," Jeff said, with a little pep left in his voice. One of the greatest joys of my summit was that Jeff hadn't turned back at all. From the South Summit, he had watched us down-climb onto the knife edge ridge and move toward the Hillary Step. Later he told me, "I simply had to follow." Behind Jeff came Erie, Michael B., Didrik, Charley, and Mike O. Sherm had been the first on the team to summit, becoming the oldest man in history to stand on the top of the world, but better than his record was the fact that his son, Brad, had stepped on to the summit right behind him. Nineteen team members made it to the summit: eleven Westerners and eight Sherpas, the most from one team to reach the top in a single day. So it was a crowded summit as we all stood together, hugging and crying on a snow platform the size of a single-car garage.

Another storm was rolling in from the north. "Weather's changing fast," PV called up on the radio. "You guys need to go down immediately." I turned to head down with Erie, when Jeff said, "Wait a second, Big E. You'll only be here once in your life. Look around. Think about where you are and what you've done." So I suspended my nerves for a moment, reached down and touched the snow through my gloved hand, listened to the Sherpa prayer flags flapping in the wind, and heard the infinite sound of space around me, as on my first rock climb. After I had gone blind almost twenty years ago, I would have been proud to find the bathroom, so I said a quick prayer and thanked God for giving me so much. Then it was time to go down.

We descended through heavy snowfall but, thankfully, little wind. Erie took over guiding me, down the Hillary Step, across the knife edge, and contrary to his fears that he wouldn't be strong enough to make the top, he was stronger and more lucid on the way down from Everest's summit than most were on the top of a peak in Colorado. Reaching our tents at about 3:00 P.M., I hugged Erie. "Today," I said, "you were my guardian angel. I'm glad you're here."

That night, Kevin radioed up to report that he had called Ellie on the sat phone with the news. "She screamed loud enough to break the neighbors' windows." He laughed. The next days were exhausting as we fought our way through the screaming wind of the South Col, down the Lhotse Face—where my rubbery legs refused to obey my brain—and finally one last trip through the icefall. At the bottom, in Superman's Palace, of course, the whole team was waiting, and the party lasted long after the sun had sunk below Pumori.

Despite our success, plenty of detractors voiced their opinions on Internet chat rooms and in letters to the editor. I've heard all the ridiculous assumptions.

"Now that a blind guy's climbed it, everyone's going to want to climb it. They're going to think it's easy. People will probably get hurt."

"Why are people thinking this is such a big deal? Anyone can be short-roped to the top by nineteen seeing-eye guides."

TAKE NOTES

Essay

There are five types of **essays**. They are **narrative**, **descriptive**, **expository**, **persuasive**, and **reflective**. What type of essay do you think this is? Explain your answer.

_____

_____

_____

_____

Essay

Read the bracketed passage. Underline the text that shows the author's **bias** against the people making the negative comments. Name one thing the author does in the bracketed passage that does not show a **bias** on his part.

_____

_____

Stop to Reflect

How do you feel about the negative comments that Weihenmayer receives?

_____

_____

_____

_____

Vocabulary Development: detractors (di TRAK terz) *n.* those who discredit someone's accomplishments

An author's **purpose** may be to inform, to entertain, to persuade, to praise, to celebrate, or to warn. What do you think is Weihenmayer's purpose? Give reasons for your answer.

_____

_____

_____

_____

Why does Erik Weihenmayer climb mountains? Underline the text that tells you. How does this reason show the author's **perspective**?

_____

_____

_____

What gives Weihenmayer secret satisfaction? Underline the text that tells you so.

My teammates constantly come to my rescue with carefully crafted comebacks like "Before you start spouting a bunch of lies over a public forum, get your facts straight, dude!"

"Don't let 'em get to you," Chris Morris said after I shared with him their comments. "You climbed every inch of that mountain, and then some."

I knew he was right. There were some who would never be convinced, others who still had no idea what to think, but many others for whom the climb forced a higher expectation of their own possibilities. I don't climb mountains to prove to anyone that blind people can do this or that. I climb for the same reason an artist paints a picture: because it brings me great joy. But I'd be lying if I didn't admit my secret satisfaction in facing those cynics and blowing through their doubts, destroying their negative stereotypes, taking their very narrow <u>parameters</u> of what's possible and what's not, and shattering them into a million pieces.

When those parameters are rebuilt, thousands and thousands of people will live with fewer barriers placed before them, and if my climbs can play a small role in opening doors of opportunity and hope for those who will come after us, then I am very proud of what we were able to achieve.

Vocabulary Development: parameters (puh RAM uh terz) *n.* boundaries or limits

---

Reader's Response: Why should it matter to you or to anyone else that a blind man climbed Mount Everest?

_____

_____

_____

_____

_____

Essays and Speeches

1. **Generalize:** Given Weihenmayer's experience, what statement can you make about turning negatives into positives?

   _____

   _____

2. **Analyze:** Use this chart to analyze decisions made by individuals or the team on Mount Everest.

Decision	Results of Decision	Importance to Team's Success

3. **Essays and Speeches:** Weihenmayer often stops his **narrative essay** to write **exposition**, or background information. In what ways does this information help you better understand his experience?

   _____

   _____

   _____

4. **Essays and Speeches:** How does Weihenmayer balance his own **perspective** with the views of others? Explain.

   _____

   _____

RESEARCH THE AUTHOR
Report

- Use Internet and library resources to write a **report** about Erik Weihenmayer's athletic accomplishments.

- Choose sports at which Weihenmayer excels, such as scuba diving, distance running, ice climbing, mountain climbing, or skiing. Record your notes here.

Sports: _____

How he learned them: _____

_____

Special techniques he uses: _____

_____

Special equipment he uses: _____

_____

Help he receives: _____

_____

Quote from Weihenmayer or others about his mastery of the sports:

_____

_____

- Watch the video interview with Erik Weihenmayer. Add what you learn in the interview to the other information you have found. Then, decide on the main point you want to make about Weihenmayer's accomplishments as an athlete.

What I learned from the interview: _____

_____

_____

_____

Main point to make in my report:

_____

_____

_____

The Spider and the Wasp • from Longitude

LITERARY ANALYSIS

An **expository essay** is a brief nonfiction work in which an author informs, defines, explains, or discusses. Often, the writer reaches a conclusion through reasoning. The writer's reasoning may be inductive or deductive.

- **Inductive reasoning**—reviewing a number of cases and then making a generalization from them
- **Deductive reasoning**—proving that a conclusion is true by applying a general idea or principle to a specific case

As you read, use this chart to map the writer's reasoning. Follow the example of inductive reasoning below.

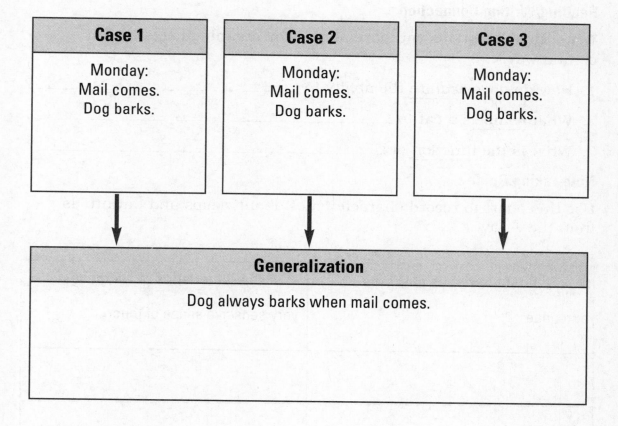

Case 1	Case 2	Case 3
Monday: Mail comes. Dog barks.	Monday: Mail comes. Dog barks.	Monday: Mail comes. Dog barks.

Generalization

Dog always barks when mail comes.

READING SKILL

To fully understand an essay, **analyze main ideas and supporting details**. Recognize each main point the writer makes and identify its relation to the ideas or facts that explain or illustrate it. Pause occasionally to summarize to organize your thoughts. When you **summarize**, you briefly restate only the main ideas and key details.

The Spider and the Wasp

Alexander Petrunkevitch

Summary Alexander Petrunkevitch looks at the difference between instinct and intelligence in animal behavior. He focuses attention on digger wasps and tarantulas. Animal behavior raises many questions, but gives no simple answers.

Reading/Writing Connection

Write three questions you have about why an animal acts in a certain way.

1. How do dogs <u>acquire</u> the ability to _____?

2. What <u>compels</u> a cat to _____?

3. What is the <u>function</u> of _____?

Note-taking Guide

Use this chart to record characteristics about wasps and tarantulas from the essay.

Characteristics of Wasps	Characteristics of Tarantulas
antennae	very sensitive sense of touch

The Spider and the Wasp
Alexander Petrunkevitch

To hold its own in the struggle for existence, every species of animal must have a regular source of food, and if it happens to live on other animals, its survival may be very delicately balanced. The hunter cannot exist without the hunted; if the latter should perish from the earth, the former would, too. When the hunted also prey on some of the hunters, the matter may become complicated.

This is nowhere better illustrated than in the insect world. Think of the complexity of a situation such as the following: There is a certain wasp, *Pimpla inquisitor*, whose larvae feed on the larvae of the tussock moth. *Pimpla* larvae in turn serve as food for the larvae of a second wasp, and the latter in their turn nourish still a third wasp. What subtle balance between fertility and mortality must exist in the case of each of these four species to prevent the extinction of all of them! An excess of mortality over fertility in a single member of the group would ultimately wipe out all four.

This is not a unique case. The two great orders of insects, Hymenoptera and Diptera, are full of such examples of interrelationship. And the spiders (which are not insects but members of a separate order of arthropods) are also killers and victims of insects.

The picture is complicated by the fact that those species which are carnivorous in the larval stage have to be provided with animal food by a vegetarian mother. The survival of the young depends on the mother's correct choice of a food which she does not eat herself.

In the feeding and safeguarding of their progeny[1] the insects and spiders exhibit some interesting analogies to reasoning and some crass examples of blind instinct. The case I propose to describe here is that of the tarantula spiders and their arch-enemy, the digger wasps of the genus Pepsis. It is a classic example of what looks like intelligence pitted against instinct—a strange situation in which the victim, though fully able to defend itself, submits unwittingly to its destruction.

Most tarantulas live in the tropics, but several species occur in the temperate zone and a few are common in the southern U.S. Some varieties are large and have powerful

---

Vocabulary Development: instinct (IN stingkt) *n.* inborn pattern of behavior, as opposed to a learned skill

---

1. **progeny** (PRAHJ uh nee) *n.* offspring; young

TAKE NOTES

Activate Prior Knowledge

Think of an animal or a pet that you have spent a great deal of time watching. What are some interesting things you remember seeing this animal do?

_____

_____

Literary Analysis

An author informs, defines, explains, or discusses a topic in an **expository essay**. What ideas does the first paragraph introduce that you think the writer will explain later?

_____

_____

Reading Skill

Analyze main ideas and supporting details to fully understand an essay. Try to recognize each main point the writer makes. Then, find the facts or ideas that support each point. Read the bracketed paragraph. Underline the supporting details that illustrate this point: Humans should not fear most tarantulas.

Inductive reasoning uses a number of cases to form generalizations. What is one generalization that the writer makes about tarantulas in the second bracketed passage?

_____

_____

_____

The following is a **main idea** about tarantulas: Tarantulas have a sensitive sense of touch. Circle two **supporting details** on this page that explain this main idea.

fangs with which they can inflict a deep wound. These formidable-looking spiders do not, however, attack man; you can hold one in your hand, if you are gentle, without being bitten. Their bite is dangerous only to insects and small mammals such as mice; for a man it is no worse than a hornet's sting.

Tarantulas <u>customarily</u> live in deep cylindrical burrows, from which they emerge at dusk and into which they retire at dawn. Mature males wander about after dark in search of females and occasionally stray into houses. After mating, the male dies in a few weeks, but a female lives much longer and can mate several years in succession. In a Paris museum is a tropical specimen which is said to have been living in captivity for 25 years.

A fertilized female tarantula lays from 200 to 400 eggs at a time; thus it is possible for a single tarantula to produce several thousand young. She takes no care of them beyond weaving a cocoon of silk to enclose the eggs. After they hatch, the young walk away, find convenient places in which to dig their burrows and spend the rest of their lives in solitude. Tarantulas feed mosly on insects and millipedes. Once their appetite is appeased, they digest the food for several days before eating again. Their sight is poor, being limited to sensing a change in the intensity of light and to the perception of moving objects. They apparently have little or no sense of hearing, for a hungry tarantula will pay no attention to a loudly chirping cricket placed in its cage unless the insect happens to touch one of its legs.

But all spiders, and especially hairy ones, have an extremely delicate sense of touch. Laboratory experiments prove that tarantulas can distinguish three types of touch: pressure against the body wall, stroking of the body hair, and riffling of certain very fine hairs on the legs called trichobothria.[2] Pressure against the body, by a finger or the end of a pencil, causes the tarantula to move off slowly for a short distance. The touch excites no defensive response unless the approach is from above where the spider can see the motion, in which case it rises on its hind legs, lifts its front legs, opens its fangs and holds this threatening posture as long as the object continues to move. When the motion stops, the spider drops back to the ground, remains quiet for a few seconds and then moves slowly away.

The entire body of a tarantula, especially its legs, is thickly clothed with hair. Some of it is short and woolly,

---

Vocabulary Development: customarily (kus tuh MER uh lee) _adv._
usually; by habit or tradition

---

2. **trichobothria** (trik uh BAHTH ree uh) _n._

some long and stiff. Touching this body hair produces one of two <u>distinct</u> reactions. When the spider is hungry, it responds with an immediate and swift attack. At the touch of a cricket's antennae the tarantula seizes the insect so swiftly that a motion picture taken at the rate of 64 frames per second shows only the result and not the process of capture. But when the spider is not hungry, the stimulation of its hairs merely causes it to shake the touched limb. An insect can walk under its hairy belly unharmed.

The trichobothria, very fine hairs growing from disklike membranes on the legs, were once thought to be the spider's hearing organs, but we now know that they have nothing to do with sound. They are sensitive only to air movement. A light breeze makes them vibrate slowly, without disturbing the common hair. When one blows gently on the trichobothria, the tarantula reacts with a quick jerk of its four front legs. If the front and hind legs are stimulated at the same time, the spider makes a sudden jump. This reaction is quite independent of the state of its appetite.

These three <u>tactile</u> responses—to pressure on the body wall, to moving of the common hair, and to flexing of the trichobothria—are so different from one another that there is no possibility of confusing them. They serve the tarantula adequately for most of its needs and enable it to avoid most annoyances and dangers. But they fail the spider completely when it meets its deadly enemy, the digger wasp Pepsis.

These solitary wasps are beautiful and formidable creatures. Most species are either a deep shiny blue all over, or deep blue with rusty wings. The largest have a wing span of about four inches. They live on nectar. When excited, they give off a pungent odor—a warning that they are ready to attack. The sting is much worse than that of a bee or common wasp, and the pain and swelling last longer. In the adult stage the wasp lives only a few months. The female produces but a few eggs, one at a time at intervals of two or three days. For each egg the mother must provide one adult tarantula, alive but paralyzed. The tarantula must be of the correct species to nourish the larva. The mother wasp attaches the egg to the paralyzed spider's abdomen. Upon hatching from the egg, the larva is many hundreds of times smaller than its living but helpless victim. It eats no other food and drinks

---

Vocabulary Development: **distinct** (di STINGKT) *adj.* clearly different; separate
tactile (TAK tuhl) *adj.* related to the sense of touch

TAKE NOTES

Reading Check

What will a tarantula do if the trichobothria on both its front and hind legs are stimulated at the same time? Circle the text that tells you the answer.

Reading Skill

Analyze main ideas and supporting details to help you organize your thoughts. **Summarize** what you now know about the hair on tarantulas.

_____
_____
_____
_____

Reading Skill

Read the bracketed passage. The first sentence in the passage tells you a **main idea** about digger wasps. Circle three details in the passage that support this main idea.

Stop to Reflect

The wasp and the tarantula are very different. Which animal would you rather spend time observing and studying? Explain your answer.

_____
_____
_____

When the writer describes the type of tarantulas that digger wasps attack, he says, "The sex of the spider makes no difference." What type of evidence could the writer present to support this claim, aided by **inductive reasoning**?

_____

_____

_____

Summarize what the wasp does to figure out if the tarantula is of the right species.

_____

_____

_____

In the beginning of this **expository essay**, the writer states, "It is a classic example of what looks like intelligence pitted against instinct." How does the writer link his descriptions of behavior to this statement?

_____

_____

_____

_____

What is the only spot on the tarantula's body that can be penetrated by the wasp? Underline the text that tells you.

no water. By the time it has finished its single gargantuan meal and become ready for wasphood, nothing remains of the tarantula but its indigestible chitinous skeleton.[3]

The mother wasp goes tarantula-hunting when the egg in her ovary is almost ready to be laid. Flying low over the ground late on a sunny afternoon, the wasp looks for its victim or for the mouth of a tarantula burrow, a round hole edged by a bit of silk. The sex of the spider makes no difference, but the mother is highly discriminating as to species. Each species of Pepsis requires a certain species of tarantula, and the wasp will not attack the wrong species. In a cage with a tarantula which is not its normal prey, the wasp avoids the spider, and is usually killed by it in the night.

Yet when a wasp finds the correct species, it is the other way about. To identify the species the wasp apparently must explore the spider with her antennae. The tarantula shows an amazing tolerance to this exploration. The wasp crawls under it and walks over it without evoking any hostile response. The molestation is so great and so persistent that the tarantula often rises on all eight legs, as if it were on stilts. It may stand this way for several minutes. Meanwhile the wasp, having satisfied itself that the victim is of the right species, moves off a few inches to dig the spider's grave. Working vigorously with legs and jaws, it excavates a hole 8 to 10 inches deep with a diameter slightly larger than the spider's girth. Now and again the wasp pops out of the hole to make sure that the spider is still there.

When the grave is finished, the wasp returns to the tarantula to complete her ghastly enterprise. First she feels it all over once more with her antennae. Then her behavior becomes more aggressive. She bends her abdomen, protruding her sting, and searches for the soft membrane at the point where the spider's leg joins its body—the only spot where she can penetrate the horny skeleton. From time to time, as the exasperated spider slowly shifts ground, the wasp turns on her back and slides along with the aid of her wings, trying to get under the tarantula for a shot at the vital spot. During all this maneuvering, which can last for several minutes, the tarantula makes no move to save itself. Finally the wasp corners it against some obstruction and grasps one of its legs in her powerful jaws. Now at last the harassed spider tries a desperate but vain defense. The two contestants roll over and over on the ground. It is a terrifying sight and the outcome is always the same. The wasp finally manages to thrust her sting into the soft spot and holds it there for a few seconds while she pumps in the poison.

---

3. **chitinous** (KY tin uhs) **skeleton** tough outer covering of an insect's body. The external skeleton gives an insect's body its structure, because an insect has no internal skeleton.

Almost immediately the tarantula falls paralyzed on its back. Its legs stop twitching; its heart stops beating. Yet it is not dead, as is shown by the fact that if taken from the wasp it can be restored to some sensitivity by being kept in a moist chamber for several months.

After paralyzing the tarantula, the wasp cleans herself by dragging her body along the ground and rubbing her feet, sucks the drop of blood oozing from the wound in the spider's abdomen, then grabs a leg of the flabby, helpless animal in her jaws and drags it down to the bottom of the grave. She stays there for many minutes, sometimes for several hours, and what she does all that time in the dark we do not know. Eventually she lays her egg and attaches it to the side of the spider's abdomen with a sticky secretion. Then she emerges, fills the grave with soil carried bit by bit in her jaws, and finally tramples the ground all around to hide any trace of the grave from prowlers. Then she flies away, leaving her descendant safely started in life.

In all this the behavior of the wasp evidently is qualitatively different from that of the spider. The wasp acts like an intelligent animal. This is not to say that instinct plays no part or that she reasons as man does. But her actions are to the point; they are not automatic and can be modified to fit the situation. We do not know for certain how she identifies the tarantula—probably it is by some olfactory or chemotactile sense[4]—but she does it purposefully and does not blindly tackle a wrong species.

On the other hand, the tarantula's behavior shows only confusion. Evidently the wasp's pawing gives it no pleasure, for it tries to move away. That the wasp is not simulating sexual stimulation is certain, because male and female tarantulas react in the same way to its advances. That the spider is not anesthetized by some odorless secretion is easily shown by blowing lightly at the tarantula and making it jump suddenly. What, then, makes the tarantula behave as stupidly as it does?

No clear, simple answer is available. Possibly the stimulation by the wasp's antennae is masked by a heavier pressure on the spider's body, so that it reacts as when prodded by a pencil. But the explanation may be much more complex. Initiative in attack is not in the nature of tarantulas; most species fight only when cornered so that escape is impossible. Their inherited patterns of behavior apparently prompt them to avoid problems rather than attack them. For example, spiders always weave their webs in three dimensions, and when a spider finds that there is insufficient space to attach

---

4. **olfactory** (ahl FAK tuh ree) . . . **chemotactile** (kee moh TAK tuhl) **sense** An olfactory sense is a sense of smell. A chemotactile sense involves sensitivity by touch to the presence of specific chemicals.

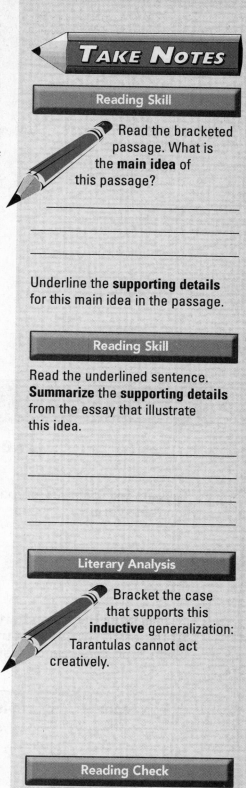

TAKE NOTES

Reading Skill

Read the bracketed passage. What is the **main idea** of this passage?

_____

_____

_____

Underline the **supporting details** for this main idea in the passage.

Reading Skill

Read the underlined sentence. **Summarize** the **supporting details** from the essay that illustrate this idea.

_____

_____

_____

_____

Literary Analysis

Bracket the case that supports this **inductive** generalization: Tarantulas cannot act creatively.

Reading Check

In how many dimensions do spiders weave their webs? Circle the sentence that tells you.

certain threads in the third dimension, it leaves the place and seeks another, instead of finishing the web in a single plane. This urge to escape seems to arise under all circumstances, in all phases of life, and to take the place of reasoning. For a spider to change the pattern of its web is as impossible as for an inexperienced man to build a bridge across a chasm obstructing his way.

In a way the instinctive urge to escape is not only easier but often more efficient than reasoning. The tarantula does exactly what is most efficient in all cases except in an encounter with a ruthless and determined attacker dependent for the existence of her own species on killing as many tarantulas as she can lay eggs. Perhaps in this case the spider follows its usual pattern of trying to escape, instead of seizing and killing the wasp, because it is not aware of its danger. In any case, the survival of the tarantula species as a whole is protected by the fact that the spider is much more fertile than the wasp.

TAKE NOTES

Reader's Response

What fact or idea in the essay surprised you the most? Explain.

_____

_____

_____

APPLY THE SKILLS

The Spider and the Wasp

1. **Compare and Contrast:** Compare the ways in which the wasp and the tarantula provide for their young.

_____

_____

2. **Reading Skill:** Use this chart to identify the **main ideas** and the **supporting details** in the essay. Write the author's main idea about the topic in your own words. Then, find and record a supporting detail for each main idea.

Topic	Spider's Sense of Touch	Spider's Response to Wasp	Wasp's Handling of Spider
Main Idea			
Supporting Detail			

SUPPORT FOR WRITING AND EXTEND YOUR LEARNING

Writing: Business Letter

Write a **business letter** in which you ask for money to study tarantulas and wasps. Answer these questions to gather ideas for your letter: To whom will you send your request? Why would this person or group be interested in your research? What is the main point of your letter? How will you spend the money if you get it?

_____

_____

_____

_____

_____

Listening and Speaking: Humorous Persuasive Speech

Write a **humorous persuasive speech** in which you encourage people to keep wasps and tarantulas as pets. Use the Venn diagram below to make notes about the characteristics of good pets.

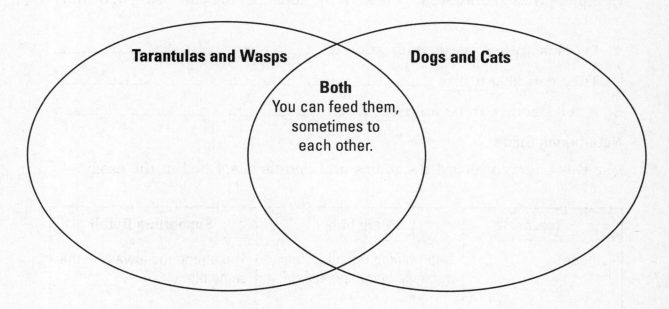

Tarantulas and Wasps

Both
You can feed them, sometimes to each other.

Dogs and Cats

Use these notes to help you write your speech.

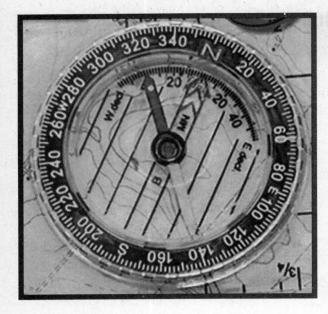

from Longitude

Dava Sobel

Summary The author points out the key difference between latitude and longitude. The laws of nature set latitude lines. However, before the prime meridian of longitude was finally fixed, lines of longitude would shift. The problem of measuring longitude made it difficult for sailors to know their ship's position. The solution was a clock that kept accurate time at sea.

Reading/Writing Connection

Complete these sentences by describing tools people can use when they are lost.

1. People can use <u>visual</u> cues such as _____.

2. They can also <u>utilize</u> _____.

3. A cell phone can be an <u>asset</u> when _____.

Note-taking Guide

Use this chart to record the topics and details described in the essay.

Topic	Main Idea	Supporting Detail
Latitude	Determining latitude is easy because latitude is fixed.	The equator is always in the same place.

from Longitude

1. **Analyze:** Why did inventing a clock that worked at sea help solve the problem of longitude? Explain.

   _____

   _____

2. **Compare and Contrast:** Why is determining latitude easier than determining longitude?

   _____

   _____

3. **Literary Analysis:** How does Sobel use **inductive reasoning** to prove that navigation was dangerous without precise longitude measurements?

   _____

   _____

4. **Reading Skill:** Use the chart below to identify the **main ideas** and the **supporting details** in the essay. Write the author's main idea about the topic in your own words. Then, write a supporting detail for each main idea.

Topic	Problem of Longitude	Importance of Longitude	Harrison's Invention
Main Idea			
Supporting Detail			

SUPPORT FOR WRITING AND EXTEND YOUR LEARNING

Writing: Business Letter

Imagine that you are John Harrison. Write a **business letter** to King George III, asking him to favor your invention.

- Take notes for your letter in the chart below.

Main Point of the letter:		
Details: your clock	Details: other clocks	How your clock will benefit the king:

Research and Technology: Abstract

Find two more articles about navigation. Write an **abstract** for each article. An abstract is a paragraph that summarizes the main points of a research article. Use this chart to help you organize the ideas for your abstract.

	Title	Author	Main Idea	Supporting Details
Article 1				
Article 2				

The Sun Parlor • from In Commemoration: One Million Volumes

LITERARY ANALYSIS

A **reflective essay** is a brief nonfiction work in which a writer presents the experiences that shaped or inspired his or her thoughts on a topic. In a reflective essay, a writer

- draws on an event, a time period, or an idea from his or her own life and experience.
- weaves a connection between personal experience and a point of general interest, such as a lesson about life.
- reflects on a specific object, scene, occasion, place, or idea.

Look for these characteristics of a reflective essay as you read.

READING SKILL

Analyze main ideas and supporting details to fully understand an essay. Recognize each main point that the writer makes and identify the ideas or facts that explain or illustrate it. To help you analyze, **ask questions** as you read.

- What is the topic of this passage?
- What is the main point being made?
- Which details support this point?

As you read, use the chart below to record the main ideas and supporting details.

Question: _____

Main Idea

Supporting Detail		Supporting Detail

The Sun Parlor

Dorothy West

Summary West recalls a time when she forgot one of her mother's lessons. West forbids a little girl, Sis, to enter the sun parlor. West later regrets her actions. She realizes that nothing is worth as much as a child.

Reading/Writing Connection

Complete the following sentences by describing a room that has a special meaning for you.

1. The room may <u>derive</u> its meaning from _____.

2. The smell of roses can <u>evoke</u> _____.

3. Being in the room may <u>generate</u> feelings of _____.

Note-taking Guide

Use this chart to record a series of events in West's reflective essay.

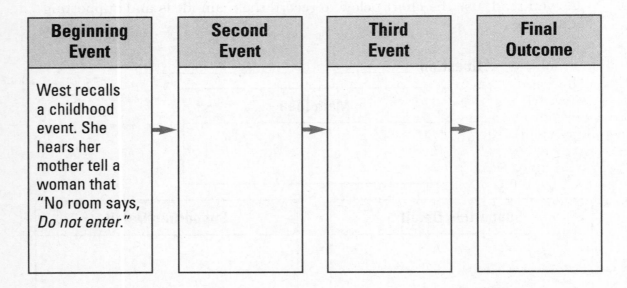

Beginning Event	Second Event	Third Event	Final Outcome
West recalls a childhood event. She hears her mother tell a woman that "No room says, *Do not enter.*"			

The Sun Parlor
Dorothy West

This is a tale with a moral. I will try not to tax your attention too long. But I have to go way back to begin because it begins with my childhood. It is about houses and children, and which came first.

There were four of us children, well-schooled in good manners, well-behaved almost all of the time, and obedient to the commands of grown-ups, the power people who could make or break us.

We lived in a beautiful house. The reason I knew that is because all my mother's friends said so, and brought their other friends to see it. On the day appointed for the tour, which included inspection of every room on every floor, my mother would gather us around her and say in her gentlest voice, "I'm sorry, children, but Mrs. So-and-so is coming today and bringing a friend to see our house. You children keep clean and play quietly while they're here. It's not a real visit. They won't stay long. It'll be over before you can say Jack Robinson."

Most often a first-time caller, having lavished praise on everything she saw, including us, proceeded out without any further remarks. But there were others who, when they saw four children good as gold, did not see beyond their size, and asked my mother in outspoken horror, "How can you bear to let children loose in a lovely house like this?"

Every time it happened we were terrified. What would happen to us if my mother decided her house was too good for us and she hated the sight of us? What would we do, where would we go, would we starve?

My mother looked at our stricken faces, and her own face softened and her eyes filled with love. Then she would say to her inquisitor, though she did not say it rudely, "The children don't belong to the house. The house belongs to the children. No room says, *Do not enter*."

I did not know I could ever forget those sentiments. But once, to my lasting regret, I did. With the passage of years I took my place with grown-ups, and there was another generation, among them the little girl, Sis, who was my mother's treasure. The summer she was eight was the one time I forgot that a child is not subordinate to a house.

Vocabulary Development: lavished (LAV ishd) *v.* gave with extreme generosity
subordinate (suh BAWRD in it) *adj.* below another in importance or rank

---

TAKE NOTES

Activate Prior Knowledge

What would a stranger think of your bedroom? Describe one object that you feel best represents you as a person.

_____

_____

_____

Literary Analysis

A **reflective essay** is a nonfiction work in which a writer presents experiences that shaped or defined his or her thoughts on a topic. Underline the sentence in this essay that tells you when the experience begins.

Reading Skill

To fully understand an essay, **analyze main ideas and supporting details**. The writer shows how the mother feels about her children. How does the mother feel about her children?

_____

Circle details from the text that support your answer.

Reading Check

What does the author say she regrets forgetting? Underline the answer.

Where and when does the experience that forms the basis of this **reflective essay** take place? Circle the answers in the text.

Read the bracketed passage. What **details support** the **main idea** that Sis's reaction to the sun parlor is exceptional?

_____

_____

_____

_____

_____

What does Sis say when she sees the sun parlor? Underline the answer.

We had a cottage in the Highlands of Oak Bluffs[1] of unimpressive size and appearance. My mother loved it for its easy care. It couldn't even stand in the shade of our city house, and there certainly were no special rules for children. No one had ever looked aghast at a child on its premises.

Except me, the summer I painted the sun parlor. I am not a painter, but I am a perfectionist. I threw my whole soul into the project, and worked with such diligence and painstaking care that when the uncounted hours ended I felt that I had painted the Sistine Chapel.[2]

School vacation began, and Sis arrived for the long holiday, the car pulling up at the edge of the brick walk, and Sis streaking into the house for a round of hugs, then turning to tear upstairs to take off her travel clothes and put on her play clothes, and suddenly her flying feet braking to a stop in front of the sun parlor, its open door inviting inspection.

She who was always in motion, she who never took time for a second look at anything, or cared whether her bed was smooth or crumpled, or noticed what was on her plate as long as it was something to eat—she, in the awakening that came when she was eight, in her first awareness of something outside herself, stood in the doorway of the sun parlor, her face filled with the joy of her discovery, and said in a voice on the edge of tears, "It's the most beautiful room I ever saw in my whole life."

I did not hear her. I did not really hear her. I did not recognize the magnitude of that moment. I let it sink to some low level of my subconscious. All I saw was that her foot was poised to cross the threshold of my chapel.

I let out a little cry of pain. "Sis," I said, "please don't go in the sun parlor. There's nothing in there to interest a child. It's not a place for children to play in. It's a place for grown-ups to sit in. Go and change. Summer is outside waiting for you to come and play wherever you please."

In a little while the sounds of Sis's soaring laughter were mingling with the happy sounds of other vacationing children. They kept any doubt I might have had from surfacing. Sis was surely more herself running free than squirming on a chair in the sun parlor.

All the same I monitored that room, looking for smudges and streaks, scanning the floor for signs of scuffing. The room bore no scars, and Sis showed no trace of frustration.

---

1. **the Highlands** (HY luhndz) **of Oak Bluffs** (ohk blufs) *n.* a village on the island of Martha's Vineyard in Massachusetts.
2. **the Sistine Chapel** (SIS teen CHAP uhl) place of worship in the Vatican, Rome, the Pope's residence. The chapel is famed for scenes painted on its walls and ceiling by Michelangelo.

The summer flowed. My friends admired the room, though they did it without superlatives. To them it was a room I had talked about redoing for a long time. Now I had done it. So much for that.

The summer waned, and Sis went home for school's reopening, as did the other summer children, taking so much life and laughter with them that the ensuing days recovered slowly.

Then my mother's sister, my favorite aunt, arrived from New York for her usual stay at summer's end. She looked ten years younger than her actual years. She seemed to bounce with energy, as if she had gone through some process of <u>rejuvenation</u>. We asked her for the secret.

There was no way for us to know in the brimful days that followed that there really was a secret she was keeping from us. She had had a heart attack some months before, and she had been ordered to follow a strict set of rules: plenty of rest during the day, early to bed at night, take her medicine faithfully, carefully watch her diet.

She was my mother's younger sister. My mother had been her babysitter. She didn't want my mother to know that she was back to being a baby again, needing to be watched over, having to be put down for a nap, having to be spoon-fed pap. She kept herself busy around the clock, walking, lifting, sitting up late, eating her favorite foods and forgetting her medicine.

And then one day standing over the stove involved in the making of a meal that a master chef might envy, she collapsed, and the doctor was called, and the doctor called the ambulance.

She was in the hospital ten days. When she was ready to come home to convalesce, we turned the sun parlor into a sickroom, for the stairs to the upper story were forbidden to her. At night we who, when she slept upstairs, would talk family talk back and forth from our beds far into the night, without her we were now quiet, not wanting our voices to wake her if she was asleep, knowing her recovery depended on rest and quiet.

But at night she slept fitfully. The sleeping house and separation from the flock were unbearable. She was afraid of the sun parlor, seeing it as an abnormal offshoot from the main part of the house, its seven long windows giving access to so many imagined terrors. She did not know if we would hear her if she called. She did not know if she would ever get well.

Vocabulary Development: rejuvenation (ri joo vuh NAY shuhn) *n.*
a restoration to a new, youthful energy or appearance

TAKE NOTES

Literary Analysis

How does the scene change in West's **reflective essay** after Sis goes back to school?

_____

_____

_____

_____

_____

Reading Skill

Read the bracketed passage. What **main idea** do the **details** about the aunt's stay in the sunroom suggest?

_____

_____

_____

Reading Check

What secret is West's aunt keeping from the family? Circle the text that tells the answer.

Reading Skill

How did the aunt's death change the sun parlor? Underline the **supporting details** in the first bracketed passage that explain this idea.

Literary Analysis

Read the second bracketed passage. How does West connect her personal experience with a lesson on life in her **reflective essay**?

_____

_____

_____

_____

Reading Check

What does West's mother say to her when West locks the sun parlor door? Underline the answer.

She did not get well. She went back to the hospital, and for our sakes was brave in her last days, comforting us more than we comforted her.

When it was over, we took the sickbed away and restored the sun parlor to its natural look. But it did not look natural. The sadness resisted the sun's cajoling. It had settled in every corner. The seven long windows streaming light did not help. I closed the door and locked it.

My mother saw the closed door and the key in my hand. She said as a simple statement of fact, "A little girl wanted to love that room, and you wouldn't let her. We learn so many lessons as we go through life."

"I know that now," I said. "I wish I had known it then."

Another summer came, and with it Sis. The sun parlor door was open again, the room full of light with the sadness trying to hide itself whenever she passed. I did not know how to say to her, "You can go in the sun parlor if you want to." I did not know whether she knew it had been a sickroom, and might say, "Take your sun parlor and you-know-what," though in less succinct phrasing. I did not know if she yet knew that nothing can be the same once it has been different.

Other summers passed, older family members died, and mine became the oldest generation. I was living on the Island year-round in the winterized cottage. The sun parlor was just another everyday room, its seven long windows reduced to three of standard size, most of the furniture replaced for sturdier sitting.

Sis was married, a mother, coming to visit when she could—coming, I think, to look for bits and pieces of my mother in me, wanting to see her ways, hear her words through me.

It was a year ago that I asked her the question that had been on my mind, it seems, forever. A dozen times I had bitten it off my tongue because I did not know what she might answer.

"Sis," I said, "do you remember the summer I painted the sun parlor and acted as if I thought more of it than I thought of you? I'm not asking you to forgive me. All I want to know is if sometimes my mother said to you when I went out, 'She's gone.'" My mother always referred to me as "she" when she was annoyed with me. " 'She said she'd be gone awhile. You go play in that sun parlor if you want to. There's nothing in there you can hurt. Nothing in that room is worth as much as a child.'"

Vocabulary Development: cajoling (kuh JOHL ing) *n.* coaxing with flattery

I saw her lips beginning to part. And I felt my heart trembling.

"I don't want to know the answer. Please don't tell me the answer. I had to ask the question. It's enough for me that you listened."

She smiled.

Reader's Response: Consider an object or a place that is very important to you. Describe it. Of what or whom does it make you think? Are you as protective of your special object or place as the author is of her sun parlor?

_____

_____

_____

_____

_____

_____

_____

_____

Stop to Reflect

What do you think Sis's answer would be if the author had allowed her to finish?

_____

_____

_____

_____

_____

_____

The Sun Parlor

1. **Infer:** Why does West tell Sis not to go into the sun parlor?

   _____

   _____

   _____

2. **Interpret:** What does West mean when she says to Sis, "It's enough for me that you listened."?

   _____

   _____

   _____

3. **Literary Analysis:** The sun parlor is the focus of this **reflective essay**. Use this chart to show how each detail you list is connected to the sun parlor.

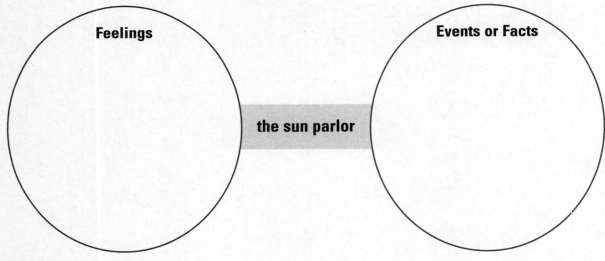

4. **Reading Skill:** Reread the first six paragraphs. What is the **main idea** of this opening section?

   _____

   _____

   _____

SUPPORT FOR WRITING AND EXTEND YOUR LEARNING

Writing: Support for Writing a Memoir

Write a brief **memoir** of a room that has been meaningful to you. A memoir is a recollection based on personal experience. Use the list below to help you write your memoir.

- What room will you write about?

  _____

- What mood does the room put you in?

  _____

- What are the most prominent features of the room?

  _____

  _____

- What does the room cause you to remember?

  _____

  _____

Research and Technology: Multimedia Presentation

Gather materials for a brief **multimedia presentation**. Discuss the developmental stages that children go through between the ages of four and nine. Take notes on these topics:

- Physical development, ages 4–9: _____

  _____

- Mental development, ages 4–9: _____

  _____

- Emotional development, ages 4–9: _____

  _____

from In Commemoration: One Million Volumes

Rudolph A. Anaya

Summary The University of New Mexico gets its millionth book. Anaya uses this event to reflect on the importance of libraries. He connects books to the people and stories that affected him as a child. Books and the stories of his elders opened his mind to the world. Libraries hold the books that open new worlds to people.

Reading/Writing Connection

Complete these sentences to describe books that have an impact on people.

1. People <u>derive</u> a sense of _____.

2. Books can <u>evoke</u> images of _____.

3. Reading can <u>formulate</u> opinions about _____.

Note-taking Guide

Use this chart to record what Anaya learned from people and places in the essay.

Source/Place	What Anaya Learned
los viejitos	riddles and stories
one-room library	

from In Commemoration: One Million Volumes

1. **Compare and Contrast:** Identify a difference and a similarity between the riddles and *cuentos* Anaya learned in childhood and the books he later read.

   _____

   _____

2. **Interpret:** What does Anaya mean when he writes that "a book at once quenches the thirst of the imagination and ignites new fires"?

   _____

   _____

3. **Literary Analysis:** Using the chart below, analyze Anaya's use of libraries as the focus of his **reflective essay**. Explain the connection of each detail you list to libraries.

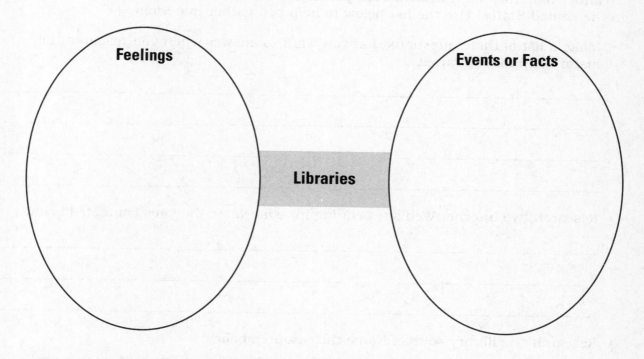

4. **Reading Skill:** Reread the text until you reach the paragraph that begins, "But a million books?" What is the **main idea** of this section?

   _____

   _____

SUPPORT FOR WRITING AND EXTEND YOUR LEARNING

Writing: Writing a Memoir

Write a brief **memoir** that focuses on a building that has been meaningful to you. A memoir is a brief recollection based on your personal experience. Use the list below to help you write your memoir.

- List four buildings you clearly remember because they are special to you.

  _____

  _____

  _____

- Choose one building from your list. Describe what happened in this building.

  _____

  _____

  _____

Research and Technology: Multimedia Presentation

Gather materials for a **multimedia presentation** on the history of public libraries in the United States. Use the list below to help you gather materials.

- Make a list of three questions that you want to answer when you research the history of public libraries.

  _____

  _____

  _____

  _____

- Research two Internet Web sites ending in *.edu.* Name the sites contacted below.

  _____

  _____

  _____

- Research one library source. Name the resource below.

  _____

  _____

  _____

Technical Directions

ABOUT TECHNICAL DIRECTIONS

Technical directions give step-by-step instructions. They tell you how to assemble, operate, or repair a product. Technical directions, as well as other informational materials that you **read to perform a task**, often have these features:

- A diagram of the product with the parts listed and labeled
- Numbered steps to follow
- A troubleshooting guide for possible problems and solutions
- Manufacturer's contact information
- Warranty information

READING SKILL

Technical directions have many parts and can be difficult to understand. To make sure that you can smoothly set up and use a new device, **preview the text**. When you preview, you look over the text before you read it word for word. Look at the headings and diagrams to get a sense of the kind of information provided. Identify any terms you don't know. Before you begin working, make sure you know the answers to the questions shown.

Questions for Previewing Technical Directions
What does the device do?
What special features does it have?
What are the main parts?
What tools or materials are needed?
What are the safety warnings?

Next, **read closely** the steps you must follow to use the device. Look for the first setup instructions. These instructions will tell you the steps you need to follow to set up the device before using it. Pay careful attention to the order in which the steps must be followed.

How To Use A Compass

Our compasses have been the accurate and easy-to-use choice of foresters, geologists, surveyors, scientific explorers, sports enthusiasts, military personnel, and many others for 50 years. Most of our compasses include these features:

- Magnetized tungsten steel needle
- Friction-free sapphire bearing
- Permanently clear, antistatic liquid
- Accurate from - 40° to +140° F

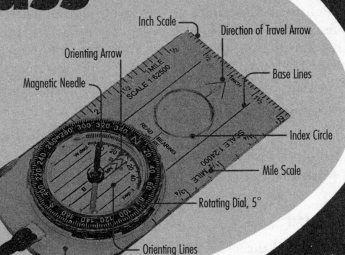

Inch Scale
Direction of Travel Arrow
Orienting Arrow
Base Lines
Magnetic Needle
Index Circle
Mile Scale
Rotating Dial, 5°
Orienting Lines
Clear Base Plate

1 Point the Base Plate to Your Destination:
Place your compass on the map with the edge along the desired line of travel.

2 Set the Compass Heading:
Turn the compass Dial until "N" points to the north on your map. Your direction in degrees is read at the Index Line on the Dial.

NOTE: Align the Dial with magnetic north if it is marked on your map. If it is not marked on your map, align the Dial with true north and adjust for declination.

3 Follow Your Heading:
- Remove the compass from your map and hold it level, so the Magnetic Needle is free to turn.
- Turn your body until the red end of the Needle aligns with the Orienting Arrow and "N" on the Dial.

Find Your Way Without a Map:

Find a heading (field bearing):

1. Select a landmark along the route you want to travel. Hold the compass level and point the Direction of Travel Arrow at the landmark.

2. Find your heading to the landmark by turning the compass dial until the "N" aligns with the red end of the Needle. Read your heading in degrees at the Index Line.

3. Keep the Needle aligned with the "N"; look up; sight on your landmark and walk to it. Repeat this procedure until you reach your destination.

When you know your heading:

1. If you've been given a heading in degrees to travel, turn the Dial so that the heading is set at the Index Line. Hold the compass level in front of you with the Direction of Travel Arrow pointing straight ahead.

2. Turn your body until the red end of the Needle is aligned with the "N" on the dial. You now face your direction of travel.

3. Pick out a landmark in line with your heading and move toward it. Repeat this procedure until you reach your destination.

NOTE: Be aware of nearby iron or steel objects. They may attract the Magnetic Needle if too close to the compass. Even a hidden nail can deflect the needle.

Compass Warranty----------------------

What Is Covered?
We warrant your compass to be free from defects in materials or workmanship, and **we guarantee its accuracy**, for the life of the compass.

What Is Not Covered?
Normal wear, abrasion, melting, misuse, alteration, abuse, or taking apart the compass is not covered by this warranty.

How To Obtain Warranty Service or Repair of Your Compass
Should your compass become defective under the terms of this warranty, call the Customer Satisfaction Department toll free at 1 (800) 123-4567 for return authorization. If, after our inspection, we find that the product was defective in material or workmanship, we shall, at our option, either repair or replace it without charge. If repairs not covered under this warranty are required, we will contact you for approval to proceed. You will be charged for the components repaired or replaced, plus a nominal charge for labor.

There are no other express warranties beyond the terms of this limited warranty. In no event shall our company be liable for incidental or consequential damages arising from using our compasses.

THINKING ABOUT THE TECHNICAL DIRECTIONS

1. Describe the three main parts of the compass.

   _____

   _____

2. How is the function of the Direction of Travel Arrow different from the function of the Magnetic Needle? Explain.

   _____

   _____

READING SKILL

3. Suppose you have been given a heading in degrees to travel. What is the first step you take in using the compass?

   _____

   _____

4. When will the company NOT repair the compass free of charge?

   _____

   _____

TIMED WRITING: PERSUASION (20 minutes)

   Write a letter to the company, asking for the repair of your compass. The compass is under warranty. Follow these steps:
   - Describe the specific damage or defect in your compass.
   - Give details from the warranty to explain why you believe the company should repair or replace your compass free of charge.

   Remember that you are writing to persuade, so use a respectful, polite tone. Make notes about each step.

   1. _____

   2. _____

Keep Memory Alive • from Nobel Lecture

LITERARY ANALYSIS

Persuasive compositions, including **speeches**, are intended to convince people that they should take a particular action or position. Writers present **arguments**, using reason to support their position. They also use **rhetorical devices**, or verbal techniques that create emphasis and appeal to emotions.

- **Repetition:** the reuse of a key word or idea for emphasis
- **Parallelism:** similar grammatical structures expressing related ideas
- **Slogans and saws:** short, catchy phrases
- **Rhetorical questions:** questions that are intended to have obvious answers, asked for effect

READING SKILL

When reading persuasive writing, **evaluate the writer's argument**. Consider whether the writer supports claims with evidence and reasoning.

Determine when **persuasive techniques** are effectively used to enhance the impact of the support, and recognize when they are used to cover up a lack of logical support. Use this chart to take notes.

Claim	Local businesses will suffer.	
Support	Prices at malls are lower.	
Technique	Rhetorical question: Do you want your neighbor to lose his business?	

Keep Memory Alive

Elie Wiesel

Summary Elie Wiesel's speech recalls the author's experiences during World War II. He explains the importance of not remaining silent in the face of injustice. He says that if people remain silent, they aid those who commit injustices.

Reading/Writing Connection

Complete the following sentences to describe why it is useful to learn lessons from the past.

1. People must <u>assess</u> unfortunate past events because _____ .

2. Examining the past can help people <u>formulate</u> _____ .

3. One thing everyone must <u>comprehend</u> about the past is _____ .

Note-taking Guide

Use this chart to record the main points that Elie Wiesel makes in "Keep Memory Alive."

Main Points of the Speech
We should never be silent when people are suffering.

Keep Memory Alive

Elie Wiesel

It is with a profound sense of humility that I accept the honor you have chosen to bestow upon me. I know: your choice transcends me. This both frightens and pleases me.

It frightens me because I wonder: do I have the right to represent the multitudes who have perished? Do I have the right to accept this great honor on their behalf? I do not. That would be <u>presumptuous</u>. No one may speak for the dead, no one may interpret their mutilated dreams and visions.

It pleases me because I may say that this honor belongs to all the survivors and their children, and through us, to the Jewish people with whose destiny I have always identified.

I remember: it happened yesterday or eternities ago. A young Jewish boy discovered the kingdom of night. I remember his <u>bewilderment</u>, I remember his anguish. It all happened so fast. The ghetto.[1] The deportation. The sealed cattle car. The fiery altar upon which the history of our people and the future of mankind were meant to be sacrificed.

I remember: he asked his father: "Can this be true? This is the 20th century, not the Middle Ages. Who would allow such crimes to be committed? How could the world remain silent?"

And now the boy is turning to me: "Tell me," he asks. "What have you done with my future? What have you done with your life?"

And I tell him that I have tried. That I have tried to keep memory alive, that I have tried to fight those who would forget. Because if we forget, we are guilty, we are <u>accomplices</u>.

Vocabulary Development: presumptuous (pri ZUMP choo uhs) *adj.* overstepping appropriate bounds; too bold
bewilderment (bi WIL duhr muhnt) *n.* confusion
accomplices (uh KAHM plis iz) *n.* people who help others commit a crime

---

1. **The ghetto** (GET oh) During the Second World War, the Nazis forced Jews in European cities to live in crowded, restricted neighborhoods, or ghettos.

Evaluate a writer's argument by looking at the ways the writer supports claims with evidence and reasoning. Many writers use **persuasive techniques** to accomplish this.

How does the fact that "the world" remained "silent" during the Holocaust support Wiesel's claim?

_____

_____

_____

_____

Stop to Reflect

Reread the last line of the speech. Do you agree with Wiesel that silence works with the tormentor? Explain your answer.

_____

_____

_____

_____

And then I explained to him how naive we were, that the world did know and remain silent. And that is why I swore never to be silent whenever and wherever human beings endure suffering and humiliation. We must always take sides. Neutrality[2] helps the oppressor, never the victim. Silence encourages the tormentor, never the tormented.

---

2. **Neutrality** (noo TRAL uh tee) *n.* state of not taking sides in a conflict; quality of being unbiased.

Reader's Response: How do you think the audience responded to Wiesel's speech?

_____

_____

APPLY THE SKILLS

Keep Memory Alive

1. **Draw Conclusions:** Wiesel accepts the award on behalf of Holocaust survivors and their children. Why does he believe that he cannot accept on behalf of those who perished?

   _____

   _____

2. **Interpret:** What do the boy Wiesel's questions imply about the adult Wiesel's responsibility?

   _____

   _____

3. **Reading Skill:** Wiesel says, "If we forget, we are guilty, we are accomplices." Explain his reasons for making the claim.

   _____

   _____

   _____

4. **Literary Analysis:** Use the chart below to identify and analyze the **rhetorical devices** that Wiesel uses in his speech.

	Repetition	Parallelism	Slogans or Saws	Rhetorical Questions
Example				
Effect				

SUPPORT FOR WRITING AND EXTEND YOUR LEARNING

Writing: Letter

Write a **letter** to Elie Wiesel. In your letter, take a position on his claim that silence makes us accomplices. Answer the following questions to help organize your ideas about his claim.

- Explain what it means to be an accomplice. How is an accomplice different from an oppressor?

  _____

  _____

- What are the specific results of silence that Wiesel points out?

  _____

  _____

- Do you agree or disagree with Wiesel's argument? Explain.

  _____

  _____

Use these notes to help write your letter to Elie Wiesel.

Listening and Speaking: Debate

Prepare for a group **debate** about Wiesel's claim that silence makes people accomplices to crime. Use your answers to the questions below to prepare for the debate.

- Will I be arguing for or against the statement?

  _____

- How can I support my argument? What examples can I give?

  _____

  _____

  _____

- What will persuade people to agree with me?

  _____

  _____

  _____

from Nobel Lecture

Alexander Solzhenitsyn

Summary Alexander Solzhenitsyn writes about the "one great heart" of world literature. He believes that readers and writers can end lies and violence. He says that the written word has the power to help solve common problems. Evil may live, but literature brings humans together against it.

Reading/Writing Connection

Imagine that it is illegal to express one of your strongest opinions aloud. Complete each sentence to describe your reaction to not being able to express an opinion.

1. When I <u>assert</u> an opinion, I expect to _____.

2. I would like to <u>ignore</u> the rules, but _____.

3. No government can <u>legislate</u> _____.

Note-taking Guide

Use this chart to identify examples in the text that support the author's purpose in writing the essay.

Author's Purpose	Examples From Text
To inform	In the past, readers did not learn about foreign writers until later so that mutual influences were delayed. Today, there is instant reciprocity.
To persuade	
To reflect	

from Nobel Lecture

1. **Interpret:** Why does Solzhenitsyn call literature "one great heart"?

   _____

   _____

2. **Analyze:** What role does Solzhenitsyn believe artists have in the struggle against injustice?

   _____

   _____

3. **Literary Analysis:** What **rhetorical devices** does the writer use to support his main argument? Use the chart below to analyze examples.

	Repetition	Parallelism	Slogans or Saws	Rhetorical Questions
Example				
Effect				

4. **Reading Skill:** Solzhenitsyn writes, "Once lies have been dispelled . . . hollow violence will collapse." Explain his reasons for making the claim.

   _____

   _____

SUPPORT FOR WRITING AND EXTEND YOUR LEARNING

Writing: Letter

Write a **letter** to Solzhenitsyn in which you evaluate his idea that telling the truth can change the world. Use your notes from the questions below to write your letter.

- Do you agree or disagree with Alexander Solzhenitsyn's argument? Explain.

  _____

  _____

  _____

- What personal example can you use to support your opinion?

  _____

  _____

  _____

- What example can you use from your reading or from news stories?

  _____

  _____

  _____

Research and Technology: Biography

Research Solzhenitsyn's life, and write a brief **biography** of him. Use library and Internet resources to research and write your biography.

- List three key questions to focus your research.

  _____

  _____

  _____

- List one library resource you checked for information.

  _____

- List two Internet resources you checked for information.

  _____

  _____

What Makes a Degas a Degas? • The American Idea

LITERARY ANALYSIS

An **analytic essay** is a brief work of nonfiction in which a writer explores a subject by breaking it into parts. In an **interpretive essay**, a writer offers a personal view of the meaning or significance of an issue. A single essay may combine features of both types of essay.

To bring readers to accept an analysis or interpretation, a writer may use **appeals**, or support, of the following types:

- Using *appeals to authority*, a writer calls on the opinions of experts or other respected people.
- Using *appeals to reason*, a writer calls on logic.
- Using *emotional appeals*, a writer taps a reader's fears, sympathy, or pride.
- Using *appeals to shared values*, a writer calls on beliefs shared by many about what is good, right, or fair.

READING SKILL

To **evaluate a writer's appeals,** decide whether the writer balances logic and facts with emotional appeals. **Distinguish between fact and opinion**. A statement of fact can be proved true. A statement of opinion expresses a belief or a viewpoint and should be supported by facts or reason.

Record details on the chart below to help you decide whether the writer has made a strong argument for a position.

Position: Main Street should be repaired.	
Position:	
Reason: Businesses are suffering.	
Reason:	
Fact: Many shops are on Main.	**Fact: Potholes cause damage.**
Fact:	Fact:

What Makes a Degas a Degas?

Richard Mühlberger

Summary The author explains how the French artist Degas produced his paintings. He helps readers understand what to see in Degas's work. He shows how Degas used point of view, color, space, and his materials to capture moments in time. The author gives details of Degas's life and connects them to his work.

Reading/Writing Connection

Complete each sentence to explain details in artwork that someone might not notice at first look.

1. An artist might try to <u>capture</u> _____.

2. The size of the figures might <u>diminish</u> with _____.

3. An artist's student might <u>identify</u> _____.

Note-taking Guide

Use this chart to record the main ideas in the essay.

What We See	Degas's Methods	Degas's Goal
Dancers, Pink and Green: poses and placement of dancers; use of space; hazy background; limited range of color		
Carriage at the Races: arrangement of space and figures		

What Makes a Degas a Degas?

1. **Analyze:** How does Degas draw attention to the main image in *Carriage at the Races*?

   _____

2. **Connect:** What qualities in Degas's paintings suggest that he might have been a good photographer when he took up that hobby? Explain.

   _____

   _____

   _____

3. **Literary Analysis:** Use the chart below to organize details of the **analytic** sections of Mühlberger's **essay**.

   Topic: _____

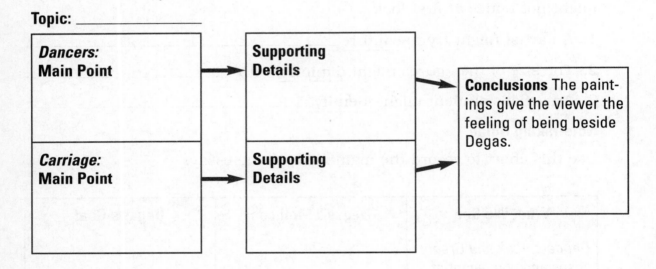

4. **Reading Skill:** List two **facts** and two **opinions** that Mühlberger includes about Degas.

   _____

   _____

SUPPORT FOR WRITING AND EXTEND YOUR LEARNING

Writing: Critique

Write a **critique**, or critical evaluation, of Mühlberger's essay. Use your answers to the following questions to write your critique.

- What is the author's purpose in this essay?

  _____

  _____

- List two things you learned about Degas in this essay.

  _____

  _____

- Name one thing Mühlberger could have done differently to help you learn.

  _____

  _____

- Would you recommend this essay to other readers? Explain.

  _____

  _____

Listening and Speaking: Persuasive Speech

Give a **persuasive speech** in which you explain and defend a new style in music, fashion, or art. Use your notes to the following questions to write your persuasive speech.

- Think about your purpose. What do you want listeners to learn about the new style?

  _____

- What do you want listeners to do after hearing your speech?

  _____

- Think about your audience. What sort of appeal will work with them?

  _____

- What information or details will persuade them to like the style?

  _____

The American Idea

Theodore H. White

Summary The author of this interpretive essay traces the development of America and its democratic ideals. He also discusses key figures in American history and how they contributed to the Declaration of Independence.

Reading/Writing Connection

Complete the following sentences to explain patriotism.

1. People feel patriotic when they see a <u>display</u> of _____.

2. Americans can <u>signify</u> their patriotism by _____.

3. The strongest way to <u>communicate</u> patriotism is to _____.

Note-taking Guide

Fill in this chart to record facts and opinions that support White's claim.

White's Main Claim	Facts That Support It	Opinions That Support It
The Declaration of Independence makes the United States unique.		

The American Idea
Theodore H. White

The idea was there at the very beginning, well before Thomas Jefferson put it into words—and the idea rang the call.

Jefferson himself could not have imagined the reach of his call across the world in time to come when he wrote:

"We hold these truths to be self-evident, that all men are created equal, that they are endowed by their Creator with certain unalienable rights, that among these are life, liberty, and the pursuit of happiness."

But over the next two centuries the call would reach the potato patches of Ireland, the ghettoes of Europe, the paddyfields of China, stirring farmers to leave their lands and townsmen their trades and thus unsettling all traditional civilizations.

It is the call from Thomas Jefferson, embodied in the great statue that looks down the Narrows of New York Harbor,[1] and in the immigrants who answered the call, that we now celebrate.

Some of the first European Americans had come to the new continent to worship God in their own way, others to seek their fortunes. But, over a century-and-a-half, the new world changed those Europeans, above all the Englishmen who had come to North America. Neither King nor Court nor Church could stretch over the ocean to the wild continent. To survive, the first emigrants had to learn to govern themselves. But the freedom of the wilderness whetted their appetites for more freedoms. By the time Jefferson drafted his call, men were in the field fighting for those new-learned freedoms, killing and being killed by English soldiers, the best-trained troops in the world, supplied by the world's greatest navy. Only something worth dying for could unite American volunteers and keep them in the field—a stated cause, a flag, a nation they could call their own.

When, on the Fourth of July, 1776, the colonial leaders who had been meeting as a Continental Congress in Philadelphia voted to approve Jefferson's Declaration of Independence, it was not puffed-up rhetoric for them to pledge to each other "our lives, our fortunes and

---

Vocabulary Development: emigrants (EM uh gruhnts) *n.* people who leave their country or region to settle elsewhere

---

1. **the great statue that looks down the Narrows of New York Harbor** Statue of Liberty.

TAKE NOTES

Activate Prior Knowledge

Theodore White discusses the meaning and significance of an issue. What issues are important to you? Explain how you might try to change people's minds about an issue you feel is important.

_____

_____

_____

Literary Analysis

A writer might use different types of **appeals**, or support, in an essay. Underline the emotional appeals White uses in the bracketed passage.

Reading Skill

It is important for readers to distinguish between **fact and opinion**. Identify one example of a statement of fact and one example of a statement of opinion expressed on this page.

_____

_____

Reading Check

Whom does White claim was responsible for putting "The American Idea" into words? Circle the person's name in the text.

TAKE NOTES

Reading Skill

Underline the sentence that tells you what, in White's **opinion**, was most important for the new Americans.

Literary Analysis

An **interpretive essay** presents a writer's view on the importance and significance of an event. Read the bracketed paragraph. Why does the author believe that the founding of America was so important to the rest of the world?

_____

_____

Stop to Reflect

Why do you think drafting the Declaration of Independence was such a difficult process?

_____

_____

Reading Check

How long did Thomas Jefferson spend writing the first draft of the Declaration of Independence? Circle the text that tells you.

our sacred honor." Unless their new "United States of America" won the war, the Congressmen would be judged traitors as relentlessly as would the irregulars-under-arms in the field . . .

The new Americans were tough men fighting for a very tough idea. How they won their battles is a story for the schoolbooks, studied by scholars, wrapped in myths by historians and poets. But what is most important is the story of the idea that made them into a nation, the idea that had an explosive power undreamed of in 1776.

All other nations had come into being among people whose families had lived for time out of mind on the same land where they were born. Englishmen are English, Frenchmen are French, Chinese are Chinese, while their governments come and go; their national states can be torn apart and remade without losing their nationhood. But Americans are a nation born of an idea; not the place, but the idea, created the United State Government.

The story we celebrate . . . is the story of how this idea worked itself out, how it stretched and changed and how the call for "life, liberty and the pursuit of happiness" does still, as it did in the beginning, mean different things to different people.

The debate began with the drafting of the Declaration of Independence. That task was left to Jefferson of Virginia, who spent two weeks in an upstairs room in a Philadelphia boarding house penning a draft, while John Adams and Benjamin Franklin questioned, edited, hardened his phrases. By the end of that hot and muggy June, the three had reached agreement: the Declaration contained the ringing universal theme Jefferson strove for and, at the same time, voiced American grievances toughly enough to please the feisty Adams and the pragmatic Franklin. After brief debate, Congress passed it.

As the years wore on, the great debate expanded between Jefferson and Adams. The young nation flourished and Jefferson chose to think of America's promise as a call to all the world, its promises universal. A few weeks before he died, he wrote, "May it be to the

Vocabulary Development: relentlessly (ri LENT lis lee) *adv.*
without pause or easing up; harshly

world, what I believe it will be (to some parts sooner, to others later, but finally to all), the signal of arousing men to burst their chains." To Adams, the call meant something else—it was the call for American independence, the cornerstone of an American state.

Their argument ran through their successive Administrations. Adams, the second President, suspected the French Revolutionaries; Alien and Sedition Acts[2] were passed during his term of office to protect the American state and its liberties against French subversion. But Jefferson, the third President, welcomed the French. The two men, once close friends, became archrivals. Still, as they grew old, their rivalry faded; there was glory enough to share in what they had made; in 1812, they began a correspondence that has since become classic, remembering and taking comfort in the triumphs of their youth.

Adams and Jefferson lived long lives and died on the same day—the Fourth of July, 1826, 50 years to the day from the Continental Congress's approval of the Declaration. Legend has it that Adams breathed on his death bed, "Thomas Jefferson still survives." As couriers set out from Braintree[3] carrying the news of Adams's death, couriers were riding north from Virginia with the news of Jefferson's death. The couriers met in Philadelphia. Horace Greeley,[4] then a youth in Vermont, later remembered: ". . . When we learned . . . that Thomas Jefferson and John Adams, the author and the great champion, respectively, of the Declaration, had both died

TAKE NOTES

Reading Skill

Underline two **facts** that White provides in the bracketed section.

Stop to Reflect

Why do you think the rivalry between Adams and Jefferson eventually became a friendship again?

_____

_____

_____

Literary Analysis

An author explores a subject by breaking it into parts in an **analytical essay**. What is White's subject?

_____

_____

What is one part of White's subject that he explores?

_____

_____

Vocabulary Development: subversion (suhb VER zhuhn) *n.* activity aimed at ruining or overthrowing something established

---

2. **Alien and Sedition Acts** laws passed by Congress in 1798 restricting immigration and regulating the expression of criticism of the government.
3. **Braintree** town in Massachusetts (now called Quincy) where John Adams lived and died.
4. **Horace Greeley** famous American newspaper publisher.

Stop to Reflect

Why do you think White chose to end his essay with this quote?

_____

_____

_____

_____

Reading Check

What were the couriers carrying, according to Greeley? Underline the text that tells you.

on that day, and that the messengers bearing South and North, respectively, the tidings of their decease, had met in Philadelphia, under the shadow of that Hall in which our independence was declared, it seemed that a Divine attestation had solemnly hallowed and sanctified the great anniversary by the impressive ministration of Death."

Reader's Response: White claims that the Declaration of Independence is part of what makes "The American Idea" of freedom and democracy so much a part of our lives. What other documents in American history do you think are also important?

_____

_____

_____

_____

The American Idea

1. **Infer:** How were various peoples of the world affected by hearing the call of the American Idea?

   _____

   _____

2. **Respond:** Which idea about America meant the most to you? Explain your choice.

   _____

   _____

3. **Reading Skill:** List two **opinions** that White includes about people or events, and explain the **facts** he uses to support each opinion.

   _____

   _____

   _____

4. **Literary Analysis:** Use the chart below to organize details of the **analytic** sections of White's essay.

   Topic: _____

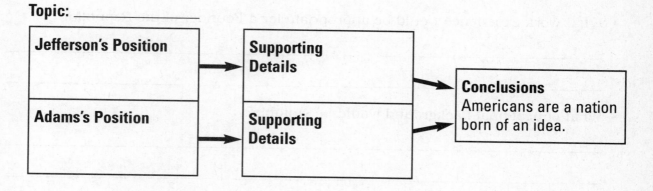

SUPPORT FOR WRITING AND EXTEND YOUR LEARNING

Writing: Critique

Write a **critique**, or critical evaluation, of White's essay. Use your answers to these questions to write your critique.

- Make a list of White's central claims.

_____

_____

_____

- What evidence supports each claim—facts, opinions, or both?

_____

_____

_____

- How relevant and convincing is the evidence for each claim?

_____

_____

_____

Research and Technology: Cover Letter and Résumé

Research one of the nation's founders, such as Thomas Jefferson, John Adams, or Benjamin Franklin. Write a **cover letter and résumé** that the person might have submitted for the position of "Founder of the Republic."

- What work experience would be appropriate for a Founder of the Republic?

_____

_____

- What educational background would be suitable?

_____

_____

- What accomplishments would be desirable?

_____

_____

Use your notes to research and write your cover letter and résumé.

Newspaper Editorials

ABOUT NEWSPAPER EDITORIALS

Most newspaper articles are meant to be objective. They contain facts and tell both sides of an issue. **Newspaper editorials** are an exception. An editorial is an essay in which a writer gives his or her opinion on a current event. Newspaper editorials usually include a clearly stated opinion about a topic in the news, background information on the topic, and arguments in support of the writer's opinion.

READING SKILL

When you read an editorial, think about the author's argument. **Analyze the author's assumptions.** Assumptions are the basic ideas that the author takes for granted. Sometimes the author states his or her assumptions. Sometimes readers need to figure them out from the points the author makes. For example, an editorial writer might write, "Sports are important to a city's life. The mayor should give money for the new stadium." The author of this statement makes several assumptions.

- Sports are important to a city's life. (This assumption is stated.)
- The mayor has the power to give money for the stadium. (This is unstated.)
- The mayor should provide for the city's cultural life, including sports. (This is unstated.)

To analyze assumptions, ask yourself whether most readers would accept each one. Decide whether the assumptions are reasonable and supported by strong evidence. Use the chart below to analyze assumptions.

WRITER'S OPINION:	
Analysis of Assumptions	**My Evaluation of Assumption**
The point is a good one IF one believes . . .	❏ Reasonable
❏ Assumption about what is right or wrong:	❏ Reasonable in part
❏ Assumption about human nature:	❏ Unreasonable
❏ Assumption about a person's character:	
❏ Other assumption:	

THE WALL STREET JOURNAL

Editorial, November 9, 1999

On this day in 1989 the world watched as the German people whom the [Berlin] Wall had divided for more than a generation attacked it with hammers, ropes and their bare hands. What the cameras could not capture was that the physical breaching of the Wall would not have been possible without the sustained moral pounding that had softened the foundation upon which it stood. It was a force most literally expressed by Ronald Wilson Reagan two years earlier when he came to Berlin to present his own challenge to the Soviet leader: "Mr. Gorbachev, tear down this wall." At the time, even many of Mr. Reagan's closest sympathizers regarded it as mere boilerplate.

Mr. Reagan knew better. For his was not an optimism grounded in denying unpleasant facts, as his critics like to think. To the contrary, his was an optimism built on a faith in freedom. Freedom, moreover, was not some distant Platonic ideal, but a practical workaday answer. Thus Mr. Reagan could at once acknowledge the threat posed by the Soviet Union while refusing to be intimidated by it. As he went on to say in his now-famous Berlin speech, "In the Communist world, we see failure, technological backwardness, declining standards of health, even want of the most basic kind—too little food."

In other words, for all its strength and brutality, communism was not the invincible monolith it was so often assumed to be by foes and sympathizers alike. [. . .]

Indeed, in looking back to the heady days of the early 1980s perhaps the most striking thing is how persistently Mr. Reagan predicted communism's fall—and how most everyone simply ignored him. Even among his fellow Cold Warriors the Gipper's[1] optimism set him apart. [. . .]

Ronald Reagan did not win the Cold War single-handedly. The contradictions of communism had been building, pushed by brave leaders like Lech Walesa and Vaclav Havel.[2] Clearly too Mikhail Gorbachev played his part, not least in his refusal to use troops to keep the Wall up. Ten years after the Wall came down, Kosovo and Chechnya[3] remind us that we have challenges we could not even have imagined then. But surely the lesson of 1989 is that human beings are born to be free, that a confidence in this proposition is infectious, and that—as Mr. Reagan would no doubt have reminded us—we would do best by our future to look at the pulling down of the Berlin Wall as a beginning, not an end.

---

1. **Cold Warriors . . . the Gipper's** (gĭ´ perz) The conflict between the Soviet Union and the United States in the decades after 1945 is known as the Cold War; Ronald Reagan was nicknamed "the Gipper."
2. **Lech Walesa** (lekh vä wen´ sä) (b. 1943) . . . **Vaclav Havel** (vä´ tslä hä´ vel) (b. 1936) Eastern European leaders of democratic reform, Walesa in Poland and Havel in Czechoslovakia.
3. **Kosovo** (kô´ sô vô´) **and Chechnya** (chech´ nye) regions that experienced bloody conflict after the Soviet Union's collapse; Kosovo is in Yugoslavia, and Chechnya was formerly part of the Soviet Union.

The New York Times

Editorial, November 10, 1999

The Berlin Wall was bound to fall eventually. But that it came down as bloodlessly as it did 10 years ago this week is largely a tribute to one leader. Today Mikhail Gorbachev is a political pariah in Russia and increasingly forgotten in the West. But history will remember him generously for his crucial role in ending the cold war and pulling back the Iron Curtain that Stalin drew across Europe in 1945.[1]

Liquidating the Soviet empire was not what Mr. Gorbachev had in mind when he came to power in 1985. He was shrewd enough to recognize that radical changes were urgently needed to stave off economic and political bankruptcy in Russia and its European satellites. [. . .][2]

Once Mr. Gorbachev lifted the lid with the openness of *glasnost* and the attempted economic restructuring of *perestroika*,[3] change took on a dynamic of its own. Similar energies were unleashed in the once-captive nations of Eastern Europe as it became clear that he would not send Soviet tanks to bail out the unpopular client regimes that had held sway there since World War II.

As political pressures began to build in the late 1980s, Mr. Gorbachev was left with two options. He could hurtle ahead toward full political and economic freedom. Or he could reverse course and crack down, as so many previous Soviet leaders had done. He chose to do neither. He was too much a creature of his Soviet Communist upbringing to subject his own power to the test of electoral democracy. But he was too enlightened to unleash the kind of thorough repression that might have preserved the Soviet empire for a few more years.

Others stepped in to accelerate the transformations Mr. Gorbachev had begun, and in 1989 fixtures of the Soviet empire began to crumble. [. . .]

Through it all, Mr. Gorbachev and his like-minded foreign minister, Eduard Shevardnadze, stayed their hand, reflecting not only their idealism about reshaping East-West relations but also a pragmatic calculation that the Soviet Union could no longer afford an empire. For permitting its dissolution, Mr. Gorbachev paid a high price. Within two years he had been pushed from power in Moscow. [. . .]

History has passed Mr. Gorbachev by. But this week, especially, he deserves to be remembered for what he did and, perhaps more important, what he refused to do. With a wisdom and decency that is sadly rare in international power politics, he chose not to defend a dying system with a final, futile spasm of murderous force.

---

1. Iron Curtain . . . 1945 At the end of the Second World War, in 1945, Europe was split between western countries, allied with the United States, and eastern countries, dominated by its rival, the Soviet Union, then led by Josef Stalin. West and East were said to be divided by an "iron curtain."
2. European satellites Eastern European countries dominated by the Soviet Union.
3. *glasnost* (glaz′ nōst) **. . . *perestroika*** (per′ ə strō̄i′ kə) policies of Gorbachev's designed to reform the Soviet Union. *Glasnost* involved lifting restrictions on free speech; *perestroika* referred to attempts to reform the government and economy.

THINKING ABOUT THE NEWSPAPER EDITORIAL

1. Compare and contrast the two writers' ideas about Gorbachev's role in the fall of the Berlin Wall. Use quotations from each editorial.

_____

_____

2. According to the *Wall Street Journal* editorial, how did Ronald Reagan contribute to the fall of the Berlin Wall? Give two examples.

_____

_____

READING SKILL

3. What assumption do both writers share about the fall of the Berlin Wall?

_____

_____

4. What assumption does the *New York Times* editorial state directly?

_____

_____

TIMED WRITING: PERSUASION (20 minutes)

Respond to one of the editorials. Answer the following questions in your response.

1. Who does the author believe most affected the fall of the Berlin Wall?

_____

2. Why does the author think this person should be remembered?

_____

3. Should other readers accept this argument? Explain.

_____

The Poetic Interpretation of the Twist • The Empty Dance Shoes

Poetry is literature in verse form. It has a controlled arrangement of lines and stanzas. Poets use concise, musical, and emotional language to express multiple layers of meaning.

Figurative language is language that is used imaginatively rather than literally. Poets use it to express ideas or feelings in new ways.

The **figures of speech** in the chart below help poets create special effects.

Figurative Language	Definition	Example
Simile	A comparison of two unlike things using the connecting words *like,* or *as*	The wind was as persistent and annoying as a buzzing fly.
Metaphor	A comparison of two unlike things in which one becomes the other	The sun was an unblinking yellow eye.
Personification	An object or animal is given human feelings, thoughts, actions, or attitudes	Black clouds peeked over the tops of buildings.

Imagery is descriptive language that creates vivid impressions. These impressions, or **images**, are developed through **sensory language**. This language provides details related to sight, sound, taste, touch, smell, and movement.

Poets also use a number of sound devices to achieve a musical quality. The chart on the next page shows types of sound devices.

Sound Device	Definition	Example
Rhythm	The pattern created by the stressed and unstressed syllables of words in sequence; an ordered pattern of rhythm is called **meter**.	"I caught a tremendous fish/ and held him beside the boat"
Rhyme	Repetition of identical sounds in the last syllables of words; a pattern of end rhymes is a **rhyme scheme**.	The man's one last wish/ Was to eat his favorite dish
Alliteration	The repetition of initial consonant sounds in nearby words	Big brown eyes were buried under his brow
Assonance	The repetition of vowel sounds in nearby words	As if this kid felt the chill
Consonance	The repetition of consonants within nearby words in which the separating vowels differ	milk/walk

Types of Poetry

There are three main types of poetry.

- **Narrative** poems tell a story. They have a plot, characters, and a setting. An **epic** is a long narrative poem about gods or heroes. A **ballad** is a songlike narrative that has short stanzas and a refrain.
- **Dramatic** poems tell a story using a character's thoughts or spoken statements.
- **Lyric** poems express the feelings of a single speaker. This is the most common type of poem in modern literature.

Poems can also be categorized by form. Poetic forms are defined by specific organizations of line and stanza length, rhythm, and rhyme.

- A **haiku** has three unrhymed lines of five, seven, and five syllables. A **tanka** has five unrhymed lines of five, seven, five, seven, and seven syllables. Both forms use imagery to convey a single vivid emotion.
- A **sonnet** is a fourteen-line lyric poem with formal patterns of rhyme, rhythm, and line structure.
- **Free verse** does not have a set pattern of rhythm or rhyme.

The Poetic Interpretation of the Twist • The Empty Dance Shoes

Cornelius Eady

Summaries In "The Poetic Interpretation of the Twist," the speaker shows what life was like in the early 1960s. In "The Empty Dance Shoes," the speaker explains what happens when a pair of dancing shoes goes unfilled. The poems are a record of memories and an explanation of the resistance to change.

Note-taking Guide

Use this chart to write the images that are described in each poem.

	The Poetic Interpretation of the Twist	The Empty Dance Shoes
What images are described?	description of a man	

TAKE NOTES

Activate Prior Knowledge

What songs or dances do you connect with your childhood? What are the reasons for the connection?

_____

_____

_____

Poetry

A **simile** is a comparison of two unlike things using a connecting word such as *like*, or *as*. Write the simile the author uses in the bracketed stanza.

_____

_____

_____

Stop to Reflect

Underline the details the speaker of the poem gives about his or her world. Why does the speaker include these details?

_____

_____

_____

Poetry

Which **sound device** is used in the underlined sentence?

_____

Circle the words in which it appears.

The Poetic Interpretation of the Twist
Cornelius Eady

I know what you're expecting to hear.
You think to yourself: Here's a guy who must
    understand what the twist was all about.
Look at the knuckles of his hands,
Look at his plain, blue shirt hanging out of the
    back of his trousers.
The twist must have been the equivalent of the
    high sign
In a secret cult.

I know
I know
I know

But listen: I am still confused by the mini-skirt
As well as the deep meaning of vinyl on everything.
The twist was just a children's game to us.
I know you expect there ought to be more to this,
The reason the whole world decided to uncouple,

But why should I lie to you? Let me pull up a chair
And in as few words as possible,
Re-create my sister,
Who was renowned for running like a giraffe.
Let me re-create my neighborhood,
A dead-end street next to the railroad tracks.
Let me re-create
My father, who would escape the house by bicycle
And do all the grocery shopping by himself.

Let's not forget the pool hall and the barbershop,
Each with their strange flavors of men,
And while we're on the subject,
I must not <u>slight</u> the ragweed,
The true rose of the street.

<u>All this will still not give you the twist.</u>

Forgive me for running on like this.
Your question has set an expectation
That is impossible to meet

Vocabulary Development: slight (slyt) *v.* to treat with disrespect
or indifference

Your question has put on my shoulders
A troublesome responsibility

Because the twist is gone.
It is the foundation of a bridge
That has made way for a housing project

And I am sorry to admit
You have come to the wrong person.
I recall the twist
The way we recall meeting a distant aunt as a baby
Or the afternoons spent in homeroom
Waiting for the last bell.

My head hurts.
I am tired of remembering.
Perhaps you can refresh my memory
And tell me
How we got on this topic?
As a favor to me,
Let's not talk anymore about old dances.

I have an entire world on the tip of my tongue.

Poetry

Alliteration is the repetition of consonant sounds in nearby words. Read the bracketed passage. Circle a place where the author uses alliteration.

Poetry

What type of poem do you think this is? Why do you think so?

_____

_____

_____

_____

_____

Reading Check

What does the author say that "Your question" has done? Underline the lines in the text that tell you.

TAKE NOTES

Poetry

When an object or an animal is given human thoughts, feelings, or actions, this is called **personification**. How does the author show personification in the bracketed stanza?

_____

_____

_____

Stop to Reflect

The author compares "an empty pair of dancing shoes" to many things in this poem. Given these comparisons, how do you think the author feels about the shoes being empty?

_____

_____

_____

_____

Poetry

What does the **image** of the flat clown and the dancing shoes suggest?

_____

_____

_____

Reading Check

What is the secret of inertia, according to the speaker? Underline the text that tells you.

The Empty Dance Shoes
Cornelius Eady

My friends,
As it has been proven in the laboratory,
An empty pair of dance shoes
Will sit on the floor like a wart
Until it is given a reason to move.

Those of us who study inertia[1]
(Those of us covered with wild hair and sleep)
Can state this without fear:
The energy in a pair of shoes at rest
Is about the same as that of a clown

Knocked flat by a sandbag.
This you can tell your friends with certainty:
A clown, flat on his back,
Is a lot like an empty pair of dancing shoes.

An empty pair of dancing shoes
Is also a lot like a leaf
Pressed in a book.
And now you know a simple truth:
A leaf pressed in, say, *The Colossus* by Sylvia
    Plath,[2]
Is no different from an empty pair of dance shoes

Even if those shoes are in the middle of the
    Stardust Ballroom
With all the lights on, and hot music shakes
    the windows up and down the block.

This is the secret of inertia:
The shoes run on their own sense of the world.
They are in sympathy with the rock the kid skips
    over the lake
After it settles to the mud.
Not with the ripples,
But with the rock.

---

1. **inertia** (i NER shuh) *n.* in physics, the tendency of matter at rest to remain at rest or, if moving, to keep doing so in the same direction unless affected by an outside force.
2. ***The Colossus* by Sylvia Plath** volume of poetry by American poet Sylvia Plath (1932–1963).

A practical and personal <u>application</u> of inertia
Can be found in the question:
Whose Turn Is It
To Take Out the Garbage?
An empty pair of dance shoes
Is a lot like the answer to this question,
As well as book-length poems
Set in the Midwest.

To sum up:
An empty pair of dance shoes
Is a lot like the sand the 98-pound weakling
    brushes from his cheeks
As the bully tows away his girlfriend.
Later,

When he spies the coupon at the back of the
    comic book,
He is about to act upon a different set of scientific
    principles.
He is ready to dance.

Vocabulary Development: application (ap li CAY shuhn) *n.* act of
                          putting something to use

Reader's Response: Which of Eady's poems do you prefer? Why?

_____

_____

_____

TAKE NOTES

Poetry

Alliteration is the repetition of consonant sounds in nearby words. Circle the use of alliteration in the bracketed passage.

Stop to Reflect

How do the last three lines of the poem shift its meaning?

_____

_____

_____

_____

_____

Poetry

1. **Cause and Effect:** In "The Poetic Interpretation of the Twist," the speaker mentions memories as he tries to recall the Twist. How is the speaker affected by these memories?

_____

_____

_____

2. **Compare and Contrast:** The speaker in "The Empty Dance Shoes" uses examples of a clown, a leaf pressed into a book, and a skipped rock to illustrate inertia. How are these examples both similar and different?

_____

_____

3. **Compare and Contrast:** How are the **speakers** of the two poems similar and different?

_____

_____

_____

4. In the first column of the chart, list examples of **figurative language** from "The Empty Dance Shoes" that compare the shoes to other things. In the second column, describe the effect of each example. In the last column, explain the meaning of the shoes in each example.

What It Says	Feeling It Creates	What It Means

RESEARCH THE AUTHOR

Annotated Poster

Create an **annotated poster** that displays the musical or dance imagery in poems by Cornelius Eady. Use your notes from the prompts below to create your poster.

- Find six poems about dance or music written by Cornelius Eady. Two of his poetry collections you may find helpful are *Victims of the Latest Dance Craze* (1986) and *The Autobiography of a Jukebox* (1997). List the names of the poems you will use. Then, briefly summarize what each poem is about.

_____

_____

_____

_____

_____

_____

- Watch the video interview with Cornelius Eady. What impact do music and dance have on his poetry?

_____

_____

- Select photographs, drawings, and other images that relate to Eady's poetry. Briefly describe your selections below.

_____

_____

_____

_____

_____

_____

_____

_____

Poetry Collection 1 • Poetry Collection 2

LITERARY ANALYSIS

In poetry, the **speaker** is the voice that says the words of the poem. The speaker may be the poet, or it may be a character the poet invents to give the poem a particular voice or viewpoint. All poems have a speaker, but some poems have qualities that set them apart as a distinct form.

- In **narrative poetry**, the speaker tells a story in verse.
- In **lyric poetry**, the speaker's thoughts, feelings, and insights create a single, unified impression. Lyric poems include **imagery**, or language that appeals to the senses.

READING SKILL

Read aloud to appreciate and share the musical qualities of poetry. As you read aloud, **read fluently** and **adjust your reading rate**.

- Read the poem slowly and carefully. Make sure that you understand it and that you can pronounce all of the words.
- Use punctuation, and group words for meaning. Do not pause at line-ends unless punctuation indicates that you should.
- Slow down to emphasize an idea or the sounds of words.

To prepare to read aloud, mark a copy of the poem to indicate adjustments to your reading rate. Use the chart below to help.

Mark the Text	Adjust Reading Rate
Circle punctuation marks.	Pause or stop.
Underline words or sounds to emphasize.	Slow down.
Bracket phrases or groups of words to read together.	Speed up.

Poetry Collection 1

Summaries In "The Bridegroom," a strong-willed woman has seen a murder. She avoids misfortune by pointing out the murderer. In "The Guitar," Lorca compares the guitar's sad sound to a wounded heart. In "The Fish," the speaker catches an old fish. The speaker sees that it has already won several battles with other fishermen. In "Danny Deever," two young soldiers must watch the hanging of another soldier. They dread what they are about to see.

Reading/Writing Connection

Complete the paragraph below to explain why a certain story or movie creates feelings of suspense, wonder, or melancholy.

One tale that <u>illustrates</u> suspense is _____.

Most people <u>guarantee</u> that this tale will _____.

People who hear this tale <u>react</u> with _____.

Note-taking Guide

Use this chart to record the speaker and the images in the poems.

Title of Poem	Speaker	Imagery
The Bridegroom	The poet	"a swift troika," "a handsome young man," "snow and mud went flying"
The Guitar		
The Fish		
Danny Deever		

The Bridegroom
Alexander Pushkin

Think of important experiences you have had during your life. Which of these experiences would make a good subject for a poem? Explain.

_____

_____

_____

Reading aloud can help you appreciate the tone, or feeling, of poetry. Read aloud the first stanza of the poem. How would you describe the tone of these lines? Explain.

_____

_____

_____

Circle details from the stanza to support your answer.

In **narrative** poetry, the **speaker** tells a story in verse. What has happened so far in this story?

_____

_____

_____

_____

For three days Natasha,
The merchant's daughter,
Was missing. The third night,
She ran in, distraught.
5 Her father and mother
Plied her with questions.
She did not hear them,
She could hardly breathe.

Stricken with foreboding
10 They pleaded, got angry,
But still she was silent;
At last they gave up.
Natasha's cheeks regained
Their rosy color.
15 And cheerfully again
She sat with her sisters.

Once at the shingle-gate
She sat with her friends
—And a swift troika[1]
20 Flashed by before them;
A handsome young man
Stood driving the horses;
Snow and mud went flying,
Splashing the girls.

25 He gazed as he flew past,
And Natasha gazed.
He flew on. Natasha froze.
Headlong she ran home.
"It was he! It was he!"
30 She cried. "I know it!
I recognized him! Papa,
Mama, save me from him!"

Vocabulary Development: foreboding (fawr BOHD ing) *n.* a feeling that something bad will happen

---

1. **troika** (TROY kuh) *n.* Russian carriage or sleigh drawn by a team of three horses.

Full of grief and fear,
They shake their heads, sighing.
35 Her father says: "My child,
Tell me everything.
If someone has harmed you,
Tell us . . . even a hint."
She weeps again and
40 Her lips remain sealed.

The next morning, the old
Matchmaking woman
Unexpectedly calls and
Sings the girl's praises;
45 Says to the father: "You
Have the goods and I
A buyer for them:
A handsome young man.

"He bows low to no one,
50 He lives like a lord
With no debts nor worries;
He's rich and he's generous,
Says he will give his bride,
On their wedding-day,
55 A fox-fur coat, a pearl,
Gold rings, brocaded² dresses,

"Yesterday, out driving,
He saw your Natasha;
Shall we shake hands
60 And get her to church?"
The woman starts to eat
A pie, and talks in riddles,
While the poor girl
Does not know where to look.

65 "Agreed," says her father;
"Go in happiness
To the altar, Natasha;
It's dull for you here;
A swallow should not spend
70 All its time singing,
It's time for you to build
A nest for your children."

2. brocaded (broh KAYD id) *adj.* with raised designs woven into the cloth.

TAKE NOTES

Reading Skill

Reading fluently involves reading in sentences. Circle the punctuation marks in the first bracketed passage. How many sentences are in this stanza?

_____

Literary Analysis

Imagery is created by language that appeals to the senses. Read the second bracketed passage. Given the matchmaking woman's description, what image do you have of the "handsome young man"?

_____

_____

_____

Stop to Reflect

How does grouping words by punctuation help you better understand poetry?

_____

_____

_____

Reading Check

Where does the young man see Natasha? Circle the text that tells you.

To **read fluently, adjust your reading rate**. You can slow down your reading rate by identifying words that need emphasis. **Read aloud** the first bracketed passage. Underline words that need emphasis.

The **speaker** is the voice that says the words of the poem. How does the lack of details in the second bracketed passage make it seem as if the speaker is a storyteller?

_____

_____

_____

What is Natasha's reaction to the matchmaker's visit? Underline the text that tells you.

Natasha leaned against
The wall and tried
75 To speak—but found herself
Sobbing; she was shuddering
And laughing. The matchmaker
Poured out a cup of water,
Gave her some to drink,
80 Splashed some in her face.

Her parents are distressed.
Then Natasha recovered,
And calmly she said:
"Your will be done. Call
85 My bridegroom to the feast,
Bake loaves for the whole world,
Brew sweet mead[3] and call
The law to the feast."

"Of course, Natasha, angel!
90 You know we'd give our lives
To make you happy!"
They bake and they brew;
The worthy guests come,
The bride is led to the feast,
95 Her maids sing and weep;
Then horses and a sledge[4]

With the groom—and all sit.
The glasses ring and clatter,
The toasting-cup is passed
100 From hand to hand in tumult,
The guests are drunk.

BRIDEGROOM
"Friends, why is my fair bride
Sad, why is she not
Feasting and serving?"

105 The bride answers the groom:
"I will tell you why
As best I can. My soul
Knows no rest, day and night
I weep; an evil dream
110 Oppresses me." Her father
Says: "My dear child, tell us
What your dream is."

---

3. mead (meed) _n._ drink made of fermented honey and water.
4. sledge (slej) _n._ sleigh.

"I dreamed," she says, "that I
Went into a forest,
115 It was late and dark;
The moon was faintly
Shining behind a cloud;
I strayed from the path;
Nothing stirred except
120 The tops of the pine-trees.

"And suddenly, as if
I was awake, I saw
A hut. I approach the hut
And knock at the door
125 —Silence. A prayer on my lips
I open the door and enter.
A candle burns. All
Is silver and gold."

BRIDEGROOM
"What is bad about that?
130 It promises wealth."

BRIDE
"Wait, sir, I've not finished.
Silently I gazed
On the silver and gold,
The cloths, the rugs, the silks
135 From Novgorod,⁵ and I
Was lost in wonder.

"Then I heard a shout
And a clatter of hoofs . . .
Someone has driven up
140 To the porch. Quickly
I slammed the door and hid
Behind the stove. Now
I hear many voices . . .
Twelve young men come in,

145 "And with them is a girl,
Pure and beautiful.
They've taken no notice
Of the ikons,⁶ they sit
To the table without
150 Praying or taking off
Their hats. At the head,
The eldest brother,
At his right, the youngest;
At his left, the girl.
155 Shouts, laughs, drunken clamor . . . "

5. **Novgorod** (NAHV guh rahd) city in northwestern Russia.
6. **ikons** (Y kahnz) *n.* sacred religious images.

TAKE NOTES

Literary Analysis

Narrative poetry tells a story. Who is the main character in this poem's story?

_____

Reading Skill

Reading aloud helps a reader appreciate the musical qualities of poetry. Read aloud the second bracketed passage. What feeling does the sound of these lines create?

_____

_____

Literary Analysis

Underline the details on this page that help the bride's **narrative** build in excitement.

Natasha acts as the **speaker** in this part of the poem. What qualities does she exhibit as she describes her dream?

_____

_____

_____

_____

To **read fluently**, use punctuation as a guide for where to pause and where to stop when reading. Read the bracketed passage. Where should you pause when reading these stanza? Where should you stop? Explain.

_____

_____

_____

What is the question that Natasha asks the Bridegroom? What is his reaction to this question? Underline the text that tells you.

BRIDEGROOM
"That betokens merriment."

BRIDE
"Wait, sir, I've not finished.
The drunken din goes on
And grows louder still.
160 Only the girl is sad.

"She sits silent, neither
Eating nor drinking;
But sheds tears in plenty;
The eldest brother
165 Takes his knife and, whistling,
Sharpens it; seizing her by
The hair he kills her
And cuts off her right hand."

"Why," says the groom, "this
170 Is nonsense! Believe me,
My love, your dream is not evil."
She looks him in the eyes.
"And from whose hand
Does this ring come?"
175 The bride said. The whole throng
Rose in the silence.

With a clatter the ring
Falls, and rolls along
The floor. The groom blanches,
180 Trembles. Confusion . . .
"Seize him!" the law commands.
He's bound, judged, put to death.
Natasha is famous!
Our song at an end.

The Guitar
Federico García Lorca

Now begins the cry
Of the guitar,
Breaking the vaults
Of dawn.
5 Now begins the cry
Of the guitar.
Useless
To still it.
Impossible
10 To still it.
It weeps monotonously
As weeps the water,
As weeps the wind
Over snow.
15 Impossible
To still it.
It weeps
For distant things,
Warm southern sands
20 Desiring white camellias.
It mourns the arrow without a target,
The evening without morning.
And the first bird dead
Upon a branch.
25 O guitar!
A wounded heart,
Wounded by five swords.

Vocabulary Development: monotonously (muh NAHT n uhs lee)
adv. in a dull, unvarying way

TAKE NOTES

Reading Skill

Read aloud the bracketed lines. Underline words that are repeated. What is the effect of Lorca's use of repetition?

_____

_____

_____

Literary Analysis

In **lyric poetry**, the **speaker's** thoughts, feelings, and insights create a single unified impression. At the end of this poem, with what impression are you left? Explain.

_____

_____

_____

Reading Check

What three things does the guitar mourn for? Circle the text that tells you.

Literary Analysis

What event in this **narrative** poem triggers the speaker's thoughts?

_____

_____

Stop to Reflect

What words and images do you associate with fish and fishing?

_____

_____

_____

_____

_____

Reading Skill

Use punctuation in this poem to **read fluently. Read aloud** lines 34–40. Circle the pauses signaled by punctuation marks.

The Fish
Elizabeth Bishop

I caught a tremendous fish
and held him beside the boat
half out of water, with my hook
fast in a corner of his mouth.
5 He didn't fight.
He hadn't fought at all.
He hung a grunting weight,
battered and venerable
and homely. Here and there
10 his brown skin hung in strips
like ancient wallpaper,
and its pattern of darker brown
was like wallpaper:
shapes like full-blown roses
15 stained and lost through age.
He was speckled with barnacles,
fine rosettes of lime,
and infested
with tiny white sea-lice,
20 and underneath two or three
rags of green weed hung down.
While his gills were breathing in
the terrible oxygen
—the frightening gills,
25 fresh and crisp with blood,
that can cut so badly—
I thought of the coarse white flesh
packed in like feathers,
the big bones and the little bones,
30 the dramatic reds and blacks
of his shiny entrails,
and the pink swim-bladder
like a big peony.
I looked into his eyes
35 which were far larger than mine
but shallower, and yellowed,
the irises backed and packed
with tarnished tinfoil
seen through the lenses
40 of old scratched isinglass.[1]

Vocabulary Development: venerable (VEN uhr uh buhl) *adj.*
worthy of respect because of age, character, or position

---

1. **isinglass** (Y zin glas) *n.* transparent material once used in windows.

They shifted a little, but not
to return my stare.
—It was more like the tipping
of an object toward the light.
45 I admired his sullen face,
the mechanism of his jaw,
and then I saw
that from his lower lip
—if you could call it a lip—
50 grim, wet, and weaponlike,
hung five old pieces of fish-line,
or four and a wire leader
with the swivel still attached,
with all their five big hooks
55 grown firmly in his mouth.
A green line, frayed at the end
where he broke it, two heavier lines,
and a fine black thread
still crimped from the strain and snap
60 when it broke and he got away.
Like medals with their ribbons
frayed and wavering,
a five-haired beard of wisdom
trailing from his aching jaw.
65 I stared and stared
and victory filled up
the little rented boat,
from the pool of bilge
where oil had spread a rainbow
70 around the rusted engine
to the bailer rusted orange,
the sun-cracked thwarts,[2]
the oarlocks on their strings,
the gunnels[3]—until everything
75 was rainbow, rainbow, rainbow!
And I let the fish go.

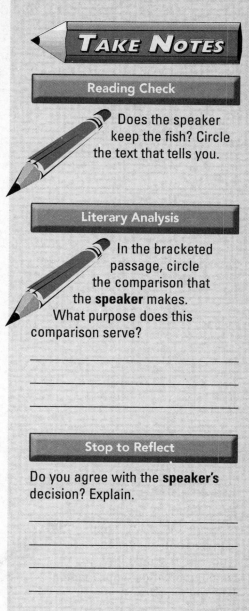

TAKE NOTES

Reading Check

Does the speaker keep the fish? Circle the text that tells you.

Literary Analysis

In the bracketed passage, circle the comparison that the **speaker** makes. What purpose does this comparison serve?

_____

_____

_____

Stop to Reflect

Do you agree with the **speaker's** decision? Explain.

_____

_____

_____

_____

_____

_____

---

2. **thwarts** (thwawrtz) *n.* seats in a boat for rowers.
3. **gunnels** (GUN uhlz) *n.* upper edges of the sides of a ship or boat.

Danny Deever

Rudyard Kipling

Compare and contrast the two characters in this poem.

_____

_____

_____

"What are the bugles blowin' for?" said
    Files-on-Parade.[1]
"To turn you out, to turn you out," the
    Color-Sergeant[2] said.
"What makes you look so white, so white?"
    said Files-on-Parade.
"I'm dreadin' what I've got to watch," the
    Color-Sergeant said.
5   For they're hangin' Danny Deever, you can hear
      the Dead March play,
    The regiment's in 'ollow square[3]—they're hangin'
      him today;
    They've taken of his buttons off an' cut his
      stripes away,
    An' they're hangin' Danny Deever in the mornin'.

"What makes the rear-rank breathe so 'ard?" said
    Files-on-Parade.
10 "It's bitter cold, it's bitter cold," the Color-
    Sergeant said.
"What makes that front-rank man fall down?" says
    Files-on-Parade.
"A touch o' sun, a touch o' sun," the Color-
    Sergeant said.
    They are hangin' Danny Deever, they are
      marchin' of 'im round,
    They 'ave 'alted Danny Deever by 'is coffin on
      the ground;
15   An' 'e'll swing in 'arf a minute for a sneakin'
      shootin' hound—
    O they're hangin' Danny Deever in the mornin'!

Read aloud the bracketed passage. Circle the beginning and end of the sentence. How should the punctuation affect your **reading rate** and pace?

_____

_____

_____

The two **speakers** in this poem use a question-and-answer format to relate events. What effect does this format have on the reader?

_____

_____

_____

_____

1. **Files-on-Parade** soldier who directs marching formation.
2. **Color-Sergeant** flag-bearer.
3. **'ollow square** At a hanging, soldiers standing in ranks form three sides of a square; the gallows occupies the fourth side.

"'Is cot was right-'and cot to mine," said
    Files-on-Parade.
"'E's sleepin' out an' far tonight," the Color-
    Sergeant said.
"I've drunk 'is beer a score o' times," said
    Files-on-Parade.
20 "'E's drinkin' bitter beer alone," the Color-
    Sergeant said.
      They are hangin' Danny Deever, you must mark
        'im to 'is place,
      For 'e shot a comrade sleepin'—you must look
        'im in the face;
      Nine 'undred of 'is county an' the regiment's
        disgrace,
      While they're hangin' Danny Deever in the
        mornin'.

25 "What's that so black agin the sun?" said Files-
    on-Parade.
"It's Danny fightin' 'ard for life," the Color-
    Sergeant said.
"What's that that whimpers over'ead?" said
    Files-on-Parade.
"It's Danny's soul that's passin' now," the
    Color-Sergeant said.
      For they're done with Danny Deever, you can
        'ear the quick-step play,
30   The regiment's in column, an' they're marchin'
        us away;
      Ho! the young recruits are shakin', an' they'll
        want their beer to-day,
      After hangin' Danny Deever in the mornin'.

Reader's Response: Which of the poems in Poetry Collection 1 is the best example of **narrative** poetry? Explain your choice.

_____

_____

_____

_____

TAKE NOTES

Reading Skill

Read aloud lines 17–24. Underline repeated words and phrases. What effect does this repetition have on the poem?

_____

_____

_____

Literary Analysis

In dramatic **narrative** poems, one or more characters speak. By using the words of these **speakers** to tell the story, the poet makes the readers feel as if they are actually witnessing the event. How does the bracketed passage help you feel as if you are witnessing the events in the poem?

_____

_____

_____

Reading Check

Why is Danny Deever being hanged? Circle the text that tells you.

Poetry Collection 1

1. **Respond:** Use this chart to record the images you find most vivid in these poems.

Title of Poem	Vivid Images
The Bridegroom	
The Guitar	
The Fish	
Danny Deever	

2. **Connect:** Think about how Natasha reacts to the matchmaker's visit. Explain what Natasha's "dream" reveals about the reasons for her reaction.

_____

_____

3. **Literary Analysis:** Compare the **speakers** in "The Guitar" and "The Fish." In your response, consider how much or how little you know about the speaker and whether the speaker is the poet or a character.

_____

_____

_____

4. **Reading Skill:** Choose one of the poems, and make notes for **reading** it **aloud**. Where will you slow down and where will you speed up to **read fluently**? Give reasons for your choices.

_____

_____

_____

SUPPORT FOR WRITING AND EXTEND YOUR LEARNING

Writing: Lyric Poem

Write your own **lyric poem** in response to one of the poems in this collection. To begin, answer the following questions.

- Name an object that is important to you.

_____

- What does the subject of your poem make you think of?

_____

- How does the subject of your poem make you feel?

_____

- What feelings do you want readers to get from reading your poem?

_____

_____

Use your notes to write your lyric poem.

Listening and Speaking: Oral Interpretation

Prepare to present an **oral interpretation** of another Kipling poem that uses dialect. Remember that dialect is a form of the language spoken by people in a particular region or group. Use your answers to prepare for the interpretation.

- What dialect is spoken in the poem?

_____

- What does the dialect used say about the characters in the poem?

_____

- Why did Kipling use the dialect in his poem?

_____

- How does the dialect bring the speaker to life?

_____

_____

Poetry Collection 2

Summaries In "A Tree Telling of Orpheus," Levertov describes emotions through the point of view of a tree that is charmed by the music of Orpheus. In "Spring and All," Williams understands that birth and death are both full of joy and difficulty. In "Mowing," Frost writes about a scythe that seems to be alive as the speaker mows. In "Making a Fist," Nye writes about a mother who answers her daughter's question about death.

Reading/Writing Connection

Complete this paragraph to describe looking at something in a new way.

The time to <u>inspect</u> something familiar is _____.

It <u>stimulates</u> the ability to _____. You will

<u>perceive</u> _____.

Note-taking Guide

Use this chart to record the speaker and the images in the poems.

Title of Poem	Speaker	Imagery
A Tree Telling of Orpheus	A tree	Foggy dawn
Spring and All		
Mowing		
Making a Fist		

Poetry Collection 2

1. **Respond:** Use the chart below to identify the images that you find most vivid in these poems.

Title of Poem	Vivid Images
A Tree Telling of Orpheus	
Spring and All	
Mowing	
Making a Fist	

2. **Analyze:** In "A Tree Telling of Orpheus," why do the trees react as they do, when Orpheus leaves?

_____

_____

3. **Literary Analysis:** How are the **speakers** in "Spring and All" and "Making a Fist" similar and different? Consider how much you know about the speaker and whether the speaker is the poet or a character.

_____

_____

4. **Reading Skill:** Choose one poem from this collection. Make notes for **reading** it **aloud**. Where will you slow down and where will you speed up to **read fluently**? Give reasons for each choice.

_____

_____

SUPPORT FOR WRITING AND EXTEND YOUR LEARNING

Writing: Lyric Poem

Write your own **lyric poem** in response to one of the poems in this collection. Use your notes below to write your lyric poem.

- Name an object that is important to you.

  _____

- What does the subject of your poem make you think of?

  _____

- How does the subject of your poem make you feel?

  _____

- What feelings do you want readers to get from reading your poem?

  _____

Research and Technology: Report Answering Research Questions

Select one poet from this collection whose work you enjoy and understand. Research the poet, and write a **report answering your research questions**. Use the Internet and library resources to find answers to your research questions. Use the chart below to organize your research questions, answers, and answer sources.

Poet's Name:	
Question:	Answer:
	Answer source:
Question:	Answer:
	Answer source:
Question:	Answer:
	Answer source:

Poetry Collection 1 • Poetry Collection 2

LITERARY ANALYSIS

To unify sounds and ideas in a poem, a poet may follow a **poetic form**, or defined structure. Each poetic form uses a set number of lines and a distinctive **meter** and pattern of **rhymes**. Traditional poetic forms include the following:

Tanka—a five-line, unrhymed Japanese form

- The first and third lines contain five syllables. The second, fourth, and fifth lines have seven syllables. (The number of syllables can vary when a tanka is translated into English.)
- The briefness of a tanka helps poets focus on a single strong image or idea.

Sonnet—a fourteen-line form

- In a type of sonnet called the **Shakespearean sonnet**, the lines are grouped into three **quatrains** (groups of four lines) and a **couplet**, a pair of rhymed lines. The rhyme scheme is *abab, cdcd, efef, gg*.
- Sonnet writers may answer the ideas in one quatrain with ideas in another, summing up the poem in the couplet.
- Sonnets are written in *iambic pentameter*. That is, each line contains five unaccented and five accented syllables in the pattern "da-DUM, da-DUM, da-DUM, da-DUM, da-DUM."

Villanelle—a nineteen-line form

- The lines are grouped into five three-line stanzas and one four-line stanza. The lines rhyme *aba, aba, aba, aba, aba, abaa*.
- Line 1 is repeated in lines 6, 12, and 18. Line 3 is repeated in lines 9, 15, and 19.
- This repetition can create a chanting effect or suggest intense passion.

Use this chart to analyze poetic forms as you read.

Analyzing the Form of a Poem	
Number of lines	
Number of syllables in each line	
Pattern of accented and unaccented syllables in each line	
Which lines rhyme?	

READING SKILL

When you **read fluently**, you read smoothly and with understanding, placing emphasis appropriately and pausing where necessary. To increase your fluency when reading a poem, **preview** the work, looking over the text in advance.

- Use footnotes and other text aids to learn unfamiliar words. Practice saying each unfamiliar word by following the pronunciation given, and learn each word's definition.
- Determine where each sentence in the poem begins and ends. If you notice that a sentence stretches over more than one line, prepare to read it "through" the end of each line, pausing only when the punctuation indicates you should. Refer to the diagram for the types of pauses associated with common marks.

Punctuation		Type of Pause
.	Period	Full stop
:	Colon	Almost as strong as a period; end with your voice raised just enough that a listener knows to expect more.
;	Semicolon	Less strong than a colon; pause briefly, with your voice raised.
,	Comma	A slight pause

- Form a rough idea of the topic and mood of the work. A quick look at the type of words used in the poem may show you whether the mood of the poem is sad or happy, serious or humorous. Read the poem with its mood in mind.

Poetry Collection 1

Summaries "The clustering clouds . . ." reflects on light and shadow. The poet reaches understanding through images of nature in "When I went to visit . . ." The speaker describes his love of city life in "My City." The speaker of "Do Not Go Gentle Into That Good Night" encourages a fight against death.

Reading/Writing Connection

Complete this paragraph to describe your favorite view.

People can <u>appreciate</u> nature when _____.

_____ helps <u>liberate</u> the mind. This peace can

<u>generate</u> _____.

Note-taking Guide

Use this chart to record the imagery and main message of each poem.

Poem	Imagery	Main Message
The clustering clouds . . .	gathering clouds; moonlight	The clouds make the moon appear even brighter.
When I went to visit . . .		
My City		
Do Not Go Gentle Into That Good Night		

Think about your favorite poem. Does this poem have a clear structure? Does it use rhyme? If so, what purpose does the structure and/or rhyme serve?

_____

_____

_____

When you **read fluently**, you read smoothly and with understanding. To increase your fluency when reading a poem, **preview** the work, or look over the text in advance. Preview the first two poems on this page. How many sentences are in each?

_____

_____

_____

A **tanka** is a five-line unrhymed Japanese form. Which features of the tanka appear in the translations of "The clustering clouds . . ." and "When I went to visit . . ."?

_____

_____

_____

_____

What type of poem is "My City"? Underline the sentence that tells you.

Tanka

The clustering clouds—
Can it be they wipe away
The lunar shadows?
Every time they clear a bit
The moonlight shines the brighter.

—Minamoto no Toshiyori
translated by **Donald Keene**

When I went to visit
The girl I love so much,
That winter night
The river blew so cold
That the plovers[1] were crying.

—Ki Tsurayuki
translated by **Geoffrey Bownas**

My City

James Weldon Johnson

Background
Poets who write Shakespearean sonnets may slightly modify the rhyme scheme. In this sonnet, Johnson uses a modified scheme in the first two quatrains, or groups of four lines. In the rest of the poem, though, he follows classic Shakespearean form.

When I come down to sleep death's endless night,
The threshold of the unknown dark to cross,
What to me then will be the keenest loss,
When this bright world blurs on my fading sight?
5 Will it be that no more I shall see the trees
Or smell the flowers or hear the singing birds
Or watch the flashing streams or patient herds?

Vocabulary Development: clustering (KLUS ter ing) *adj.* gathering; forming in a group
lunar (LOO ner) *adj.* of the moon
threshold (THRESH hohld) *n.* the bottom of a doorway; entrance or a point of beginning

---

1. **plovers** (PLUV uhrz) *n.* shorebirds with short tails and long, pointed wings.

No, I am sure it will be none of these.
But, ah! Manhattan's sights and sounds,
 her smells,
10 Her crowds, her throbbing force, the thrill
 that comes
From being of her a part, her subtile spells,
 Her shining towers, her avenues, her slums—
 O God! the stark, unutterable pity,
To be dead, and never again behold my city!

Do Not Go Gentle Into That Good Night

Dylan Thomas

Do not go gentle into that good night,
Old age should burn and rave at close of day;
Rage, rage against the dying of the light.

Though wise men at their end know dark is right,
5 Because their words had forked no lightning they
Do not go gentle into that good night.

Good men, the last wave by, crying how bright
Their frail deeds might have danced in a green bay,
Rage, rage against the dying of the light.

10 Wild men who caught and sang the sun in flight,
And learn, too late, they grieved it on its way,
Do not go gentle into that good night.

Grave men, near death, who see with blinding sight
Blind eyes could blaze like meteors and be gay,
15 Rage, rage against the dying of the light.

And you, my father, there on the sad height,
Curse, bless, me now with your fierce tears, I pray.
Do not go gentle into that good night.
Rage, rage against the dying of the light.

Reader's Response: Which image from the poems in Poetry
Collection 1 made the strongest impression on you? Explain.

_____

_____

_____

Stop to Reflect

Read the poem by Dylan Thomas.
Think about Thomas's message to
his father. Do you agree with his
message?

_____

_____

_____

Reading Skill

Reading in sen-
tences can help you
read fluently. Circle the
punctuation in lines 16–19
that indicates where you will
pause when reading.

Reading Check

Underline the four types of men
Thomas describes. What disappointment does each type
of man face at the
end of life?

_____

_____

_____

_____

Poetry Collection 1

1. **Infer:** In "When I went to visit . . .", what does the speaker's reaction to the weather indicate about his love? Explain.

   _____

   _____

2. **Interpret:** In "The clustering clouds . . .," the clouds obscure the moon and the moonlight. The speaker brings meaning to this event. What does the poem suggest about the effect of contrasts on our perceptions?

   _____

   _____

3. **Literary Analysis:** Using the chart below, analyze the meaning of the three **quatrains** and the **couplet** in the **sonnet** "My City."

Message of Quatrain 1	Connection: Quatrains 1 and 2	Connection: Quatrains 2 and 3	Connection: Couplet to Quatrains

4. **Literary Analysis:** What feeling do the repeated lines in the **villanelle** "Do Not Go Gentle Into That Good Night" help create?

   _____

   _____

5. **Reading Skill:** By **previewing** the first eight lines of "My City," what information about vocabulary and sentence structure can a reader learn?

   _____

   _____

SUPPORT FOR WRITING AND EXTEND YOUR LEARNING

Writing: Tanka

Write your own **tanka**. Follow the traditional Japanese form. Remember that a tanka is a five-line, unrhymed poem. The first and third lines contain five syllables. The second, fourth, and fifth lines have seven syllables. Answer the following questions to begin:

- What mood do you want to create? _____

- What descriptive words will express that mood? List three words.

  _____

- What image would capture or express the mood? _____

  _____

- List three words that describe the image. _____

  _____

Research and Technology: Visual Presentation

Prepare a **visual presentation** on Japanese art.

- Use library and Internet resources to find two works of Japanese art that illustrate the general mood or specific descriptions in the tanka in this collection.

- Fill in the chart below with descriptive words for the tanka and for the art you find.

Notes for a Visual Presentation on Japanese Art	
Mood of the poem "The clustering clouds . . ."	Mood of the poem "When I went to visit . . ."
Mood of the picture I located:	Mood of the picture I located:
How the picture creates the mood:	How the picture creates the mood:
Picture source:	Picture source:

Poetry Collection 2

Summaries "One cannot ask loneliness . . ." reflects on loneliness. The speaker in "Was it that I went to sleep . . ." longs for a loved one who appears in a dream. The speaker in "The Waking" suggests that waking up to life is a gradual, unplanned process. The poet of "Sonnet 18" speaks of the power of poetry to immortalize a loved one.

Reading/Writing Connection

Complete this paragraph about the value of thinking through something on your own.

When people <u>evaluate</u> their lives, _____.

They <u>assess</u> _____. They <u>restore</u> their sense

_____.

Note-taking Guide

Use this chart to record the thoughts and feelings you find in each poem.

Title of Poem	Speaker's Thoughts	Speaker's Feelings
One cannot ask loneliness . . .	Speaker is thinking about loneliness	lonely
Was it that I went to sleep . . .		
The Waking		
Sonnet 18		

APPLY THE SKILLS

Poetry Collection 2

1. **Respond:** Which poem made the greatest impact on you? Why?

_____

_____

_____

2. **Infer:** In "Was it that I went to sleep . . .," what do the speaker's comments reveal about her feelings for the man?

_____

_____

3. **Literary Strategy:** Fill in the chart below to analyze the meaning of the three **quatrains** and the **couplet** in the **sonnet** Sonnet 18.

Message of Quatrain 1	Connection: Quatrains 1 and 2	Connection: Quatrains 2 and 3	Connection: Couplet to Quatrains

4. **Reading Skill:** By **previewing** the first four lines of Sonnet 18, what information about vocabulary and sentence structure can the reader learn?

_____

_____

SUPPORT FOR WRITING AND EXTEND YOUR LEARNING

Writing: Tanka

Write your own **tanka**. Follow the traditional Japanese form.

- Many Japanese poems are about nature or love. Find a natural scene or favorite object to observe for your tanka.

  _____

- How does the subject make you feel? Think of two descriptive terms.

  _____

  _____

- Use your descriptive terms in one short sentence to express a mood or emotion.

  _____

Listening and Speaking: Poetry Reading Discussion

Hold a **poetry reading discussion** on a recording of Shakespeare's Sonnet 18. Use the following questions to prepare for your discussion.

- How did you feel about the sonnet before listening to the recording?

  _____

  _____

- How did you feel about the sonnet after listening to the recording?

  _____

  _____

- Did the recording add to your appreciation of the sonnet? Explain.

  _____

  _____

Research Sources

ABOUT RESEARCH SOURCES

A **research source** is a text that gives reliable information about a subject. Some examples of research sources include encyclopedias, articles, and databases. These research sources usually have text aids that make it easier for readers to find the information they need. Some text aids are called "navigational" aids. Navigational aids include:

- an index
- a table of contents
- entries listed in alphabetical order
- a search engine (for Web sources)

Research sources also use formatting aids to help you find important information. These aids include boldface headings and color-coded features.

READING SKILL

To find information quickly in a research source, you should **preview the text**. Follow these steps to preview the text:

1. **Skim** the text. Quickly read through the table of contents, introduction, and conclusion.

2. **Scan** the source. Look over boldface headings and other main elements.

3. Notice the **text structure** as you skim and scan. The text structure is the pattern of organization in the source. (Common text structures are shown in the chart.)

4. Find sections in the source that are likely to contain the information you need.

Common Text Structures
Sequence, or **chronological order**—giving information about events in the order of their occurence
Spatial order—giving information about different things according to their location
Order of importance—organizing ideas in a logical progression: for example, discussing a whole and then its parts
Comparison-and-contrast—organizing ideas according to the ways they are similar and different

The History of the Guitar
Thomas A. Hill

When we attempt to pinpoint the origins of deliberately produced, carefully designed instruments, we run into problems, because the very first instrument makers were not very concerned with posterity. They did not leave written records. One approach we might try, in an effort to find out where the guitar came from, would be an examination of languages.

Ancient Beginnings

The ancient Assyrians,[1] four thousand years ago, had an instrument that they called a *chetarah.* We know little more about it other than that it was a stringed instrument with a sound-box, but the name is intriguing. The ancient Hebrews had their *kinnura,* the Chaldeans[2] their *qitra,* and the Greeks their *cithara* and *citharis*—which Greek writers of the day were careful to emphasize were *not* the same instrument. It is with the Greeks, in fact, that the first clear history of the evolution of an instrument begins; some of this history can again be traced with purely linguistic devices. The cithara and citharis were members of a family of musical instruments called *fides*—a word that is ancient Greek for "strings." From the *fides* family it is easy to draw lines to the medieval French *vielle,* the German *fiedel,* the English *fithele* or *fiddle,* and the *vihuela,* national instrument of medieval Spain. Significantly, much of the music for the vihuela (of which a great deal survives to the present day) can easily be transcribed[3] for the guitar.

In England, the influences of the cithara and citharis led to the evolution of such instruments as the *cither, zither, cittern,* and *gittern,* with which instrument the linguistic parallel we seek is fairly easy to draw. Gitterns dating back to 1330 can be seen in the British Museum. In Spain, there is music for the vihuela that dates back at least that far.

What did these instruments look like? Superficially, they bore a substantial resemblance to the guitar as we know it today, although the

---

1. **Assyrians** (ə sir´ ē ənz) founders of an ancient empire in the Middle East, flourishing in the seventh century B.C.
2. **Chaldeans** (kal dē´ ənz) a people that rose to power in Babylon, an ancient empire of the Middle East, during the sixth century B.C.
3. **transcribed** (tran skrībd´) *v.* adapted a piece of music for an instrument other than the one for which it was originally written.

sides seldom curved in as far as do the sides of the modern guitar. They were usually strung with *pairs* of strings, or *courses,* much like a modern twelve-string guitar. The two strings of each course were tuned either in unison or an octave[4] apart. For a while, there seemed to be no standard for the number of courses an instrument should have; there are both vihuelas and gitterns with as few as four courses and as many as seven. By the fifteenth century, the vihuela seems to have settled on six as the standard number of courses. . . . In England, the gittern settled down to four courses. . . . Historians of this period do note the existence in Spain of an instrument called the *guitarra*. . . . But no music was being written for this instrument, and nobody seems to have been paying much attention to it.

The African Link

Meanwhile, in Africa, the Arabs had been playing an instrument that they called *al-ud,* or "the wood," for centuries. When the Moors crossed the Straits of Gibraltar[5] in the twelfth century to conquer Spain, they brought this instrument with them. It quickly became popular, and by the time anybody who spoke English was talking about it, al-ud had become *lute.* The lute's main contribution to the evolution of the guitar as we know

it today seems to have been the fret, a metal bar on the finger-board. Until the arrival of the lute, the European forerunners of the guitar had no frets at all. Since the fret made it a little easier to play the same tune the same way more than once, and helped to standardize tunings, it was a resounding success. The first Arabic lutes in Europe had movable frets, tied to the neck, usually about eight in number. Consequently, the first vihuelas to which frets were added also had movable ones.

The lute—or rather the people who brought it to Europe—made another important contribution. The Moorish artistic influence, blowing the cobwebs away from stodgy Spanish art and society, created an artistic climate that encouraged music to flourish. And so the instruments on which the music was played flourished as well, and continued to evolve and improve. This is a contribution that cannot be overestimated.

If any general lines can be drawn, perhaps it can be said that descendants of the original al-ud, crossing the Straits of Gibraltar, collided in Spain with the descendants of the Greek cithara and citharis. Sprinkled with a little bit of gittern influence from England, the result led ultimately to what we know today as the guitar.

---

4. **unison** (yo͞on′ ə sən) . . . **octave** (äk′ tiv) A unison consists of two tones of the same pitch. An octave consists of two tones that are eight notes apart in the scale. The pitches in an octave sound "the same" and are named by the same note.

5. **Moors** (mo͞orz) . . . **Gibraltar** (ji brôl′ tər) Groups of Moors, an Arab people of North Africa, invaded Spain at various times, beginning in the eighth century A.D. The Straits of Gibraltar are waters dividing Spain from Africa.

THINKING ABOUT THE RESEARCH SOURCE

1. From which part of the world did the earliest instrument described in the essay come?

   _____

2. How does this essay show the way that one country can have a powerful influence on another?

   _____

   _____

   _____

READING SKILL

3. Skim the first and last paragraphs of this essay. What pattern of organization does this article have?

   _____

4. What pattern of organization does Hill use in the second paragraph?

   _____

TIMED WRITING: RESEARCH (20 minutes)

Write a letter to the author of this article. Complete the following steps to help you write your letter.

- Comment on "The History of the Guitar." Describe at least two things that you enjoyed about the article.

   _____

   _____

   _____

- Ask two questions that are not answered by the article.

   _____

   _____

Poetry Collection 1 • Poetry Collection 2

LITERARY ANALYSIS

Figurative language is language that is not meant to be taken literally. Poets often use the following **figures of speech**, or specific types of figurative language, to convey their ideas in fresh and innovative ways. Each of these figures of speech is a kind of **analogy**, or comparison of two things that are alike in certain respects but not in others.

- A **simile** is a comparison of unlike things using the words *like* or *as*. *Example:* He runs *like* a cheetah.

- In a **metaphor**, one thing is spoken about as if it were something else. *Example:* During the holidays, the stores *are* zoos.

- In **personification**, an object, an animal, or an idea is spoken of as if it were human. *Example:* Our cow was queen of the fair.

Because figurative language is often used to express meaning in concrete pictures, it is an important source of **imagery**, or word-pictures, in poetry.

READING SKILL

To understand a poem, **paraphrase** it, or restate the meaning of lines in your own words. Begin by **picturing the imagery**, forming clear pictures of the descriptive details in the poem. Then, consider how the lines you will paraphrase are connected with these pictures. Use a chart like the one below to paraphrase passages as you read.

Descriptive Details	What I Picture	My Paraphrase
"A snapshot in the radiant flood, / Raccoon glares, as any outlaw should. / His craft lies knotted in his paws; / His canny forest ways undo suburban laws."	a raccoon caught in the light when someone opens the back door	The raccoon freezes in the light of an open door. He is clever with his paws and can outsmart the person whose yard he is visiting.

Poetry Collection 1

Summaries In "Glory," a baseball game gives its players hope for the future. The speaker in "Metaphor" gives an optimistic view of life. The poet of "The Wind—tapped like a tired Man" gives a force of nature human qualities.

Reading/Writing Connection

Describe how an ordinary daily event can make a person's day special.

1. Events that <u>enrich</u> a person's day can include _____.

2. These events <u>create</u> a feeling of _____.

3. People <u>maximize</u> this feeling by _____.

Note-taking Guide

Use this chart to record the figures of speech you find in each poem.

Poem	Figure of Speech
Glory	"a promise / Like a hesitation pitch always / At the edge of their lives"
Metaphor	
The Wind—tapped like a tired Man	

Glory
Yusef Komunyakaa

Most were married teenagers
Working knockout shifts daybreak
To sunset six days a week—
Already old men playing ball
5   In a field between a row of shotgun houses
& the Magazine Lumber Company.
They were all Jackie Robinson
& Willie Mays, a touch of
Josh Gibson & Satchell Paige[1]
10   In each stance & swing, a promise
Like a hesitation pitch always
At the edge of their lives,
Arms sharp as rifles.
The Sunday afternoon heat
15   Flared like thin flowered skirts
As children & wives cheered.
The men were like cats
Running backwards to snag
Pop-ups & high-flies off
20   Fences, stealing each other's glory.
The old deacons & raconteurs[2]
Who umpired made an *Out* or *Safe*
Into a song & dance routine.
Runners hit the dirt
25   & slid into homeplate,
Cleats catching light,
As they conjured escapes, outfoxing
Double plays. In the few seconds
It took a man to eye a woman
30   Upon the makeshift bleachers,
A stolen base or homerun
Would help another man
Survive the new week.

TAKE NOTES

Activate Prior Knowledge

This poem is about hope. What purpose does hope serve in your life? Explain.

_____

_____

Literary Analysis

A **simile** compares unlike things using *like* or *as*. Read the bracketed section. Underline the simile. What does the simile tell you about the way in which the heat is rising?

_____

_____

_____

Reading Skill

To help you understand a poem, **paraphrase** it, or restate it in your own words. Paraphrase lines 24–28.

_____

_____

_____

_____

Reading Check

What does the speaker say would "help another man survive the new week"? Underline the text that tells you.

Poets often use **imagery**, or word-pictures, to express meaning in a poem. What image does the poet use to convey the idea that each morning is a new start?

_____

_____

Paraphrase "Metaphor."

_____

_____

_____

_____

_____

Compare your paraphrase of "Metaphor" with the original poem. What qualities does the poem have that your paraphrase does not?

_____

_____

_____

What happens to the sheet of paper at night? Circle the lines that tell you.

Metaphor
Eve Merriam

Morning is
a new sheet of paper
for you to write on.

Whatever you want to say,
5 all day,
until night
folds it up
and files it away.

The bright words and the dark words
10 are gone
until dawn
and a new day
to write on.

The Wind—tapped like a tired Man
Emily Dickinson

The Wind—tapped like a tired Man—
And like a Host—"Come in"
I boldly answered—entered then
My Residence within

5　A Rapid—footless Guest—
To offer whom a Chair
Were as impossible as hand
A Sofa to the Air—

No Bone had He to bind Him—
10　His Speech was like the Push
Of numerous Humming Birds at once
From a superior Bush—

His Countenance—a Billow—
His Fingers, as He passed
15　Let go a music—as of tunes
Blown tremulous in Glass—

He visited—still flitting—
Then like a timid Man
Again, He tapped—'twas flurriedly—
20　And I became alone—

Vocabulary Development: countenance (KOWN ten uhns) *n.* face;
the look of a person's face, showing his
or her nature or feelings
tremulous (TREM yoo luhs) *adj.*
trembling; quivering

Reader's Response: Which poem spoke to you most directly?
Explain.

_____

_____

_____

_____

Reading Skill

Picturing the imagery helps you
form clear pictures of the descriptive details in a poem. Describe the
image you picture when reading
the third stanza of "The Wind—
tapped like a tired Man."

_____

_____

_____

Literary Analysis

In **personification**, an object, animal, or idea is spoken of as if it
were human. Describe two examples of personification in the bracketed stanzas.

_____

_____

_____

_____

_____

_____

Reading Check

What are three ways in which the
wind is unlike any other
guest? Underline
the text that tells
you.

Poetry Collection 1

1. **Analyze Cause and Effect:** In "Glory," what does the phrase "already old men" suggest about the effect of the men's work schedule?

_____

_____

2. **Hypothesize:** In "The Wind—tapped like a tired Man," do you think the speaker sees the wind as menacing or kind? Explain.

_____

_____

3. **Literary Analysis:** Poets use **figurative language** devices to express their ideas in new ways. Use this chart to explain a **simile**, a **metaphor**, or an example of **personification** you find in one of the three poems.

Poem	Device	Explanation

5. **Reading Skill: Paraphrase** the third stanza of "The Wind—tapped like a tired Man."

_____

_____

_____

SUPPORT FOR WRITING AND EXTEND YOUR LEARNING

Writing: Critical Essay

Write a **critical essay** to explain which one of the poems in Poetry Collection 1 you found most effective.

• What does the poem communicate to you?

_____

_____

• What is your reaction to the poem?

_____

_____

• Reread the poem. Look for similes, metaphors, and personification. Explain how figurative language increases your enjoyment of the poem.

_____

_____

Listening and Speaking: Group Discussion

Hold a **group discussion** of Merriam's claim that each day is a new sheet of paper.

• Explain Merriam's metaphor in your own words.

_____

_____

• Do you find the metaphor effective? Explain.

_____

_____

• In what ways could you elaborate the metaphor?

_____

_____

Use your responses to prepare for the group discussion.

Poetry Collection 2

Summaries "Conscientious Objector" introduces a proud speaker who will not help Death. "Pride" shows how a small thing can reveal the weaknesses that people take pride in hiding. "Tell all the Truth but tell it slant—" suggests that it is not wise to tell all the truth at once.

Reading/Writing Connection

Complete this paragraph to describe how a person might overcome a limitation.

He wanted to <u>rely</u> more on his _____. The only way

to <u>adapt</u> was to _____. Over time, he <u>achieved</u>

_____.

Note-taking Guide

Use this chart to record the main topic of each poem. Explain what each poem says about its main topic.

Poem	Main Topic	Explanation
Conscientious Objector		
Pride		
Tell all the Truth, but tell it slant—		

Poetry Collection 2

1. **Extend:** What advice would the speaker in "Pride" give to someone dealing with stress or grief?

_____

_____

2. **Interpret:** What does the speaker in "Tell all the Truth, but tell it slant—" mean by the expression "tell it slant"?

_____

_____

3. **Literary Analysis:** Poets use **figurative language** devices to express their ideas in new ways. Use this chart to explain a **simile**, a **metaphor**, or an example of **personification** you find in one of the three poems.

Poem	Device	Explanation

4. **Reading Skill: Paraphrase** the last two stanzas of "Conscientious Objector."

_____

_____

_____

SUPPORT FOR WRITING AND EXTEND YOUR LEARNING

Writing: Critical Essay

Write a **critical essay** to explain which one of the poems in Poetry Collection 2 you found most effective.

• What does the poem communicate to you?

_____

_____

• What is your reaction to the poem?

_____

• Reread the poem. Look for similes, metaphors, and personification. Explain how figurative language increases your enjoyment of the poem.

_____

_____

Research and Technology: Literary History Report

Write and present a brief **literary history report** on Edna St. Vincent Millay's career.

• *Literary criticism* is an expert's judgment about a writer's work. Find two sources of literary criticism about Millay's work. Use a positive and a negative evaluation of Millay's work in your report.

_____

_____

• Reliable books or articles do not contain bias and do not confuse opinion with fact. List two reliable books or encyclopedia articles.

_____

_____

• Reliable Web sites show what sources the authors of the sites used for information. List two reliable Web sites.

_____

_____

Use these sources to help you write your report.

Poetry Collection 1 • Poetry Collection 2

LITERARY ANALYSIS

To spark the music in words, poets use a variety of **sound devices**, or patterns of word-sounds. These include the following:

- **Alliteration:** repetition of consonant sounds at the beginnings of nearby words, as in *"silent song"*
- **Assonance:** repetition of vowel sounds in nearby stressed syllables, as in *"deep* and *dream'* less." Unlike rhyming syllables, assonant syllables end in different consonants.
- **Consonance:** repetition of consonant sounds at the ends of nearby stressed syllables with different vowel sounds, as in *"heat* of l*ight'* ning"
- **Onomatopoeia:** use of words to imitate actual sounds, such as *buzz, tap,* or *splash*

Sound devices can add to the mood of a poem, imitate the sounds of events, or reflect or emphasize a poem's meaning. As you read, note how poets use sound devices to create a mood or emphasize their ideas.

READING SKILL

To help you understand poetry, **paraphrase** poems, restating the ideas in your own words. First, **break down long sentences** into parts. Identify the main actions and who or what performs them. Identify details that show when, where, how, or why each action is performed. As you read, use a chart like this one to break down sentences.

Breaking Down Long Sentences to Paraphrase
"When fighting for his country, he lost an arm and was suddenly afraid: 'From now on, I shall only be able to do things by halves. . . .'" from "A Man," by Nina Cassian
Who? he **Did what?** lost an arm, was suddenly afraid
Paraphrase: He lost his arm fighting in a war and was afraid of what his life would be like.

Poetry Collection 1

Summaries The speaker of "The Weary Blues" uses vivid words to describe the blues. "In Flanders Fields" encourages the living to think about what they owe the dead. Language mirrors the rhythm of jazz in "Jazz Fantasia."

Reading/Writing Connection

Complete this paragraph to describe your favorite type of music.

One album by _____ captures _____. The best songs on the album <u>demonstrate</u> _____. After listening to this album, people can <u>appreciate</u> _____.

Note-taking Guide

Use this chart to identify sound devices used in each poem.

Poem	Alliteration	Assonance	Consonance	Onomatopoeia
The Weary Blues	"poor piano"	"lazy sway"	"Rocking back"	"thump"
In Flanders Fields				
Jazz Fantasia				

The Weary Blues
Langston Hughes

Droning a drowsy syncopated[1] tune,
Rocking back and forth to a mellow croon,
    I heard a Negro play.
Down on Lenox Avenue[2] the other night
5 By the pale dull <u>pallor</u> of an old gas light
    He did a lazy sway. . . .
    He did a lazy sway. . . .
To the tune o' those Weary Blues.
With his <u>ebony</u> hands on each ivory key
10 He made that poor piano moan with melody.
    O Blues!
Swaying to and fro on his rickety stool
He played that sad raggy tune like a musical fool.
    Sweet Blues!
15 Coming from a black man's soul.
    O Blues!
In a deep song voice with a <u>melancholy</u> tone
I heard that Negro sing, that old piano moan—
    "Ain't got nobody in all this world,
20   Ain't got nobody but ma self.
    I's gwine to quit ma frownin'
    And put ma troubles on the shelf."
Thump, thump, thump, went his foot on the floor.
He played a few chords then he sang some more—
25   "I got the Weary Blues
    And I can't be satisfied.
    Got the Weary Blues
    And can't be satisfied—
    I ain't happy no mo'
30   And I wish that I had died."
And far into the night he crooned that tune.
The stars went out and so did the moon.
The singer stopped playing and went to bed
While the Weary Blues echoed through his head.
35 He slept like a rock or a man that's dead.

Vocabulary Development: pallor (PAL er) *n.* lack of color; paleness
ebony (EB uh nee) *adj.* black
melancholy (MEL uhn kahl ee) *adj.* sad;
gloomy

---

1. **syncopated** (SING kuh payt id) *adj.* with a catchy or emphatic rhythm created by
accenting beats that are usually unaccented.
2. **Lenox Avenue** street in Harlem, a historic African American neighborhood in New
York City.

TAKE NOTES

Activate Prior Knowledge

Is music an important part of your life? Explain.

_____

_____

_____

_____

Reading Skill

Breaking down long sentences can help you understand poetry. Read the bracketed passage. What are the main actions described in the passage?

_____

_____

Who is completing the actions?

_____

_____

Literary Analysis

Onomatopoeia is the use of words to imitate actual sounds. Why is "thump, thump, thump" an example of onomatopoeia?

_____

_____

Reading Check

What adjectives does Hughes use to describe the music? Circle them in the text.

TAKE NOTES

Reading Skill

To **paraphrase** means to restate something in your own words. Paraphrase the underlined text.

_____

_____

_____

_____

Literary Analysis

Alliteration is the repetition of consonant sounds at the beginnings of nearby words. Identify examples of alliteration in "In Flanders Fields."

_____

_____

_____

_____

Stop to Reflect

What does the use of alliteration add to this poem?

_____

_____

_____

_____

Reading Check

Who is speaking in this poem? Underline the sentence that tells you.

In Flanders Fields
John McCrae

Background
The devastation of the First World War (1914–1918) brought forth a sad beauty. In the torn-up battlegrounds of Flanders, a region of Belgium, thousands of poppies sprang up, flourishing in the fields cleared by war. McCrae turned these flowers into a symbol that generations have worn to honor the dead.

In Flanders fields the poppies blow
Between the crosses, row on row,
   That mark our place; and in the sky
   The larks, still bravely singing, fly
5 Scarce heard amid the guns below.

    We are the Dead. Short days ago
    We lived, felt dawn, saw sunset glow,
      Loved and were loved, and now we lie
      In Flanders fields.

10 Take up our quarrel with the foe:
    To you from failing hands we throw
      The torch; be yours to hold it high.
      If ye break faith with us who die
15 We shall not sleep, though poppies grow
      In Flanders fields.

Jazz Fantasia
Carl Sandburg

Drum on your drums, batter on your banjoes,
sob on the long cool winding saxophones.
Go to it, O jazzmen.

Sling your knuckles on the bottoms of the happy
5 tin pans, let your trombones ooze, and go husha-
husha-hush with the slippery sand-paper.

Moan like an autumn wind high in the lonesome
    treetops,
moan soft like you wanted somebody terrible,
    cry like a
racing car slipping away from a motorcycle cop,
10 bang-bang! you jazzmen, bang altogether drums,
    traps,
banjoes, horns, tin cans—make two people fight
    on the
top of a stairway and scratch each other's eyes in a
clinch[1] tumbling down the stairs.

Can[2] the rough stuff . . . now a Mississippi
    steamboat
15 pushes up the night river with a hoo-hoo-
    hoo-oo . . . and
the green lanterns calling to the high soft stars . . .
    a red
moon rides on the humps of the low river hills . . .
    go to it,
O jazzmen.

---

1. **clinch** *n.* in boxing, the act of gripping the opponent's body with the arms.
2. **Can** *v.* slang for "stop" or "cease."

Reader's Response: Which poem affected you most strongly?
Explain.

_____

_____

_____

_____

Literary Analysis

Assonance is the repetition of vowel sounds in nearby stressed syllables. Circle the example of assonance in the bracketed passage.

Reading Skill

When you **paraphrase** a poem, you restate its ideas in your own words. Paraphrase the third stanza of "Jazz Fantasia."

_____

_____

_____

How does this paraphrase help you understand the poem?

_____

_____

Reading Check

To whom is the speaker talking? Circle the words that tell you.

Poetry Collection 1

1. **Contrast:** Explain the contrasts in the first stanza of "In Flanders Fields" and the contrasts in the second stanza.

_____

_____

2. **Draw Conclusions:** What do the changing moods in "Jazz Fantasia" suggest about the power of jazz to capture human experience?

_____

_____

3. **Literary Analysis:** Complete the chart below. Identify examples of **sound devices** in "Jazz Fantasia" and "The Weary Blues."

Alliteration	Consonance	Assonance	Onomatopoeia

4. **Reading Skill:** Break down the sentence in the first stanza of "In Flanders Fields" by identifying the action and who or what is completing the action.

_____

_____

SUPPORT FOR WRITING AND EXTEND YOUR LEARNING

Writing: Poem

Write a **poem** about your favorite kind of music. Use sound devices to capture the sounds that you describe. Use your answers to the following questions to help you write your poem.

- What is your favorite type of music? Name two favorite songs of this type.

  _____

- What do your favorite songs have in common?

  _____

- What will your poem say about the music?

  _____

- What sound devices could express the attitude or mood of your poem?

  _____

Research and Technology: Visual Arts Presentation

Learn more about the Harlem Renaissance, a movement that Langston Hughes helped define. Choose a visual artist from the movement. Prepare a **visual arts presentation** about three of his or her works. In your presentation, compare the artwork to Hughes's poem. Fill in the chart below to help you plan. Use your notes to prepare your presentation.

Artist:	
Artwork:	
Notes on artist and works:	How works compare to Hughes's poem:
Information sources:	

Poetry Collection 2

Summaries The reader meets a sea monster that lives at the bottom of the ocean in "The Kraken." "Meeting at Night" describes two people who meet on a warm, moonlit night. Reapers are too busy to notice an injured field rat in "Reapers."

Reading/Writing Connection

Complete this paragraph to describe an "unpoetic" animal that you would not expect to appear in a poem.

_____ <u>embody</u> the idea of

_____ . They <u>display</u> _____ .

They <u>illustrate</u> _____ .

Note-taking Guide

Use this chart to record sounds used in the poems.

Title of Poem	Sounds in the Poem
The Kraken	Thunders, roaring
Meeting at Night	
Reapers	

Poetry Collection 2

1. **Infer:** In "The Kraken," what is the only thing that could cause a change in the Kraken's activity?

_____

_____

2. **Draw Conclusions:** What is the situation of the two people in "Meeting at Night"?

_____

_____

3. **Literary Analysis:** Use the chart below to identify examples of **sound devices** in "The Kraken" and "Reapers."

Alliteration	Consonance	Assonance	Onomatopoeia

4. **Reading Skill: Paraphrase** the second stanza of "Meeting at Night."

_____

_____

SUPPORT FOR WRITING AND EXTEND YOUR LEARNING

Writing: Poem

Write a **poem** that, like "The Kraken" or "Reapers," tells about a collision between nature and the world of people.

- Summarize the situation or story your poem will relate.

_____

_____

- Describe the atmosphere or mood you want your poem to have.

_____

- What words or sound devices will create that mood? List three you will use.

_____

_____

Listening and Speaking: Poetry Listening

Choose three poets whose work you would like to hear. Use the library or the Internet to find recordings of their poems. Hold a **poetry listening** with a group of classmates. Use the chart below to help you discuss what you hear.

	Title of Poem	Reactions
Poet 1:		
Poet 2:		
Poet 3:		

Feature Articles

ABOUT FEATURE ARTICLES

A **feature article** is a type of newspaper or magazine article. It gives a full description of a person, place, event, activity, or current subject of interest. Feature articles often include the following elements:

- a clear topic presented from a certain "angle," or point of view
- quotations from experts, people involved, or people who saw what happened
- photos, drawings, maps, or other graphics that give information

READING SKILL

Sometimes you will need to **take notes** on a feature article or other source. Think about ways you will present the information you gather.

- **Quoting** from a source means repeating a section of text word-for-word. Use quotation marks to set off quoted words from your own words.
- **Paraphrasing** a source means restating the ideas or information in your own words. You must give credit to the source for any paraphrased information that is not common knowledge.
- **Critiquing** a source means looking at it closely to decide whether it is a good source of information.

Review the chart for note-taking strategies.

	Note-taking Strategy	Example
Quotation	• Copy the statement word-for-word. • Clearly identify the source.	According to cultural historian Ann Douglas, be-bop music reflected "the international mix, the fluidity and speed of New York life."
Paraphrase	• Note the key facts, double-checking numbers, the spelling of names, and so on. • Clearly identify the source.	According to the most recent count, the 2000 census, New York City has a population of just over 8 million.

Feel the City's PULSE?
It's Be-bop, Man!

ANN DOUGLAS

In 1964, Thelonious Monk, one of the pioneers of be-bop and perhaps jazz's greatest composer, was asked by an interviewer to define jazz. Though Monk disliked questions and usually ignored them, this time he didn't miss a beat: "New York, man. You can feel it. It's around in the air. . . ."

Be-bop (bop for short) was sometimes labeled "New York Jazz," and it is, in fact, the only major school of jazz to which the city can lay proprietary claim. Jazz of the '20s, dominated by Louis Armstrong, originated in New Orleans, migrating to New York only after a formative detour in Chicago. Armstrong inspired '30s swing, the music of the big bands led by Benny Goodman, Artie Shaw, Glenn Miller, Count Basie and Duke Ellington, the "mother bands," as Gillespie called them, whose music the be-boppers both emulated and revolutionized. . . .

Bop's wideranging allusiveness, its quicksilver expressivity, angular dissonance and shockingly extended palette of pitches and rhythms echoed the international mix, the fluidity and speed of New York life.

Jamming After Hours

Bop began at roughly the same time as World War II, in 1940 when Monk, then 23, was hired to play with Kenny (Klook) Clarke, the man who transformed jazz drumming, at Minton's Playhouse in Harlem. Gillespie jammed with them after his regular engagement, and Parker joined them a year later. When Minton's closed for the night, they adjourned to Clark Monroe's Uptown House, an after-hours club where an extraordinary teen-age drummer named Max Roach played in the band.

The nation's entrance into the war in late 1941 imposed gas rationing, entertainment taxes and curfews, sharply restricting travel. The swing bands were touring bands, and some of them continued to tour, but now everyone was looking for a long-term base in a big city, easily accessible by public transit.

What hurt swing helped be-bop. The expense and risks of touring (especially down South) had been far greater for black musicians than for white. The cramped quarters of many city clubs suited the young bop musicians, eager to work with the small ensembles that maximized opportunities for experimentation . . . .

The word "be-bop," which both Monk and Gillespie claimed to have coined, described the music's unconventional stop-and-start form, especially Gillespie and Parker's witty eighth-note pair conclusions. The purpose of bop's irregular phrasings, side-sliding harmonies and whirlwind pace, was, in Kenny Clarke's words, to "raise the standards of musicianship," to tell people, "Whatever you go into, go into it intelligently." The be-boppers were the real New York intellectuals, the hippest, smartest men in town.

SITES OF BOP'S TRIUMPHS AND TRAGEDIES

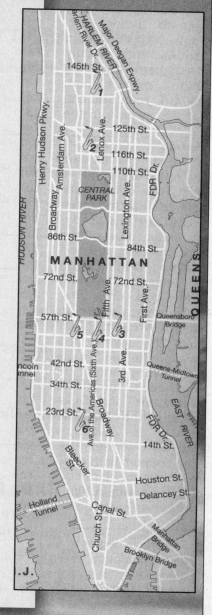

1. **Savoy Ballroom** Lenox Avenue and 140th Street, Harlem. Charlie Parker played in this legendary jazz and dance hall with the Jay McShann Orchestra in his early days in New York. . . .

2. **Minton's Playhouse** 210 West 118th Street, Morningside Heights. Charlie Christian, Kenny Clarke, Thelonious Monk, Parker and Gillespie made musical history here in the early 1940s.

3. **St. Peter's Church** 54th Street and Lexington Avenue, Manhattan (also its current site). Monk's funeral took place here on Feb. 22, 1982, with musicians playing for three hours.

4. **52nd Street** between Fifth and Sixth Avenues, known as "The Street." A magical block of jazz clubs . . . including the Onyx, Spotlite, Three Deuces and Kelly's Stable.

5. **Birdland** 1678 Broadway, at 53rd Street, Manhattan. It opened on Dec. 15, 1949, with dozens of (caged) birds on view and Charlie (Bird) Parker presiding.

6. **216 West 19th Street** Eager to become "a New York musician," Gillespie lived here with his brother, . . . when he first came to town from Philadelphia in 1937, eating for 25 cents a day.

THINKING ABOUT THE FEATURE ARTICLE

1. Name two distinctive qualities of be-bop that Douglas describes.

   _____

   _____

2. Explain how the Second World War encouraged be-bop.

   _____

   _____

   _____

READING SKILL

3. **Quote** the final sentence of Ann Douglas's article.

   _____

4. **Paraphrase** the first sentence of the second paragraph.

   _____

TIMED WRITING: PERSUASION (25–30 minutes)

Write a persuasive essay in which you explain why you agree or disagree with the quotation below.

> "Music reflects culture. It is a central means by which a group asserts its relationship to past generations, distinguishes insiders from outsiders, and addresses the future."

Complete the following steps to help you start your essay.

• Choose a position. Do you agree or disagree with the quotation?

   _____

• Choose three quotations from the article that help support your argument.

   1. _____

   2. _____

   3. _____

from Tibet Through the Red Box

Drama shares many of the characteristics of fiction. The **characters** in a play face a **conflict**. This struggle sparks a sequence of events called the **plot**. Sometimes, a drama has **parallel plots**, or two sequences of events that develop at the same time. The conflict reaches a **climax**. The climax is the point of greatest intensity before the conflict is solved in the **resolution**. Unlike fiction, however, a drama does not usually have a narrator. Instead, it is a story written to be performed by actors speaking **dialogue**. Dialogue is the characters' words.

The elements in the chart below are specific to drama. In a performance, they combine to produce the illusion of reality known as **dramatic effect**. The dramatic effect allows the playwright to explore a **theme**, or central message about life.

Elements of Drama	Definition	Example
Act	One of the main divisions of a play	Act I
Scene	The main division of an act	Act I, scene ii
Script	The text of a play; includes dialogue and stage directions	a hardcopy text of *Tibet Through the Red Box*
Stage directions	The author's notes that tell how the play is to be performed, or staged; often italicized or bracketed	*(Enter SENTRY from left.)* *(Pause. No sign from CREON.)*
Dialogue	Words the characters say	**PETER.** I read the last one.
Sets	Constructions that show where the drama takes place	painted backdrops, staircases, city sidewalks, a bedroom
Props	Movable objects that the actors use on stage	a walking stick, a water pitcher, a coat rack, a book

The ancient Greeks developed drama, making two basic types of plays. These two types are tragedy and comedy.

- A **tragedy** shows the downfall or death of the **tragic hero**, or main character. The hero is an outstanding person brought low by a **tragic flaw**. A tragic flaw is a mistaken action or a fault in character. A **chorus**, or group of performers, sings, dances, and comments on events. The hero's downfall is meant to bring about a **catharsis**. A catharsis is a calming release of tension in the audience.

    William Shakespeare's tragedies differ from Greek tragedies in several ways. In **Shakespearean tragedy**

    - The hero has greater free will, or power of choice, and reveals more of an inner life.
    - There is no formal chorus. One or more characters may comment on the action.
    - Patterns of **imagery**, or sensory language, reinforce themes.

- A **comedy** ends happily after an amusing series of problems. Tragedy stresses human greatness, but comedy emphasizes human faults and the weaknesses of society.

In addition to dialogue, dramatists use these types of **dramatic speech**:
- In a **monologue**, a character speaks at length to silent listeners.
- In a **soliloquy**, a character alone on stage reveals private thoughts.
- In an **aside**, a character briefly expresses private thoughts to the audience that other characters on stage cannot hear.

from Tibet Through the Red Box

David Henry Hwang

Summary A young boy named Peter deals with his injury and his fears. He is angry with his father. His father makes films. He has been sent to record the Chinese as they prepare to invade Tibet. Various fantasy characters help bring father and son together so that Peter understands the importance of his father's work.

Note-taking Guide

Use this sequence chart to record the events in the selection.

First Event	Next Event	Next Event	Final Event
Peter's mother brings a letter from Peter's father.			

Have you ever awakened from a dream, convinced that it was real? Tell about the dream and what made it seem as if the events in the dream had really happened.

_____

_____

_____

_____

_____

_____

_____

_____

Drama

Dialogue is the words that **characters** say. What do you learn about the character of the mother through her dialogue?

_____

_____

_____

_____

Reading Check

Where is Peter's father? Underline the text that tells you.

from Tibet Through the Red Box
David Henry Hwang

Cast of Characters

PETER A boy

ALENKA Peter's mother

THE BOY SPIRIT A guiding spirit who assumes many forms, including those of a cat and the Jingle-Bell Boy

VLADIMIR Peter's father, a filmmaker

YETI Abominable Snowman

ENSEMBLE 1 AND 2 Groups of characters who act as a chorus and serve different functions

Background

The play is set in Czechoslovakia and Tibet during the second half of the twentieth century. At that time, the Soviet Union, with Russia as its dominant state, occupied Czechoslovakia. It was also during this period that China, a rival of the Soviet Union, invaded Tibet. In Act I, the Russian government has sent Peter's father to Tibet to film preparations that the Chinese are making to invade. During his father's absence, Peter was injured while making trouble for the Russian troops. As a result, he is confined to bed. At the same time, an avalanche strands Vladimir in Tibet. Helped by various fantasy characters, including the Boy Spirit, father and son communicate through messages and dreams.

from Act II

ALENKA. (O.S.) Peter, we received another letter—from your Father!

Lights reveal ALENKA *and* PETER, *in bed. She holds the same letter that the* JINGLE-BELL BOY *pinched from* VLADIMIR.

ALENKA. All covered with a strange postmark, and these odd little stamps, and characters that can only be Chinese or maybe Japanese or—Peter, he's still alive! (*pause*)

I had to run down to the post office to sign for it, and on the way home, of course, I couldn't wait to read it. He is having the most amazing adventures. In a land so strange—lamas, castles, even an abominable snowman! Here—read it.

PETER. I read the last one.

ALENKA. What is wrong with you?

PETER. Everytime we get a letter, it's like we have a big party. If he really cares about us, how come he's not home yet?

ALENKA. You are so brave, Peter. The hardest thing of all is not knowing. Where he is, or whether he's even still—whether he's all right. You don't know how strong you are.

PETER. Does Father know?

ALENKA. Oh, I bet he does. And when he returns you'll be all better, running around like your old self.

PETER. How can I get better unless he comes home? *(Pause)* How much money does Father make?

ALENKA. Why are you—? Enough to survive, like everyone else.

PETER. How come, all of a sudden, we can afford paints?

ALENKA. I make it a <u>priority</u>, what kind of—?

PETER. Is Father a traitor?

ALENKA. Who says such a—?

PETER. It doesn't matter.

ALENKA. Do your friends talk like that? The delinquents?

PETER. Mother, they're not—

ALENKA. He was sent away by the Russians. But he had no choice!

PETER. You said he did.

ALENKA. I never said any such—

PETER. Before he left.

ALENKA. Who are you? The secret police? You tell your friends, your Father loves his country, he's a man of peace. Then send them to me—and I'll cuff them on their pointed heads!

ALENKA *exits, leaving the letter behind.* THE BOY SPIRIT *enters, as the cat.*

THE BOY SPIRIT. Meow. Spreading joy and happiness everywhere?

PETER. Want me to pull your tail?

THE BOY SPIRIT. *(re: the letter)* Oh, you got it.

PETER. But I'm not gonna read it. That'll show him.

THE BOY SPIRIT. Show him what?

PETER. He can't soften me up with, "I miss you, I love you." Not when I know the truth about him.

THE BOY SPIRIT. Does that mean you're not even curious about the Abominable Snowman?

The YETI, *an abominable snowman, enters. He is very tall.*

PETER. "Abominable snowman."

The YETI *approaches* THE BOY SPIRIT, *who flees, running around the stage.*

PETER. Who ever heard of such a stupid—?

Vocabulary Development: priority (pry AWR uh tee) *n.* something given or meriting more attention than competing alternatives

---

TAKE NOTES

Drama

A **conflict** is a struggle. How does the dialogue between Alenka and Peter show the conflict between mother and son?

_____

_____

_____

_____

Underline the text that supports your answer.

Stop to Reflect

How might the Boy Spirit be able to help Peter?

_____

_____

_____

_____

Drama

What purpose might the playwright have to introduce a mythical creature like a Yeti, or Abominable Snowman, as a **character**?

_____

How does the **dialogue** create humor in this meeting between Peter and the Yeti?

_____

_____

_____

Underline the text that supports your answer.

How would you describe the Yeti to someone who has not read the play?

_____

_____

_____

_____

How do you think this **scene** contributes to the audience's understanding of the **conflict** of the play?

_____

_____

_____

_____

_____

The YETI *is tall enough to stand eye to eye with* PETER *in his bed.*

YETI. Hello, there!

THE BOY SPIRIT. Meow meow meow!

PETER. What the—?

YETI. Could you help me?

PETER. It's the abominable snowman!

YETI. Oh my god! Where?

PETER. "Where?" You *are* the abominable snowman!

YETI. Snowmen are made of snow. This is fur. I am a Yeti. I'm trying to find a city called Prague. In a country called Chicken-slovakia. A boy, about twelve years old, who's stuck in a bed, and can't get himself out. You know anyone like that?

PETER. You've got to be kidding.

(off YETI'S *confusion)*

Boy? Twelve? Bed?

YETI. Oh! Oh! Oh! So you're Peter. When he sent me on this mission, I wasn't sure—

PETER. "He?"

YETI. I mean, to travel all the way to Europe—and, you know, no one will issue me a passport.

PETER. Who sent you?

YETI. Your Father, of course. Haven't you read his letter yet?

PETER. Why's everyone keep asking me that?

YETI. Not to be boastful or anything, but . . . a lot of it is about me. *(pause)* If you read it, I'll grant you a magical wish.

PETER. Anything?

YETI. Anything.

PETER. *(pulls out the letter)* All right . . . sucker. *(reads:)* "I was crossing a mountain pass when suddenly—"

Paper cutouts of snowflakes are projected onto the U.S. wall, moving. MUSICIANS *enter with percussion, simulating the sounds of a snowstorm. U.S.,* VLADIMIR *enters, fighting his way against a blizzard.*

VLADIMIR. "A snowstorm took me by surprise. I was looking for shelter, but the winds and snow pushed me to the ground."

U.S., VLADIMIR *is forced to the ground. He sits in a cross-legged meditation position for the rest of the scene.*

VLADIMIR. "I probably lost consciousness, but have some vague memory—like a dream—"

PETER. "Of being lifted up—" Hey!

The YETI *mimes lifting* PETER, *as he flies out of his bed.*

VLADIMIR. "Lifted up and carried!"

PETER *flies across the stage, with the* YETI *beneath, "carrying" him. Together, they move O.S.*

PETER. *(to* YETI.*)* What are you doing?

YETI. Welcome to the Land of Magic.

YETI *releases* PETER. *He finds he can stand on his own two legs.*

VLADIMIR. I awoke in a dark cave, on a bed of leaves. Beside me was a potion of honey and herbs. I drank this potion, and soon my strength began to return.

The projections of snowflakes become silhouettes of YETIS, *moving across the stage.*

VLADIMIR. One day, I finally felt well-enough to <u>venture</u> out of my dark cave.

PETER *re-enters (having detached his wires), carried by the* YETI. DANCERS *enter in Yeti-like costumes, begin to move through a series of warm-up rituals resembling Tai Chi.*

VLADIMIR. After my eyes had adjusted to the light, I could see giant fairy beings moving gently in a kind of slow motion throughout the valley.

YETI *starts to put* PETER *down amidst the* DANCERS.

VLADIMIR. They seemed to be working, gathering, tending to young ones, playing in the streams and waterfalls. Was this a lost civilization? I did not know. I crawled back into the cave, but this time I managed not to fall asleep. And I saw . . .

One of the YETIS *places food before* VLADIMIR.

VLADIMIR. Slowly, these gentle giants nursed me to recovery.

The DANCERS *begin to assume the almost martial exercises lamas perform when practicing their theological dialectics.*

PETER. *(to* YETI.*)* What are they doing now?

YETI. Practicing for battle.

PETER. How tough are you guys, anyway?

YETI. Look at us—we're big, we're strong, and we love to work out.

PETER. And you've got big teeth.

YETI. With excellent gums.

PETER. Ok, I order you to help me fight the Russians. This is gonna be a heck of a lot better than stealing their lunches.

YETI. Wait a second.

Vocabulary Development: venture (VEN cher) *v.* to do or go at some risk

---

from Tibet Through the Red Box **321**

TAKE NOTES

Drama

Stage directions show how the play should be performed. How does the playwright stage the scene when Peter finally reads the letter? Underline the stage directions that tell you. Why do you think the playwright decided to stage the scene this way?

_____

_____

Stop to Reflect

How are Vladimir's impressions of the Yeti different from other characters' impressions?

_____

_____

_____

_____

Reading Check

Where does the Yeti carry Peter? Underline the text that tells you.

A **chorus**, or ensemble, is a group of performers that comments on the event. What role does the ensemble play in this drama?

_____

_____

Why might playwrights use the repetition of a musical theme?

_____

_____

_____

What is happening in the bracketed passage? Underline clues in the text that tell you. What does this reveal about the **characters** of the play?

_____

_____

_____

Where are the Yetis and Peter doing battle? Underline the text that tells you.

PETER. You promised, remember? Want the whole world to learn Yetis are big liars?

YETI. *(to other* YETIS.*)* Guys, we're being called to battle!

ENSEMBLE 1. Battle?

PETER. We're gonna get the Russians.

ENSEMBLE 2. The who?

YETI. I . . . granted the boy a wish.

ENSEMBLE 2. Oh. Great.

YETI. It's a long story, but a wish is a wish!

ENSEMBLE 1. Where are we going?

PETER. Prague. Czechoslovakia.

ENSEMBLE 2. Is the food any good?

MUSICIANS *reprise the drumbeat which underscored the attack on the Russians in Act One.*

PETER. All right. Let's go back to when everything went wrong. I threw the rock at the Russian soldier, then he followed me into the dead-end alley.

ENSEMBLE 1, ENSEMBLE 2, *and the* YETI *criss-cross the stage, recalling the sequence in Act I.*

PETER. This time he's in for a surprise!

THE BOY SPIRIT *enters, dressed as a Russian soldier.*

PETER. And here comes the Rooskie!

THE BOY SPIRIT. Nyet! Nyet!

PETER. I climb up the wall—the exit's blocked!

THE BOY SPIRIT. *(bad Russian accent)* Stop, you stupid kid-ski!

PETER. He sees me!

THE BOY SPIRIT. I say, stop!

PETER. Only this time, I don't even try to escape.

THE BOY SPIRIT. Nyet! We have you cornered!

PETER. I just stand there, spitting down at them.

THE BOY SPIRIT. I never again will lose another lunch to you!

PETER. Doing my little victory dance.

THE BOY SPIRIT. That's disgusting! Come down—else, I shoot!

PETER. Suddenly, out of nowhere—

THE BOY SPIRIT. One, two—

PETER. The Yeti cavalry appears!

Vocabulary Development: reprise (ri PRYZ) *v.* repeat a song, or part of a song, performed earlier

THE BOY SPIRIT. What?

YETIS rush THE BOY SPIRIT.

YETIS. Roar!

THE BOY SPIRIT. Oh my god-ski!

PETER. He's so scared, he can't even move!

THE BOY SPIRIT. The Abominable Snowman?

YETI. We're Yeti, why does everyone get that wrong?

PETER. Tries to use his gun—

THE BOY SPIRIT. N-n-nice snowman . . .

PETER. —but his hands are shaking.

YETIS. Roar!

THE BOY SPIRIT. Bang, bang-ski!

YETI. Bullets can't go through our fur.

THE BOY SPIRIT. Mama!

ENSEMBLE 2. They only make us angrier!

YETIS. Roar, roar!

YETIS duplicate their martial exercises, which buffet the "SOLDIER" without actually touching him.

PETER. They close in, clutching their paws around the soldier's throat—

YETIS mime the action, as the "SOLDIER" falls, clutching his throat.

THE BOY SPIRIT. Aaaargh!

PETER. He falls to his knees—

THE BOY SPIRIT. *(choking)* Please, please spare me—

PETER. I see fear in his eyes—

THE BOY SPIRIT. You don't understand—I didn't want to come here—

PETER. *(to YETIS)* Well hurry up? Aren't you supposed to— you know—?

YETI. We're waiting for your command.

PETER. Me?

ENSEMBLE 2. After all, this is *your* wish.

ENSEMBLE 1. We're waiting.

THE BOY SPIRIT. I have wife and a son . . . just like you.

PETER. No you don't. You're nothing like me. You're a monster.

YETI. Actually, *we're* the monsters here.

PETER. *(to YETI.)* Shut up! *(to THE BOY SPIRIT.)* I mean you're not a human being.

THE BOY SPIRIT. In my back pocket . . .

PETER. Not a real one anyway.

THE BOY SPIRIT. A letter . . .

A **theme** is a central message about life. What do you think is the theme of this selection?

_____

_____

_____

_____

_____

Drama

Props are movable objects used on stage. What role does the red box play?

_____

_____

_____

Reading Check

What does Alenka show Peter? Underline the text that tells you.

PETER. You're . . . you're . . .

THE BOY SPIRIT. Send it to my son.

YETI. Hey, um, Peter, it's hard to hold this position.

ENSEMBLE 2. Yeah, so will you make up your mind?

PETER *screams in frustration.*

PETER. All right, let him go.

YETIS *release* THE BOY SPIRIT.

THE BOY SPIRIT. Thank you, thank you for showing mercy.

PETER. Get out of here. Before I change my mind.

THE BOY SPIRIT. I will remember you always.

PETER. *(to* YETIS.*)* All of you!

YETI. But your wish . . .

PETER. I don't want any wishes, I'm sick of magic, of Tibet, of this whole stupid business!

(he flies back into his bed)

Everyone just leave me alone.

All exit.

ALENKA. *(O.S.)* Peter? I have something to show you.

ALENKA *enters, carrying a beautifully lacquered red box.*

ALENKA. Isn't it beautiful?

PETER. Where'd you get this?

ALENKA. I made it—with my own two hands. You think your old mother can only cook and clean and nag? *(pause)*

I thought you might like a box—to store your paintings in.

PETER. What makes you think I'm painting?

ALENKA. Oh, I know you're not. But maybe you will someday. So I am giving you this beautiful red box . . . for all the paintings you have never made.

ALENKA *exits.*

Reader's Response: Has your reading of this act made you want to read the rest of the play? Explain your reasons.

_____

_____

_____

_____

Drama

1. **Infer:** What accusations have some of Peter's friends made against Vladimir, Peter's father? Explain how you know.

_____

_____

2. **Analyze:** In what ways do the fantasy characters help Peter connect with his father?

_____

_____

3. **Drama:** In the chart below, list the **conflicts** Peter experiences in this drama. Then, note **dialogue** and **stage directions** that the playwright uses to dramatize each conflict. Finally, analyze the effects that the playwright produces in each conflict.

Peter's Conflicts	Stage Direction/Dialogue	What It Shows

4. **Drama:** In addition to Peter, which **character** is most important in this excerpt of the play? Explain your choice, using examples from the play.

_____

_____

_____

RESEARCH THE AUTHOR

Poster

Make a **poster** to advertise a speaking appearance at your school by David Henry Hwang. The suggestions in the following bullets will help you find material for your poster.

- Do some Internet research about other works by David Henry Hwang. Write the names of several works that you want to include on the poster.

  _____

  _____

- Do some Internet research to find critics' reviews of Hwang's plays. Write several quotations from critics that you want to use on your poster.

  _____

  _____

- Review your research notes, and decide what major points you want to make about David Henry Hwang. List the major points:

  _____

  _____

  _____

- Watch the video interview with David Henry Hwang. Use it to answer these questions.

  1. What did you learn about David Henry Hwang's life that may explain his literary work?

     _____

     _____

  2. What information about Hwang may interest people in attending his speaking engagement at your school?

     _____

     _____

Antigone, Prologue through Scene 2

LITERARY ANALYSIS

Greek tragedies, like many other plays and stories, typically feature a **protagonist**, or a main character, and an **antagonist**, the character who is in conflict with the protagonist. These two terms were first applied to Greek tragedies such as *Antigone*.

READING SKILL

A **summary** is a short statement of the main ideas and events in a work.

- To summarize, pause occasionally to **retell** what you have read, using only the most important information.
- Summarizing improves your understanding of a literary work because it leads you to identify the key elements of the work.

As you read *Antigone*, pause to summarize scenes and conversations. Use this chart to identify the key elements.

Who is the most important character?
What does the character want?
Who or what gets in the character's way?
What is the outcome?

Antigone, Prologue through Scene 2

Sophocles

Summary Eteocles and Polyneices are brothers. The two brothers fight and kill each other in battle. Their uncle, Creon, becomes king. He forbids anyone to bury Polyneices, but Antigone, Polyneices' sister, buries him. In Scene 1, Creon finds out that someone has buried Polyneices.

Reading/Writing Connection

Complete each sentence to explain why you should or should not try to compromise with someone who disagrees with you.

1. When people compromise with someone, they <u>display</u> _____.

2. A compromise will usually <u>benefit</u> _____.

3. To compromise, people must <u>abandon</u> _____.

Note-taking Guide

Use this chart to record details about Creon's speech to the chorus.

What does Creon think is more important—public welfare or private friendship?
Why does Creon think that Eteocles should be buried?
Why does Creon think that Polyneices should not be buried?

Antigone

Sophocles
Translated by Dudley Fitts and Robert Fitzgerald

Persons Represented

ANTIGONE (an TIG uh nee), daughter of Oedipus, former King of Thebes

ISMENE (is MEE nee), another daughter of Oedipus

EURYDICE (yoo RID i see), wife of Creon

CREON (kree AHN), King of Thebes, uncle of Antigone and Ismene

HAIMON (HY muhn), Creon's son, engaged to Antigone

TEIRESIAS (ty REE see uhs), a blind prophet

A SENTRY

A MESSENGER

CHORUS

CHORAGOS (koh RAY guhs), leader of the chorus

A BOY who leads Teiresias

GUARDS

SERVANTS

> *In the Prologue, Antigone announces that she will bury her brother Polyneices. Antigone believes that it is her duty to bury him. She explains that she is following the laws of the gods. Her sister Ismene tries to convince Antigone not to bury Polyneices. Ismene does not want Antigone to disobey Creon's law. Creon passed a law against burying Polyneices. Ismene fears that Antigone could be put to death. Antigone refuses to listen to Ismene. She says that the laws of the gods are more important than the laws of humans. She leaves to bury their brother.*

Scene 1

    CHORAGOS. But now at last our new King is coming:
        Creon of Thebes, Menoikeus'[1] son.
        In this auspicious dawn of his reign
        What are the new complexities
5   That shifting Fate has woven for him?
        What is his counsel? Why has he summoned
        The old men to hear him?

    (Enter CREON *from the Palace, center. He addresses the* CHORUS *from the top step.)*

    CREON. Gentlemen: I have the honor to inform you that our
        Ship of State, which recent storms have threatened to
10   destroy, has come safely to harbor at last, guided by the merciful

---

1. **Menoikeus'** (me NOI kee us)

TAKE NOTES

Activate Prior Knowledge

Think about a strong belief that you have. Would you go against your belief to make someone else happy? Explain.

_____

_____

Literary Analysis

The **protagonist** is the main character of a literary work. The **antagonist** is in conflict with the protagonist. Read the bracketed paragraph. Who do you think is the protagonist of this play? Why?

_____

_____

Who do you think is the antagonist? Why?

_____

_____

Reading Skill

What reason does Antigone give for defying the law and burying her brother? Underline the answer. What laws does Antigone believe she must follow?

_____

_____

Note: The speeches of most characters in *Antigone* are written as poetry with clear line breaks. Creon's speeches are in paragraph form. His words in the Reader's Notebook have been set so that the line numbers match those in the student edition.

A **summary** is a short statement that gives the main ideas and events of a work. Summarize the main points of Creon's speech.

_____

_____

_____

_____

_____

_____

Stop to Reflect

Do you think Creon is a strong ruler? Explain.

_____

_____

_____

_____

_____

Reading Check

What does Creon think is more important than private friend- ship? Circle the text that tells you.

wisdom of Heaven. I have summoned you here this morning because I know that I can depend upon
   you: your
devotion to King Laïos was absolute; you never
   hesitated in
your duty to our late ruler Oedipus; and when
   Oedipus died,

15 your loyalty was transferred to his children.
   Unfortunately,
as you know, his two sons, the princes Eteocles and
Polyneices, have killed each other in battle; and I, as
the next in blood, have succeeded to the full power of
the throne.

20 I am aware, of course, that no Ruler can expect
   complete
loyalty from his subjects until he has been tested in
office. Nevertheless, I say to you at the very outset
   that I have nothing but contempt for the kind of
Governor who is afraid, for whatever reason, to follow

25 the course that he knows is best for the State; and
   as for
the man who sets private friendship above the public
welfare,—I have no use for him, either. I call God to
witness that if I saw my country headed for ruin, I
should not be afraid to speak out plainly; and I need

30 hardly remind you that I would never have any
   dealings
with an enemy of the people. No one values
   friendship more
highly than I; but we must remember that friends
   made at
the risk of wrecking our Ship are not real friends
   at all.
These are my principles, at any rate, and that is why I

35 have made the following decision concerning the
   sons of
Oedipus: Eteocles, who died as a man should die,
fighting for his country, is to be buried with full
   military
honors, with all the ceremony that is usual when
   the greatest
heroes die; but his brother Polyneices, who broke his

40 exile to come back with fire and sword against his
   native
city and the shrines of his fathers' gods, whose one
   idea
was to spill the blood of his blood and sell his own
   people
into slavery—Polyneices, I say, is to have no burial:
   no man
is to touch him or say the least prayer for him; he
   shall lie

45 on the plain, unburied; and the birds and the scavenging

    dogs can do with him whatever they like.

    This is my command, and you can see the wisdom behind it. <u>As</u>

    <u>long as I am King, no traitor is going to be honored with</u>

    <u>the loyal man. But whoever shows by word and deed that</u>

50 <u>he is on the side of the State,—he shall have my respect</u>

    <u>while he is living, and my reverence when he is dead.</u>

CHORAGOS. If that is your will, Creon son of Menoikeus,

    You have the right to enforce it: we are yours.

55 **CREON.** That is my will. Take care that you do your part.

CHORAGOS. We are old men: let the younger ones carry it out.

CREON. I do not mean that: the sentries have been appointed.

CHORAGOS. Then what is it that you would have us do?

CREON. You will give no support to whoever breaks this law.

60 **CHORAGOS.** Only a crazy man is in love with death!

CREON. And death it is; yet money talks, and the wisest

    Have sometimes been known to count a few coins too many.

(Enter SENTRY *from left.)*

SENTRY. I'll not say that I'm out of breath from running, King,

    because every time I stopped to think about what I have to

65 tell you, I felt like going back. And all the time a voice kept

    saying, "You fool, don't you know you're walking straight into

    trouble?"; and then another voice: "Yes, but if you let somebody

    else get the news to Creon first, it will be even worse than

    that for you!" But good sense won out, at least I hope it was

70 good sense, and here I am with a story that makes no sense

TAKE NOTES

Reading Skill

Read the underlined text. **Summarize** Creon's reason for not burying Polyneices.

_____

_____

_____

_____

Literary Analysis

How does the bracketed passage build the conflict between the **protagonist** and **antagonist**?

_____

_____

_____

_____

Reading Check

What would Creon have Choragos do? Draw a box around the answer.

Summarize how Polyneices was buried.

_____

_____

_____

_____

Why do you think Polyneices is so lightly buried?

_____

_____

_____

_____

Why is the sentry afraid to give Creon the news? Underline the answer.

at all; but I'll tell it anyhow, because, as they say, what's
going to happen's going to happen, and—

CREON. Come to the point. What have you to say?

SENTRY. I did not do it. I did not see who did it. You must not
75 punish me for what someone else has done.

CREON. A comprehensive defense! More effective, perhaps,
If I knew its purpose. Come: what is it?

SENTRY. A dreadful thing . . . I don't know how to put it—

CREON. Out with it!

80 **SENTRY.**   Well, then;
The dead man—
          Polyneices—

(Pause. The SENTRY *is overcome, fumbles for words.* CREON *waits impassively.)*
               out there—
                  someone,—
New dust on the slimy flesh!

(Pause. No sign from CREON.*)*
Someone has given it burial that way, and
85 Gone . . .

(Long pause. CREON *finally speaks with deadly control.)*

CREON. And the man who dared do this?

SENTRY.   I swear I
Do not know! You must believe me!
                  Listen:
90 The ground was dry, not a sign of digging, no,
Not a wheeltrack in the dust, no trace of anyone.
It was when they relieved us this morning: and one of them,
The corporal, pointed to it.
               There it was,
95 The strangest—
          Look:
The body, just mounded over with light dust: you see?
Not buried really, but as if they'd covered it
Just enough for the ghost's peace. And no sign
100 Of dogs or any wild animal that had been there.
And then what a scene there was! Every man of us
Accusing the other: we all proved the other man did it,

We all had proof that we could not have done it.
We were ready to take hot iron in our hands,
105 Walk through fire, swear by all the gods,
It was not I! I do not know who it was, but it was not I!

(CREON's *rage has been mounting steadily, but the*
SENTRY *is too intent upon his story to notice it.*)

And then, when this came to nothing, someone said
A thing that silenced us and made us stare
110 Down at the ground: you had to be told the news,
And one of us had to do it! We threw the dice,
And the bad luck fell to me. So here I am,
No happier to be here than you are to have me:
Nobody likes the man who brings bad news.

115 **CHORAGOS.** I have been wondering, King: can it be that the
gods have done this?

CREON. *(Furiously)* Stop!
Must you doddering wrecks
Go out of your heads entirely? "The gods!"
120 Intolerable!
The gods favor this corpse? Why? How had he
served them?
Tried to loot their temples, burn their images,
Yes, and the whole State, and its laws with it!
Is it your <u>senile</u> opinion that the gods love to honor
bad men?
125 A pious thought!—
                        No, from the very beginning
There have been those who have whispered
together,
Stiff-necked anarchists, putting their heads
together,
Scheming against me in alleys. These are the men,
And they have bribed my own guard to do this thing.
130 Money!   *(Sententiously)*
There's nothing in the world so demoralizing as
money.
Down go your cities,
Homes gone, men gone, honest hearts corrupted,
Crookedness of all kinds, and all for money!

Vocabulary Development: senile (SEE nyl) *adj.* confused or
behaving strangely because of old age
sententiously (sen TEN shuhs lee) *adv.*
in a way that shows excessive fondness
for wise sayings; in lecturing tones

TAKE NOTES

Literary Analysis

Antigone says that she will follow the laws of the gods rather than the laws of the state. Read the bracketed lines. How does the Choragos suggest that Creon is the **antagonist**?

_____

_____

_____

_____

Reading Skill

Creon does not think the gods would want Polyneices buried because his actions would not be acceptable to them. Draw a box around Creon's **summary** of Polyneices' actions.

Stop to Reflect

An anarchist is someone who believes that people should not be governed. Why do you think Creon believes that anarchists buried Polyneices?

_____

_____

_____

_____

Reading Check

Who does the sentry say nobody likes? Circle the answer.

Read the bracketed passage. Circle a detail that shows that Creon is in conflict with Antigone, and is therefore, the **antagonist** of the play.

Summarize what has taken place between Creon and the sentry.

_____

_____

_____

_____

_____

Read the underlined text. What does the sentry mean by this comment?

_____

_____

_____

_____

What does Creon threaten to do to the sentry? Circle the answer.

135 *(To* SENTRY*)* But you—!
I swear by God and by the throne of God,
The man who has done this thing shall pay for it!
Find that man, bring him here to me, or your death
Will be the least of your problems: I'll string you up
140 Alive, and there will be certain ways to make you
Discover your employer before you die;
And the process may teach you a lesson you seem
   to have missed:
The dearest profit is sometimes all too dear:
That depends on the source. Do you understand me?
145 A fortune won is often misfortune.

SENTRY. King, may I speak?

CREON. Your very voice distresses me.

SENTRY. Are you sure that it is my voice, and not
   your conscience?

CREON. By God, he wants to analyze me now!

150 SENTRY. It is not what I say, but what has been
   done, that hurts you.

CREON. You talk too much.

SENTRY. Maybe; but I've done nothing.

CREON. Sold your soul for some silver: that's all
   you've done.

SENTRY. How dreadful it is when the right judge
judges wrong!

155 CREON. Your figures of speech
May entertain you now; but unless you bring me
   the man,
You will get little profit from them in the end.

(Exit CREON *into the Palace.)*

SENTRY. "Bring me the man"—!
I'd like nothing better than bringing him the man!
160 But bring him or not, you have seen the last of
   me here.
At any rate, I am safe!

(Exit SENTRY.*)*

Ode I

CHORUS. (STROPHE 1)
Numberless are the world's wonders, but none
More wonderful than man; the stormgray sea
Yields to his prows, the huge crests bear him high;
Earth, holy and inexhaustible, is graven
5 With shining furrows where his plows have gone
Year after year, the timeless labor of stallions.

(ANTISTROPHE 1)

The lightboned birds and beasts that cling to cover,
The lithe fish lighting their reaches of dim water,
All are taken, tamed in the net of his mind;
10 The lion on the hill, the wild horse windy-maned,
Resign to him; and his blunt yoke has broken
The sultry shoulders of the mountain bull.

(STROPHE 2)

Words also, and thought as rapid as air,
He fashions to his good use; statecraft is his,
15 And his the skill that <u>deflects</u> the arrows of snow,
The spears of winter rain: from every wind
He has made himself secure—from all but one:
In the late wind of death he cannot stand.

(ANTISTROPHE 2)

O clear intelligence, force beyond all measure!
20 O fate of man, working both good and evil!
When the laws are kept, how proudly his city stands!
When the laws are broken, what of his city then?
Never may the anarchic man find rest at my hearth,
Never be it said that my thoughts are his thoughts.

*The sentry returns to the palace at the beginning of Scene 2.
He brings Antigone. He tells Creon that he caught Antigone
burying Polyneices. Antigone admits that she buried her
brother. Creon tells Antigone that she has broken a law
and bragged about breaking the law. Then Creon tells his
servants to arrest Ismene. Ismene knew about Antigone's
crime. She did not report it. Ismene must be punished too.
Ismene admits that she is guilty. Then she defends Antigone.
She asks Creon how he could kill his son's bride. Creon tells
the guards to watch that Antigone and Ismene do not escape.*

Vocabulary Development: deflects (dih FLEKTS) *v.* turns or
makes go to one side

Reader's Response: Do you agree or disagree with the Creon's
reasons for not burying Polyneices? Explain.

_____

_____

_____

_____

TAKE NOTES

Reading Skill

Summarize what the Chorus says
in the bracketed passage.

_____

_____

_____

_____

Literary Analysis

Does this passage support or
oppose the **antagonist**? Explain.

_____

_____

_____

_____

_____

Stop to Reflect

Why do you think Ismene defends
Antigone?

_____

_____

_____

Reading Check

What does Ismene admit in
Scene 2? Underline the
lines that tell
you.

Antigone, Prologue through Scene 2

1. **Analyze:** What is the key belief or principle that Creon states in his speech about "the Ship of State"?

_____

_____

2. **Compare and Contrast:** Antigone and Creon have different ideas about laws. Compare Antigone's position with Creon's.

_____

_____

_____

3. **Literary Analysis:** Use the chart to identify actions and language that present Antigone, the **protagonist**, in a sympathetic light. Then identify passages that show that Creon, the **antagonist**, is hostile toward her.

Protagonist: Antigone	vs.	Antagonist: Creon

4. **Reading Skill: Summarize** what has happened to Antigone so far in the play.

_____

_____

_____

SUPPORT FOR WRITING AND EXTEND YOUR LEARNING

Writing: Essay

The theme in **Antigone** is the conflict between the individual and society. Prepare to write an **essay** in which you explore this theme.

- Summarize Creon's reasons for not wanting Polyneices to be buried.

_____

_____

- What do Creon's reasons say about his view of the individual in society?

_____

- Summarize Antigone's reasons for wanting to bury Polyneices.

_____

_____

- What do Antigone's reasons say about her view of the individual in society?

_____

Listening and Speaking: Oral Report

Research and prepare an **oral report** on the way that Greek myths still influence culture today. Use library and Internet resources to research at least three examples of English words that have been influenced by Greek myths. Use this chart to organize what you have learned.

English Word	Definition	Greek Myth Related to Word

Antigone, Scenes 3 through 5

LITERARY ANALYSIS

Greek tragedies are serious dramas that were written for festivals in the fifth century B.C. in Greece. They all share certain characteristics:

- They are based on myths that were familiar to the original audience of the time.
- They tell of a reversal of fortune, from good to bad, experienced by a man or woman of noble birth.
- This downfall results from the main character's own actions.
- *Fate* is the force ensuring that the character's actions will bring doom.
- The main character may have a *tragic flaw,* a characteristic that allows him or her to be trapped in the events that lead to his or her downfall.

The **theme,** or central message, of a Greek tragedy is often a warning against human excess, such as pride or passion. Also, these plays concern the limitations of human knowledge, sympathy, and foresight. Tragedies remind us that every decision involves choosing—and living with the unforeseen consequences.

READING SKILL

To **summarize** a play, briefly state the most important actions and ideas in your own words. To gather details for a summary, **take notes.** Write down the most important elements of what you read: the characters, the places, the problem, and the key events. Use this chart to take notes that will help you summarize *Antigone.*

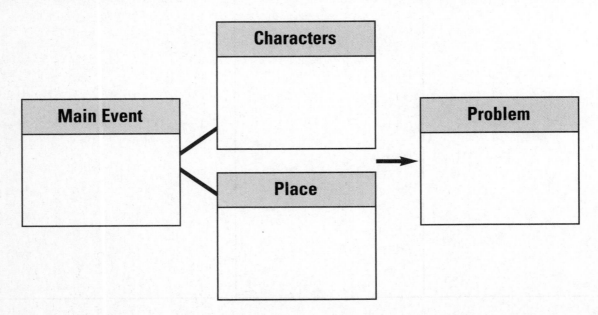

Antigone, Scenes 3 through 5

Sophocles

Summary Haimon tries to persuade his father, Creon, to change his decision about Antigone. Creon insists upon being obeyed. He places Antigone in a vault, where he expects her to die. Teiresias, the blind prophet, urges the king to admit that he is wrong before it is too late.

Note-taking Guide

Use this character wheel to record details about Antigone's character.

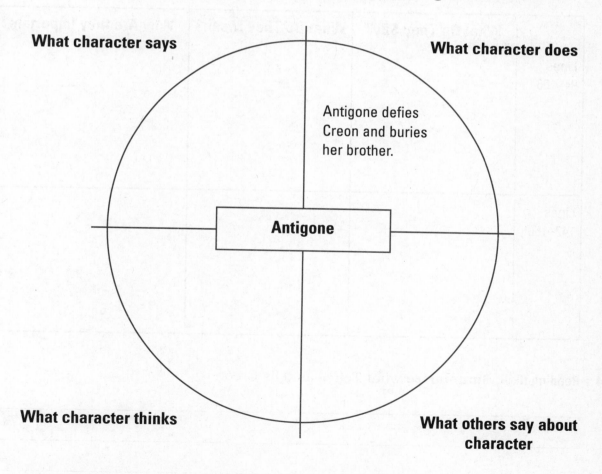

What character says

What character does

Antigone defies Creon and buries her brother.

Antigone

What character thinks

What others say about character

Antigone, Scenes 3 through 5

1. **Contrast:** Contrast Haimon's main concerns with Creon's.

   _____

   _____

   _____

2. **Analyze Cause and Effect:** What action does Creon take because of Teiresias' prophecy?

   _____

   _____

3. **Literary Analysis:** Fill in the chart below to explore the **theme** of the play.

	What Do They Say?	**What Do They Mean?**	**Why Are they Important?**
Lines 94–106			
Lines 142–150			

4. **Reading Skill: Summarize** what Teiresias tells Creon.

   _____

   _____

   _____

SUPPORT FOR WRITING AND EXTEND YOUR LEARNING

Writing: Reflective Essay

Plan a **reflective essay** in which you examine Creon's tragedy. Use your notes from the items below to write your reflective essay.

- Is Creon responsible for his downfall, or is his downfall a result of fate?

  _____

  _____

- Collect details to support your answer by summarizing the following passages:

  Haimon's words to his father: _____

  _____

  Teiresias' prediction: _____

  _____

  The words of the Chorus: _____

  _____

  The words of the Choragos: _____

  _____

Research and Technology: Playbill Note

Prepare a one-paragraph **playbill note** on the history of Thebes. Give your audience the background they need to understand *Antigone.* Use library and Internet resources to research "Thebes." List the source of your information beside the notes you take in the chart below. Then, use the chart to help compose your playbill note.

Thebes	Notes	Source of Information
Geographic location		
Beginnings		
Place in history		
Significance		

Drama Reviews

ABOUT DRAMA REVIEWS

Drama reviews are essays that tell a writer's opinion about a play that he or she has seen. A writer who writes drama reviews is called a critic. Critics examine each part of a play. Their reviews help readers decide whether they want to see a performance. Drama reviews include these features:

- a useful summary of the story line
- judgments about the direction and acting to explain whether the message of the play is expressed clearly
- examples, quotations, facts, and other support for opinions
- judgments about the staging, lighting, makeup, sound, and set design

READING SKILL

The critic who writes a drama review should give a summary of the play. The critic should also offer his or her judgments about the quality of the play and how it is performed. The way the play is performed is called the production. Readers have less reason to trust a review if the critic leaves out important information. Readers should not trust a critic who shows a lack of knowledge or does not support his or her judgments with examples. Use the chart below to help you **evaluate a critic's summaries and responses**.

	Criticisms	Specific Reason Given	Was This Aspect of the Production Omitted From the Review?
Acting			
Directing			
Sound and Lighting			
Costuming			
Scenery			

A "Prequel" to *Antigone*

A Review of *Antigone: As Played and Danced by the Three Fates on Their Way to Becoming the Three Graces*

Elyse Sommers

The 55-minute dance theater piece currently at the Classic Stage Theater is a collaboration made in avant-garde[1] heaven: a text by the wizard of word play Mac Wellman, direction and musical staging by the Big Dance Theater's director Paul Lazar and choreographer Annie-B Parsons.

The prolific and always surprising Wellman's first journey into Greek myth is more musical tone poem than play. His deconstruction or prequel to Sophocles' *Antigone* is brilliantly acted out and danced by the production's four performers.

Wellman has kept all the traditional parts: Creon, Antigone's sister Ismene, Creon's son Haemon, Creon's wife Eurydice (who in Wellman's version is also Teiresias) and the chorus of Theban citizens. But in this highly stylized collaboration, all these parts are played by the chameleonic,[2] mask-less Three Fates (Deirdre O'Connell, Molly Hickock and Rebecca Wisocky), who are also Three Facts, on their way to becoming the Three Graces. O'Connell is a moving Antigone. Wisocky, an actor-dancer

Author: Mac Wellman
Director: Paul Lazar
Choreography & Musical Staging: Annie-B Parson
Cast: Nancy Ellis, Molly Hickok, Leroy Logan, Deirdre O'Connell & Rebecca Wisocky
Songs: Cynthia Hopkins
Running time: 60 minutes without intermission

Classic Stage
136 East 13th Street
(212/677-4210)
www.classicstage.org
4/27/04 through 5/23/04;
opening 5/02/04
Tuesday through Friday
8:00pm / Saturday 2:00pm &
8:00pm / Sunday 3:00pm

whose enormous range I've long admired, is a mesmerizing and quite humorous Creon whose kingly edicts are delivered into a microphone. Hickock takes on the roles of Teiresias and Eurydice, as well as sharing the Chorus scenes with a fourth Fate, Nancy Ellis.

If all this sounds more than a little confusing and inaccessible, anyone not well schooled in the Greek tale is indeed likely to be swept with a sense of "this is all Greek to me." Still, if you just sit back and watch the four women dance and deliver the bursts of babbling dialogue, you'll gradually get the general sense if not all of it.

To add to the fun (yes, much of this IS fun with quite a few laugh-out-loud moments), there's a non-dancing narrator with the intriguing name of Shriek Operator. This character is zestfully portrayed by Leroy Logan. The staging overall is appropriately spare with just a few simple but apt and often amusing props.

---

1. **avant-garde** (a vahnt GAHRD) *adj.* any new or unconventional movements, especially in the arts.
2. **chameleonic** (kuh mee lee AHN ik) *adj.* capable of assuming a variety of appearances.

Santa Claus Meets Sophocles

A Review of *Antigone: As Played and Danced by the Three Fates on Their Way to Becoming the Three Graces*

MATTHEW MURRAY

If you're familiar with Sophocles's classic Greek tragedy and have a solid working knowledge of Greek mythology, you might well appreciate the opportunity to see Big Dance Theater's production of Wellman's interpretation of the story, which is playing at Classic Stage Company through May 23. If you don't know Sophocles's original, or you have only a casual familiarity with it, chances are you'll be utterly baffled by what you see onstage.

The full title of Wellman's play is *Antigone: As Played and Danced by the Three Fates On Their Way to Becoming the Three Graces.* That should give you an idea of what you're in for: a highly deconstructed[1] take on Sophocles's story.

As the Fates (one who spins the thread of life, one who weaves it into actions, and one who determines when it must be snipped) existed eons before Sophocles, this story bears only a perfunctory similarity to his. The story the Fates enact features a handful of characters from the play, and is overseen by a narrator (and disc jockey) named E Shriek, whom Wellman describes as "an unknown god of unknown origin."

As the play progresses, the Fates become the Three Graces, and pass along the story of the young Antigone and the steadfast uncle she defied to Sophocles himself. (Well, as represented by a hand puppet.) The story is told and retold until it reaches the version we currently know, at which point the play stops: what *is* is of no interest to Wellman. He's more concerned with what was and what might have been.

That idea, and the stagecraft used to present it, are the most engaging parts of this *Antigone.* Director Paul Lazar and choreographer[2] Annie-B Parson have done an excellent job of making the play visually appealing, providing almost constant movement onstage, and no shortage of surprises in the way the Fates' journeys are conveyed. (They employ microphones, dust busters, yellow slippers and toy pianos.)

Cynthia Hopkins has provided a few attractive songs for the production; Joanne Howard's set design is spartan,[3] but handsome and occasionally surprising; Claudia Stephens's costumes provide nice definition for the characters; Jay Ryan's lights are colorful and inventive; and Jane Shaw's sound design is never overdone. Leroy Logan, as E Shriek, is a fine combination of paternal and frightening, Santa Claus by way of Socrates (and Sophocles).

It's the lack of immediacy and freshness that hurts this *Antigone* more than anything else: the production never feels as crisp and well-defined as it needs to be. The theatrical concept on which Wellman and Lazar have collaborated is daring and intelligent, but it's currently missing the piquant[4] energy needed to really put it across.

---

1. **deconstructed** (dee kuhn STRUK tid) *adj.* (said of a text) having been broken into its elements in order to question its meaning.
2. **choreographer** (kor ee AHG ruh fer) *n.* a person who creates and directs dances.
3. **spartan** (SPART uhn) *adj.* very plain; lacking ornament.
4. **piquant** (PEE kahnt) *adj.* exciting agreeable interest or curiosity.

THINKING ABOUT THE DRAMA REVIEW

1. Find a passage from each review that talks about the same part of the production. Compare the critics' opinions.

_____

_____

2. How does each review affect your desire to see this production? Give examples from each review to support your answer.

_____

_____

READING SKILL

3. Read the opening paragraphs of each review. How does each critic prepare readers for what they can expect in this production?

_____

_____

4. What detail supports Sommers's opinion that this play is confusing?

_____

_____

TIMED WRITING: EXPOSITION (30 minutes)

Write a short essay about each reviewer's overall response to the play. In your essay, include

- a summary of each critic's overall opinion
- your evaluation of each critic's overall opinion
- specific examples from both reviews to support your opinions

To help you get started, choose one quotation from each review that shows the critic's overall opinion. Write it on the lines below.

_____

_____

The Tragedy of Julius Caesar, Act I

LITERARY ANALYSIS

Like other tragedies, **Shakespeare's tragedies** are plays that tell of a reversal of fortune, from good to bad, experienced by a man or woman, usually of noble birth. Shakespeare's tragedies also have these distinctive features:

- They are sometimes based on **historical characters**.
- The **hero** often displays a **tragic flaw**, a characteristic that brings about his or her downfall.
- Shakespeare emphasizes the hero's **internal conflict**.
- Commoners often play key **supporting roles** and provide **comic relief**, humorous scenes that serve as a break from the intense emotions of the play.

Shakespeare's plays are structured in five acts. In his tragedies, the **crisis**—the turning point that determines how the play will end—occurs in Act III. The **climax**, or point of greatest emotional intensity, often occurs in Act V, when the **catastrophe**, or disaster, befalls the hero.

As you read, use this chart to trace the structure of the play.

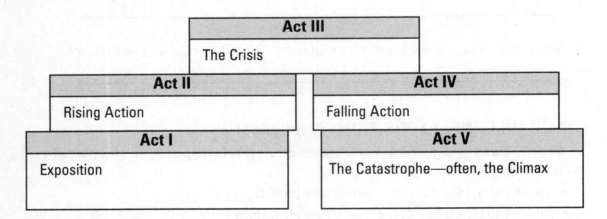

Act III
The Crisis

Act II	Act IV
Rising Action	Falling Action

Act I	Act V
Exposition	The Catastrophe—often, the Climax

READING SKILL

Shakespeare's plays contain unfamiliar language and references. When **reading Shakespearean drama, use text aids:**

- Review the list of *dramatis personae* (the cast of characters).
- Read the background information provided.

As you read the play, consult the notes, called **glosses**, beside the text. These notes define words and explain references.

The Tragedy of Julius Caesar, Act I

William Shakespeare

Summary Julius Caesar has overthrown the Roman government and wants to become emperor. A soothsayer warns Caesar to beware of danger to come. Caesar dismisses the warning. Cassius plans to ask Brutus to join the plot to overthrow Caesar. Caesar is suspicious of Cassius. The conspirators plan ways to get Brutus to join them.

Reading/Writing Connection

Complete this paragraph to explain the different ways in which people may react to another person's success.

A person's success can <u>stimulate</u> _____. Others may <u>speculate</u> _____. Some people cannot <u>tolerate</u> when _____.

Note-taking Guide

Fill in this character wheel to analyze the character of Julius Caesar.

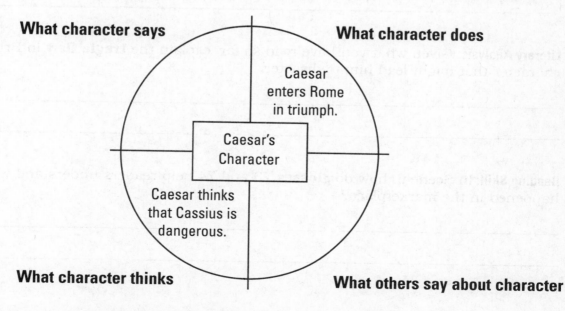

What character says

What character does

Caesar enters Rome in triumph.

Caesar's Character

Caesar thinks that Cassius is dangerous.

What character thinks

What others say about character

The Tragedy of Julius Caesar, Act I

1. **Interpret:** What do noble Romans such as Flavius and Cassius fear or resent about Caesar's success?

_____

_____

2. **Infer:** What does Caesar's reaction to the soothsayer's warning show about him?

_____

_____

3. **Analyze:** Use this chart to analyze Brutus' expression of his values in his speech in Scene ii.

	Speech	**What Does It Say?**	**What Does It Mean?**	**Why Is It Important?**
Brutus	Scene ii, lines 82–89			

4. **Literary Analysis:** Given what you have read so far, explain the **tragic flaw** in Brutus' character that might lead him to disaster.

_____

_____

5. **Reading Skill:** In Scene ii, how do **glosses** 73 and 74 help readers understand what happened in the marketplace?

_____

_____

SUPPORT FOR WRITING AND EXTEND YOUR LEARNING

Writing: Character Descriptions

Write **character descriptions** that would help actors prepare to play the roles of Caesar, Brutus, Cassius, and Antony. Take notes by answering these questions:

• What motivates this character?

_____

• What does this character say in Act I?

_____

_____

• What does this character do in Act I?

_____

_____

• How does he interact with other characters?

_____

_____

Research and Technology: Timeline

Make a **timeline** showing important events in the transition from republic to empire in ancient Rome. Use library and Internet sources to research information. Use "Roman republic" as key words. Fill in the chart below with your notes.

From Republic to Empire in Ancient Rome		
Event	**Date**	**Significance**

The Tragedy of Julius Caesar, Act II

LITERARY ANALYSIS

The Tragedy of Julius Caesar is written in blank verse. **Blank verse** is a poetic form characterized by unrhymed lines written in iambic pentameter.

- An **iamb** is a *foot* (unit of rhythm) in which an unstressed syllable is followed by a stressed syllable: da-DUH.
- **Pentameter** refers to a rhythmic pattern in which each line has five feet.
- In **iambic pentameter**, the typical line has five iambs, or five stressed syllables, each preceded by an unstressed syllable.

Shakespeare's "upperclass" characters speak in iambic pentameter. Lower-born characters speak in prose. Sometimes, Shakespeare breaks the rhythmic pattern in a line to add contrast or emphasis.

READING SKILL

Paraphrasing a line or passage from a work means restating its meaning in your own words. To paraphrase when **reading Shakespearean drama**, follow these steps:

- Look for punctuation showing where sentences end.
- For each sentence, identify the subject and verb and put them into the usual order. You may also need to add helping verbs and use modern verb and pronoun forms.

As you read, use the diagram below to help you paraphrase.

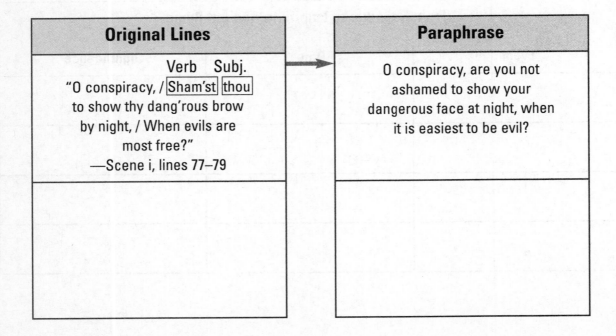

Original Lines	Paraphrase
Verb Subj. "O conspiracy, / Sham'st thou to show thy dang'rous brow by night, / When evils are most free?" —Scene i, lines 77–79	O conspiracy, are you not ashamed to show your dangerous face at night, when it is easiest to be evil?

The Tragedy of Julius Caesar, Act II

William Shakespeare

Summary Brutus decides to join and lead the conspiracy. Calpurnia dreams of Caesar's murder and begs Caesar not to leave the house. Decius gives Calpurnia's dream a different interpretation. He encourages Caesar to go to the Senate and be crowned emperor. Caesar receives a letter naming the conspirators, but he does not read it.

Note-taking Guide

Use this diagram to list events that build suspense in Act II.

Climax

Event: _____

Event: _____

Event: _____

Event: Brutus reveals his inner conflict about the conspiracy.

Rising Action Act II

Act I
Exposition

The Tragedy of Julius Caesar, Act II

1. **Evaluate:** Are Brutus' reasons for joining the conspiracy convincing or flawed? Explain.

_____

_____

2. **Draw Conclusions:** In the chart below, write Caesar's reactions to the events listed. In the third column, explain what each reaction reveals about Caesar's character and values.

Event	Caesar's Reaction	What It Reveals
Augurer's sacrifice		
Decius' flattery		

3. **Literary Analysis:** Copy lines 42–43 of Scene ii and mark them to indicate the stressed (´) and unstressed (˜) syllables. Which line of **blank verse** illustrates perfect **iambic pentameter**?

_____

_____

_____

4. **Reading Skill: Paraphrase** Brutus' words in lines 234–236 of Scene i. Make your new sentences sound like modern English.

_____

_____

SUPPORT FOR WRITING AND EXTEND YOUR LEARNING

Writing: Character Analysis

Write a brief **character analysis** of Brutus. Explain his motivations, strengths, and weaknesses. Use the questions below to help you write your character analysis.

- What decisions does Brutus make in Act II?

  _____

  _____

  _____

- Why does he make each decision you listed?

  _____

  _____

  _____

Listening and Speaking: Debate

Plan a **debate** on this question: *Are the conspirators justified in plotting against Caesar?*

- List two reasons for saying that the conspirators were right to plot against Caesar.

  _____

  _____

- Now, list two reasons for saying that the conspirators were wrong to plot against Caesar.

  _____

  _____

- Decide which side of the debate you will take. Do you think the conspirators were right or wrong to plot against Caesar?

  _____

The Tragedy of Julius Caesar, Act III, Scene i

LITERARY ANALYSIS

In plays, characters' words and actions express most of the information. Plays feature the following types of **dramatic speeches:**

- **Dialogue:** the conversations between characters
- **Soliloquy:** a long speech in which a character, usually alone on stage, speaks as if to himself or herself, unheard by any other character
- **Aside:** a remark, usually to the audience, that is not heard by other characters on stage
- **Monologue:** a long speech by one character, usually heard by the other characters

As you read, notice what characters reveal in soliloquies and asides.

READING SKILL

Writers sometimes use **imagery**, or language that appeals to the senses to make abstract ideas vivid and concrete. In Act III, Shakespeare uses many images that focus on violence and the body:

- wounds that speak
- burying Caesar's body rather than speaking praise of him
- "plucking" a poet's name out of his heart

In each case, a reference to words—speech, praise, names—is coupled with an image of a person's wounds—a corpse, blood, the heart. Shakespeare links violence in Rome with disrespect for laws—the words that bind society. Use this chart to record images like these.

Text	Text
And waving our red weapons o'er our heads Let's all cry "Peace, freedom, and liberty!"	
Imagery	**Imagery**
Swords covered in blood from Caesar's body	
Connection	**Connection**
The words name the ideals the conspirators use to justify killing Caesar.	

The Tragedy of Julius Caesar, Act III, Scene i

William Shakespeare

Summary Caesar arrives at the Capitol. The conspirators surround Caesar and stab him to death. Brutus tells Antony that the murder is for the good of Rome. Antony asks to speak at Caesar's funeral. Brutus agrees that Antony may speak after Brutus himself has spoken. Antony declares his resolve to use his speech to test the feelings of the Roman people.

Note-taking Guide

Use this chart to record important details of this scene.

What is the Senate's plan?
What do the nobles conspire to do?
What happens to Caesar?
How does Antony feel at the end of the scene?

The art of persuasion plays an important part in this play. Describe a time when you persuaded someone to do or believe something.

_____

_____

_____

_____

Reading Skill

Imagery is language that appeals to the senses to make abstract ideas vivid and concrete. How does Calpurnia's dream add imagery to the soothsayer's warning?

_____

_____

_____

Stop to Reflect

The letter that Artemidorus wants to give Caesar explains the plot and names the conspirators. How might Caesar have reacted if he had read the letter before going to the Capitol?

_____

_____

_____

_____

Reading Check

Underline the warning that the soothsayer tells Caesar.

The Tragedy of Julius Caesar, Act III, Scene i
William Shakespeare

Based on historical events in ancient Rome, Shakespeare's The Tragedy of Julius Caesar is a study of character set in a political arena. Much of the plot hinges on the character and internal conflict of Caesar's friend Brutus, who is drawn into an assassination plot against Caesar. Brutus struggles with the conflict between his personal loyalty and his patriotic duty.

As Act I opens, the people of Rome are celebrating the victory of Caesar and his army over Pompey's sons. Pompey, a Roman general, had challenged Caesar's rise to power, and Caesar had him murdered. Marullus scolds some common laborers for so easily shifting their allegiance to Caesar. Caesar is warned by a soothsayer—a predictor of the future—to "beware the ides of March." Cassius tries to find out how Brutus feels about Caesar's ambition. Although a crowd calls out for him to accept the emperor's crown, Caesar refuses it three times. Yet, some doubt his sincerity.

In Act II, Brutus meets with Cassius and other nobles who conspire to murder Caesar. Cassius also wants to kill Antony, but Brutus objects. Caesar reassures his wife, Calpurnia, who has dreamt that his statue is dripping blood. Artemidorus waits near the Capitol with a letter warning Caesar of the plot against him.

Act III is the turning point that sets irreversible events in motion.

Act III
Scene i. Rome. Before the Capitol.

(Flourish of trumpets. Enter CAESAR, BRUTUS, CASSIUS, CASCA, DECIUS, METELLUS CIMBER, TREBONIUS, CINNA, ANTONY, LEPIDUS, ARTEMIDORUS, PUBLIUS, POPILIUS, *and the* SOOTHSAYER.*)*

CAESAR. The ides of March are come.

SOOTHSAYER. Ay, Caesar, but not gone.

ARTEMIDORUS. Hail, Caesar! Read this schedule.[1]

DECIUS. Trebonius doth desire you to o'er-read,
5 At your best leisure, this his humble suit.[2]

---

1. **schedule** (SKE juhl) *n.* paper.
2. **suit** *n.* petition; plea.

ARTEMIDORUS. O Caesar, read mine first; for mine's
a suit
That touches[3] Caesar nearer. Read it, great Caesar.

CAESAR. What touches us ourself shall be last
served.

ARTEMIDORUS. Delay not, Caesar; read it instantly.

CAESAR. What, is the fellow mad?

10 **PUBLIUS.**   Sirrah, give place.[4]

CASSIUS. What, urge you your petitions in the street?
Come to the Capitol.

(CAESAR *goes to the Capitol, the rest following.*)

PUBLIUS. I wish your enterprise today may thrive.

CASSIUS. What enterprise, Popilius?

PUBLIUS.   Fare you well.

(*Advances to* CAESAR)

15 **BRUTUS.** What said Popilius Lena?

CASSIUS. He wished today our enterprise might
thrive.
I fear our purpose is discoverèd.

BRUTUS. Look how he makes to[5] Caesar; mark him.

CASSIUS. Casca, be sudden,[6] for we fear prevention.
20 Brutus, what shall be done? If this be known,
Cassius or Caesar never shall turn back,[7]
For I will slay myself.

BRUTUS.   Cassius, be constant.[8]
Popilius Lena speaks not of our purposes;
For look, he smiles, and Caesar doth not change.[9]

25 **CASSIUS.** Trebonius knows his time; for look you,
Brutus,
He draws Mark Antony out of the way.

(*Exit* ANTONY *and* TREBONIUS.)

DECIUS. Where is Metellus Cimber? Let him go
And presently prefer his suit[10] to Caesar.

---

3. **touches** *v.* concerns.
4. **give place** get out of the way.
5. **makes to** approaches.
6. **be sudden** be quick.
7. **Cassius . . . back** either Cassius or Caesar will not return alive.
8. **constant** *adj.* firm; calm.
9. **change** *v.* that is, change the expression on his face.
10. **presently prefer his suit** immediately present his petition.

TAKE NOTES

Stop to Reflect

Why do you think Artemidorus is so insistent about Caesar's reading of the letter?

_____

_____

_____

Literary Analysis

Dramatic speeches express information about characters and events. **Dialogue** is the conversations between characters and is a type of dramatic speech. How does the dialogue between Artemidorus and Caesar create suspense?

_____

_____

_____

_____

_____

Reading Check

How does Brutus reassure Cassius that their plot has not been discovered? Underline the words that tell you the answer.

_____

_____

_____

_____

What does this **dialogue** among Decius, Brutus, and Cinna reveal about how the conspirators plan to attack Caesar?

_____

_____

_____

_____

_____

_____

Read the bracketed passage. What **imagery** does Caesar use to describe Metellus Cimber's bowing and begging?

_____

_____

_____

_____

_____

What does Metellus Cimber request from Caesar? Underline the answer.

BRUTUS. He is addressed.[11] Press near and second[12] him.

30 **CINNA.** Casca, you are the first that rears your hand.

CAESAR. Are we all ready? What is now amiss
That Caesar and his Senate must redress?[13]

METELLUS CIMBER. Most high, most mighty, and most
    puissant[14] Caesar,
Metellus Cimber throws before thy seat
An humble heart.

(Kneeling)

35 **CAESAR.**   I must prevent thee, Cimber.
These couchings and these lowly courtesies[15]
Might fire the blood of ordinary men,
And turn preordinance and first decree
Into the law of children.[16]
Be not fond[17]
40 To think that Caesar bears such rebel blood
That will be thawed from the true quality[18]
With that which melteth fools—I mean sweet words,
Low-crookèd curtsies, and base spaniel fawning.[19]
Thy brother by decree is banished.
45 If thou dost bend and pray and fawn for him,
I spurn[20] thee like a cur out of my way.
Know, Caesar doth not wrong, nor without cause
Will he be satisfied.

METELLUS CIMBER. Is there no voice more worthy
    than my own,
50 To sound more sweetly in great Caesar's ear
For the repealing[21] of my banished brother?

---

11. **addressed** *adj.* ready.
12. **second** *v.* support.
13. **amiss . . . redress** wrong that Caesar and his Senate must correct.
14. **puissant** (PYOO i suhnt) *adj.* powerful.
15. **couchings . . . courtesies** low bowings and humble gestures of reverence.
16. **And turn . . . law of children** and change what has already been decided as children might change their minds.
17. **fond** *adj.* foolish.
18. **rebel . . . quality** unstable disposition that will be changed from firmness.
19. **base spaniel fawning** low, doglike cringing.
20. **spurn** *v.* kick disdainfully.
21. **repealing** *n.* recalling; ending the banishment.

BRUTUS. I kiss thy hand, but not in flattery, Caesar,
    Desiring thee that Publius Cimber may
    Have an immediate freedom of repeal.[22]

CAESAR. What, Brutus?

55 **CASSIUS.**   Pardon, Caesar; Caesar, pardon!
    As low as to thy foot doth Cassius fall
    To beg enfranchisement[23] for Publius Cimber.

CAESAR. I could be well moved, if I were as you;
    If I could pray to move,[24] prayers would move me;
60   But I am constant as the Northern Star,
    Of whose true-fixed and resting[25] quality
    There is no fellow[26] in the firmament.[27]

    The skies are painted with unnumb'red sparks,
    They are all fire and every one doth shine;
65   But there's but one in all doth hold his[28] place.
    So in the world; 'tis furnished well with men,
    And men are flesh and blood, and apprehensive;[29]
    Yet in the number I do know but one
    That unassailable holds on his rank,[30]
70   Unshaked of motion;[31] and that I am he,
    Let me a little show it, even in this—
    That I was constant[32] Cimber should be banished,
    And constant do remain to keep him so.

CINNA. O Caesar—

CAESAR.   Hence! Wilt thou lift up Olympus?[33]

DECIUS. Great Caesar—

22. **freedom of repeal** permission to be recalled.
23. **enfranchisement** (in FRAN chyz muhnt) *n.* freedom.
24. **pray to move** beg others to change their minds.
25. **resting** *adj.* immovable.
26. **fellow** *n.* equal.
27. **firmament** (FER muh muhnt) *n.* sky.
28. **his** *pron.* its.
29. **apprehensive** (ap ri HEN siv) *adj.* able to understand.
30. **unassailable . . . rank** unattackable, he maintains his position.
31. **Unshaked of motion** unmoved by his own or others' impulses.
32. **constant** *adj.* determined.
33. **Olympus** (oh LIM puhs) *n.* mountain in Greece on which the Greek gods were said to live.

TAKE NOTES

Literary Analysis

In lines 58–73, Caesar delivers a **monologue**, a type of long **dramatic speech** given by one character and heard by other characters. What point does Caesar make about himself in this monologue?

_____

_____

_____

Reading Skill

What **imagery** does Caesar use in his monologue to describe himself?

_____

_____

_____

_____

Reading Check

How do Brutus and Cassius respond to Metellus Cimber's request of Caesar? Underline the lines that support your answer.

_____

_____

_____

_____

Study the **imagery** in line 76. In what way do Casca's words combine ideas of words with images of violence?

_____

_____

_____

_____

Read the **dialogue** of the conspirators after Caesar's death. Why did they kill Caesar?

_____

_____

_____

_____

_____

Circle the passage that describes what the conspirators do to Caesar.

75 **CAESAR.**   Doth not Brutus bootless[34] kneel?

CASCA. Speak hands for me! *(They stab* CAESAR.*)*

CAESAR. Et tu, Brutè?[35] Then fall, Caesar.

(Dies)

CINNA. Liberty! Freedom! Tyranny is dead!
     Run hence, proclaim, cry it about the streets.

80 **CASSIUS.** Some to the common pulpits,[36]
     and cry out
     "Liberty, freedom, and enfranchisement!"

BRUTUS. People, and senators, be not affrighted.
     Fly not; stand still; ambition's debt is paid.[37]

CASCA. Go to the pulpit, Brutus.

DECIUS.   And Cassius too.

85 **BRUTUS.** Where's Publius?[38]

CINNA. Here, quite confounded with this mutiny.[39]

METELLUS CIMBER. Stand fast together, lest some
     friend of Caesar's
     Should chance—

BRUTUS. Talk not of standing. Publius, good cheer;
90   There is no harm intended to your person,
     Nor to no Roman else. So tell them, Publius.

CASSIUS. And leave us, Publius, lest that the people
     Rushing on us should do your age some mischief.

Vocabulary Development: confounded (kuhn FOWND id) *adj.*
                          made to feel confused; bewildered

---

34. **bootless** (BOOT lis) *adv.* uselessly.
35. **Et tu, Brutè?** Latin for "And you, too, Brutus?"
36. **pulpits** (PUL pits) *n.* speakers' platforms.
37. **ambition's . . . paid** ambition received what it deserved.
38. **Publius** an elderly senator.
39. **mutiny** (MYOOT uhn ee) *n.* revolt against authority, such as a rebellion of soldiers against their officers.

BRUTUS. Do so; and let no man abide[40] this deed
95   But we the doers.

(Enter TREBONIUS.*)*

    CASSIUS. Where is Antony?
    TREBONIUS: Fled to his house amazed.[41]
    Men, wives, and children stare, cry out and run,
    As[42] it were doomsday.

    BRUTUS.   Fates, we will know your pleasures.
    That we shall die, we know; 'tis but the time,
100   And drawing days out, that men stand upon.[43]

    CASCA. Why, he that cuts off twenty years of life
    Cuts off so many years of fearing death.

    BRUTUS. Grant that, and then is death a benefit.
    So are we Caesar's friends, that have abridged
105   His time of fearing death. Stoop, Romans, stoop,
    And let us bathe our hands in Caesar's blood
    Up to the elbows, and besmear our swords.
    Then walk we forth, even to the market place,[44]
    And waving our red weapons o'er our heads,
110   Let's all cry "Peace, freedom, and liberty!"

    CASSIUS. Stoop then, and wash. How many ages
        hence
    Shall this our lofty scene be acted over
    In states unborn and accents yet unknown!

    BRUTUS. How many times shall Caesar bleed in
        sport,[45]
115   That now on Pompey's basis lies along[46]
    No worthier than the dust!

---

40. **let no man abide** let no man take responsibility for.
41. **amazed** *adj.* astounded.
42. **As** *conj.* as if.
43. **drawing . . . upon** prolonging life that people care about.
44. **market place** the open area of the Roman Forum, the center of government, business, and public life in ancient Rome.
45. **in sport** for amusement that is, the deed will be acted out in plays.
46. **on Pompey's basis lies along** by the pedestal of Pompey's statue lies stretched out.

TAKE NOTES

Stop to Reflect

Brutus argues that the conspirators are Caesar's friends because they have shortened the time that he has to fear death. Do you think this is a valid argument? Explain.

_____

_____

_____

Reading Skill

Underline an example of the use of **imagery** on this page. Explain how the image links blood and words.

_____

_____

Literary Analysis

Read the bracketed passage. What does the **dialogue** between Cassius and Brutus reveal about how they think their act will be remembered in the future?

_____

_____

_____

_____

Cassius says that he and the other conspirators are the "boldest and best hearts of Rome." Do you agree with him? Explain your answer.

_____

_____

_____

_____

Literary Analysis

Explain what the servant is asking of Brutus in the **monologue** beginning at line 123.

_____

_____

_____

_____

_____

_____

Reading Check

Who will lead the conspirators into the market place? Underline the answer in the text.

CASSIUS.   So oft as that shall be,
So often shall the knot⁴⁷ of us be called
The men that gave their country liberty.

DECIUS. What, shall we forth?

CASSIUS.   Ay, every man away.
120 Brutus shall lead, and we will grace his heels⁴⁸
With the most boldest and best hearts of Rome.

(Enter a SERVANT.*)*

BRUTUS. Soft,⁴⁹ who comes here? A friend of Antony's.

SERVANT. Thus, Brutus, did my master bid me kneel;
Thus did Mark Antony bid me fall down;
125 And, being prostrate, thus he bade me say:
Brutus is noble, wise, valiant, and honest;
Caesar was mighty, bold, royal,⁵⁰ and loving.
Say I love Brutus and I honor him;
Say I feared Caesar, honored him, and loved him.
130 If Brutus will vouchsafe that Antony
May safely come to him and be resolved⁵¹
How Caesar hath deserved to lie in death,
Mark Antony shall not love Caesar dead
So well as Brutus living; but will follow
135 The fortunes and affairs of noble Brutus
Thorough the hazards of this untrod state⁵²
With all true faith. So says my master Antony.

BRUTUS. Thy master is a wise and valiant Roman;
I never thought him worse.
140 Tell him, so⁵³ please him come unto this place,
He shall be satisfied and, by my honor,
Depart untouched.

SERVANT.   I'll fetch him presently.⁵⁴

(Exit SERVANT*)*

---

47. **knot** *n.* group.
48. **grace his heels** do honor to his heels; that is, follow him.
49. **Soft** wait.
50. **royal** showing noble generosity.
51. **be resolved** have it explained.
52. **Thorough . . . state** through the dangers of this new state of affairs.
53. **so** *conj.* if it should.
54. **presently** *adv.* immediately.

BRUTUS. I know that we shall have him well to friend.[55]

CASSIUS. I wish we may. But yet have I a mind
145   That fears him much; and my misgiving still
  Falls shrewdly to the purpose.[56]

(Enter ANTONY.*)*

BRUTUS. But here comes Antony. Welcome, Mark Antony.

ANTONY. O mighty Caesar! Dost thou lie so low?
  Are all thy conquests, glories, triumphs, spoils,
150   Shrunk to this little measure? Fare thee well.
  I know not, gentlemen, what you intend,
  Who else must be let blood,[57] who else is rank.[58]
  If I myself, there is no hour so fit
  As Caesar's death's hour, nor no instrument
155   Of half that worth as those your swords, made rich
  With the most noble blood of all this world.
  I do beseech ye, if you bear me hard,[59]
  Now, whilst your purpled hands[60] do reek and smoke,
  Fulfill your pleasure. Live[61] a thousand years,
160   I shall not find myself so apt[62] to die;
  No place will please me so, no mean of death,[63]
  As here by Caesar, and by you cut off,
  The choice and master spirits of this age.

BRUTUS. O Antony, beg not your death of us!
165   Though now we must appear bloody and cruel,
  As by our hands and this our present act
  You see we do, yet see you but our hands
  And this the bleeding business they have done.
  Our hearts you see not; they are pitiful;[64]
170   And pity to the general wrong of Rome—
  As fire drives out fire, so pity pity[65]—
  Hath done this deed on Caesar. For your part,

TAKE NOTES

Literary Analysis

What is Antony's purpose in delivering the **monologue** beginning with line 148?

_____
_____
_____
_____
_____
_____

Reading Skill

Study the **imagery** in line 158. Explain the meaning of the image of "purpled hands" that "reek and smoke."

_____
_____
_____
_____
_____

Reading Check

Underline the lines that describe how Cassius feels about Antony.

---

55. **to friend** as a friend.
56. **my misgiving . . . to the purpose** my doubts always turn out to be justified.
57. **be let blood** (a pun) be bled for medical purposes; be killed.
58. **rank** (a pun) too powerful; swollen with disease and therefore in need of bloodletting.
59. **bear me hard** have a grudge against me.
60. **purpled hands** bloody hands.
61. **Live** if I live.
62. **apt** *adj.* ready.
63. **mean of death** way of dying.
64. **pitiful** *adj.* full of pity or compassion.
65. **pity pity** pity for Rome drove out pity for Caesar.

Read Antony's **monologue** that begins at line 183. What is his response to Brutus and Cassius' offer of friendship?

_____

_____

_____

_____

_____

_____

Do you think Antony should accept the friendship of the conspirators? Explain your answer.

_____

_____

_____

_____

_____

In lines 200–203, what **imagery** does Antony use to contrast his real grief with his words of friendship? Underline the language that appeals to your senses.

_____

_____

_____

_____

To you our swords have leaden⁶⁶ points, Mark
    Antony.
Our arms in strength of malice, and our hearts
175 Of brothers' temper,⁶⁷ do receive you in
With all kind love, good thoughts, and reverence.

CASSIUS. Your voice⁶⁸ shall be as strong as any man's
In the disposing of new dignities.⁶⁹

BRUTUS. Only be patient till we have appeased
180 The multitude, beside themselves with fear,
And then we will deliver⁷⁰ you the cause
Why I, that did love Caesar when I struck him,
Have thus proceeded.

ANTONY.   I doubt not of your wisdom.
Let each man render me his bloody hand.
185 First, Marcus Brutus, will I shake with you;
Next, Caius Cassius, do I take your hand;
Now, Decius Brutus, yours; now yours, Metellus;
Yours, Cinna; and, my valiant Casca, yours;
Though last, not least in love, yours, good
    Trebonius.
190 Gentlemen all—alas, what shall I say?
My credit⁷¹ now stands on such slippery ground
That one of two bad ways you must conceit⁷² me,
Either a coward or a flatterer.
That I did love thee, Caesar, O, 'tis true!
195 If then thy spirit look upon us now,
Shall it not grieve thee dearer⁷³ than thy death
To see thy Antony making his peace,
Shaking the bloody fingers of thy foes,
Most noble, in the presence of thy corse?⁷⁴
200 Had I as many eyes as thou hast wounds,
Weeping as fast as they stream forth thy blood,
It would become me better than to close⁷⁵
In terms of friendship with thine enemies.

---

66. **leaden** _adj._ dull; blunt.
67. **Our arms . . . / Of brothers' temper** our arms strengthened with the desire to do harm and our hearts filled with brotherly feelings.
68. **voice** _n._ vote.
69. **dignities** _n._ offices.
70. **deliver** _v._ tell to.
71. **credit** _n._ reputation.
72. **conceit** (kuhn SEET) _v._ think of.
73. **dearer** _adv._ more deeply.
74. **corse** _n._ corpse.
75. **close** (klohz) _v._ reach an agreement.

Pardon me, Julius! Here wast thou bayed,[76]
          brave hart;[77]
205   Here didst thou fall, and here thy hunters stand,
      Signed in thy spoil[78] and crimsoned in thy Lethe.[79]
      O world, thou wast the forest to this hart;
      And this indeed, O world, the heart of thee.
      How like a deer, stroken[80] by many princes.
210   Dost thou here lie!

      CASSIUS. Mark Antony—

      ANTONY.   Pardon me, Caius Cassius.
      The enemies of Caesar shall say this;
      Then, in a friend, it is cold modesty.[81]

      CASSIUS. I blame you not for praising Caesar so;
215   But what compact[82] mean you to have with us?
      Will you be pricked[83] in number of our friends,
      Or shall we on,[84] and not depend on you?

      ANTONY. Therefore I took your hands, but was indeed
      Swayed from the point by looking down on Caesar.
220   Friends am I with you all, and love you all,
      Upon this hope, that you shall give me reasons
      Why, and wherein, Caesar was dangerous.

      BRUTUS. Or else were this a savage spectacle.
      Our reasons are so full of good regard[85]
225   That were you, Antony, the son of Caesar,
      You should be satisfied.

      ANTONY.   That's all I seek;
      And am moreover suitor that I may

Vocabulary Development: spectacle (SPEK tuh kuhl) *n.* strange
                  or remarkable sight

---

76. **bayed** *v.* cornered.
77. **hart** (hahrt) *n.* deer.
78. **Signed in thy spoil** marked by signs of your slaughter.
79. **Lethe** river in Hades, the mythological Greek underworld inhabited by the dead;
    here, a river of blood.
80. **stroken** *v.* struck down.
81. **cold modesty** calm, moderate speech.
82. **compact** (KAHM pakt) *n.* agreement.
83. **pricked** *v.* marked down; included.
84. **on** proceed.
85. **so full of good regard** so carefully considered.

TAKE NOTES

Reading Skill

Read the bracketed passage. What **imagery** does Mark Antony use to describe Caesar's murder?

_____

_____

_____

_____

_____

_____

Literary Analysis

Read the **dialogue** among Cassius, Antony, and Brutus on this page. What does the dialogue reveal about Cassius' feelings?

_____

_____

_____

What does the **dialogue** reveal about Brutus' feelings?

_____

_____

_____

Reading Check

What does Antony want Brutus and Cassius to tell him? Circle the text that tells the answer.

An **aside** is a remark made by a character. It is not heard by other characters. Read the aside that Cassius speaks to Brutus. Why does Cassius wish to prevent others from hearing what he says in this aside?

_____

_____

_____

_____

_____

What do you think Brutus thinks might happen if he does not set rules for Antony's funeral speech?

_____

_____

_____

_____

Underline the rules that Antony must follow in delivering his funeral speech for Caesar. How does Antony respond to these rules outlined by Brutus?

_____

_____

Produce[86] his body to the market place,
And in the pulpit, as becomes a friend,
230   Speak in the order[87] of his funeral.

BRUTUS. You shall, Mark Antony.

CASSIUS.   Brutus, a word with you.
   (*Aside to* BRUTUS) You know not what you do;
      do not consent
   That Antony speak in his funeral.
   Know you how much the people may be moved
   By that which he will utter?

235 **BRUTUS.**   By your pardon:
   I will myself into the pulpit first,
   And show the reason of our Caesar's death.
   What Antony shall speak, I will protest[88]
   He speaks by leave and by permission,
240   And that we are contented Caesar shall
   Have all true rites and lawful ceremonies.
   It shall advantage more than do us wrong.[89]

CASSIUS. I know not what may fall;[90]
   I like it not.

BRUTUS. Mark Antony, here, take you Caesar's body.
245   You shall not in your funeral speech blame us,
   But speak all good you can devise of Caesar,
   And say you do't by our permission;
   Else shall you not have any hand at all
   About his funeral. And you shall speak
250   In the same pulpit whereto I am going,
   After my speech is ended.

ANTONY.   Be it so;
   I do desire no more.

BRUTUS. Prepare the body then, and follow us.

                              (*Exit all but* ANTONY.)

---

86. **Produce** *v.* bring forth.
87. **order** *n.* course of the ceremonies.
88. **protest** *v.* declare.
89. **advantage . . . wrong** benefit us more than hurt us.
90. **what may fall** what may happen.

ANTONY. O pardon me, thou bleeding piece of earth,
255   That I am meek and gentle with these butchers!
    Thou art the ruins of the noblest man
    That ever lived in the tide of times.[91]
    Woe to the hand that shed this costly blood!
    Over thy wounds now do I prophesy
260   (Which like dumb mouths do ope their ruby lips
    To beg the voice and utterance of my tongue),
    A curse shall light upon the limbs of men;
    Domestic fury and fierce civil strife
    Shall cumber[92] all the parts of Italy;
265   Blood and destruction shall be so in use,[93]
    And dreadful objects so familiar,
    That mothers shall but smile when they behold
    Their infants quartered with the hands of war,
    All pity choked with custom of fell deeds;[94]
270   And Caesar's spirit, ranging[95] for revenge,
    With Atè[96] by his side come hot from hell,
    Shall in these confines[97] with a monarch's voice
    Cry "Havoc,"[98] and let slip[99] the dogs of war,
    That this foul deed shall smell above the earth
275   With carrion[100] men, groaning for burial.

(Enter OCTAVIUS' SERVANT.*)*

    You serve Octavius Caesar, do you not?

SERVANT. I do, Mark Antony.

ANTONY. Caesar did write for him to come to Rome.

SERVANT. He did receive his letters and is coming,
280   And bid me say to you by word of mouth—
    O Caesar! *(Seeing the body)*

TAKE NOTES

Reading Skill

Study the **imagery** in lines 259–262. How does Shakespeare link the image of bodies with the use of words?

_____

_____

_____

_____

Literary Analysis

A **soliloquy** is a type of **dramatic speech** in which a character, usually alone on the stage, speaks as if to himself or herself. Other characters do not hear the speech. What does Antony's soliloquy in lines 254–275 reveal to the audience that other characters do not know?

_____

_____

_____

_____

Reading Check

Circle the line that shows Antony is interrupted in his soliloquy. What message does the servant bring?

_____

Vocabulary Development: prophesy (PRAHF uh sy) *v.* predict what will happen
strife (stryf) *n.* struggle; conflict

---

91. **tide of times** course of all history.
92. **cumber** (KUM buhr) *v.* distress; burden.
93. **in use** customary.
94. **custom of fell deeds** being used to cruel acts.
95. **ranging** *adj.* roaming like a wild beast in search of prey.
96. **Atè** Greek goddess personifying criminal folly or reckless ambition in people.
97. **confines** (KAHN fynz) *n.* boundaries.
98. **Havoc** Latin for "no quarter," a signal for general slaughter.
99. **let slip** release from a leash.
100. **carrion** (KAR ee uhn) *adj.* dead and rotting.

Reading Skill

What is Antony describing in the **image** "beads of sorrow"?

_____

_____

Literary Analysis

What plans does Antony reveal in his **dialogue** with the servant?

_____

_____

_____

What does Antony hope to accomplish with these plans?

_____

_____

_____

Reading Check

What is Antony's message to Octavius? Circle the text that tells the answer.

ANTONY. Thy heart is big;[101] get thee apart and weep.
  Passion, I see, is catching, for mine eyes,
  Seeing those beads of sorrow stand in thine,
285 Began to water. Is thy master coming?

SERVANT. He lies tonight within seven leagues[102]
  of Rome.

ANTONY. Post[103] back with speed, and tell him what
  hath chanced.[104]
  Here is a mourning Rome, a dangerous Rome,
  No Rome of safety for Octavius yet.
290 Hie hence and tell him so. Yet stay awhile;
  Thou shalt not back till I have borne this corse
  Into the market place; there shall I try[105]
  In my oration[106] how the people take
  The cruel issue[107] of these bloody men;
295 According to the which, thou shalt discourse
  To young Octavius of the state of things.
  Lend me your hand.

(Exit)

Vocabulary Development: discourse (DIS kawrs) *v.* speak (on a topic) formally and at length

---

101. **big** *adj.* swollen with grief.
102. **leagues** (leegz) *n.* units of measure, each equivalent in Roman times to about a mile and a half.
103. **Post** *v.* hasten.
104. **hath chanced** has happened.
105. **try** *v.* test.
106. **oration** (aw RAY shuhn) *n.* formal public speech.
107. **cruel issue** outcome of the cruelty.

Reader's Response: Do you think that Antony does the right thing in the end? Explain.

_____

_____

_____

The Tragedy of Julius Caesar, Act III, Scene i

1. **Respond:** As a Roman, would you have agreed with Antony's words in lines 254–275?

   _____

   _____

   _____

2. **Make a Judgment:** Is Caesar responsible for his own death? Explain.

   _____

   _____

   _____

3. **Literary Analysis:** In the chart below, identify each speech as an **aside**, a **soliloquy**, or a **monologue**. Then, paraphrase the speech and identify those who hear it.

Lines	Type of Speech	Paraphrase	Who Hears It?
Scene i, lines 148–163			
Scene i, lines 232–234			
Scene i, lines 254–275			

4. **Reading Skill:** Find two examples of **imagery** in Act III, Scene i, that are related to the human body and to words.

   _____

   _____

   _____

   _____

SUPPORT FOR WRITING AND EXTEND YOUR LEARNING

Writing: Letter to the Editor

Write a **letter to the editor** of the *Roman Times* that discusses your feelings about how the common people of Rome change their loyalties. Use the following questions to record answers from the text and to record your opinion about these facts.

Question	Answer From Text	Your Opinion
Who kills Caesar?		
Why is Caesar killed?		
Who is sad about Caesar's death?		
Who is happy about Caesar's death?		

Use your notes to prepare your letter.

Research and Technology: Map

Prepare a **map** of ancient Rome that shows the important sites in the city. Focus on sites which appear in Act III, scene i, of *The Tragedy of Julius Caesar*.

As you prepare the annotations for your map, ask yourself these questions:

- Where did the conspirators gather to meet Caesar as he came to the Senate?

_____

- At what location was Caesar actually assassinated?

_____

- Where did Brutus and Mark Antony plan to give their funeral speeches?

_____

- What other buildings were nearby?

_____

Use these notes to help you write the annotations for your map.

The Tragedy of Julius Caesar, Act IV

LITERARY ANALYSIS

Conflict, a struggle between opposing forces, creates drama.

- In an **external conflict**, a character struggles with an outside force, such as another character, a group of characters, or a force such as the weather.

- In an **internal conflict**, the character struggles with his or her own opposing beliefs, desires, or values.

The Tragedy of Julius Caesar involves a number of different conflicts. Internal and external conflicts are in many cases directly related. For instance, earlier in the play, the external conflict between Brutus and Caesar creates an internal conflict for Brutus—he wishes to check Caesar's ambition, but he also considers Caesar a friend.

READING SKILL

When **reading Shakespearean drama**, you need to **read between the lines** to find the deeper meaning of a character's words or actions.

- Keep the larger situation in mind as you read. For instance, early in Act IV, Antony describes Lepidus as "Meet to be sent on errands." Note that Antony has been deciding which of his political rivals will die and which will share power. Between the lines, he is saying, "Fit to run errands—and nothing else."

- Follow indirect references. For example, when Lucilius reports on Cassius, Brutus says, "Thou has described / A hot friend cooling." "A hot friend" refers to Cassius, whom Brutus worries is no longer his ally.

Use the chart below to read between the lines.

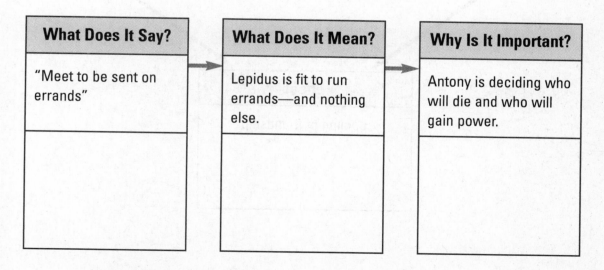

What Does It Say?	What Does It Mean?	Why Is It Important?
"Meet to be sent on errands"	Lepidus is fit to run errands—and nothing else.	Antony is deciding who will die and who will gain power.

The Tragedy of Julius Caesar, Act IV

William Shakespeare

Summary Antony, Octavius, and Lepidus meet in Rome to decide who will live and who will die. Brutus and Cassius feel wronged by each other, and the two argue. Brutus learns of Portia's suicide. Brutus and Cassius disagree about military strategy. Caesar's ghost visits Brutus and hints at dangers to come.

Note-taking Guide

Use the diagram to record the reasons for the conflict between Brutus and Cassius.

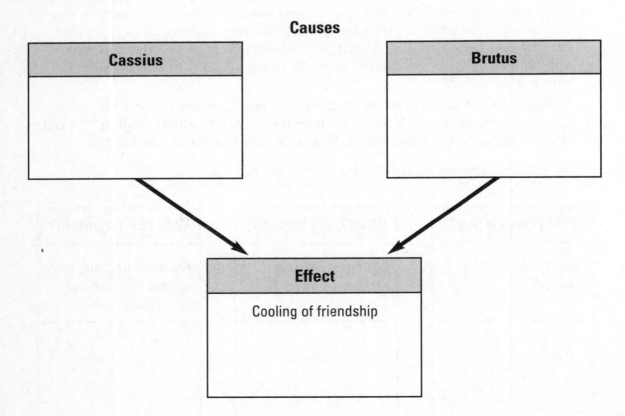

Causes

Cassius	Brutus

Effect

Cooling of friendship

The Tragedy of Julius Caesar, Act IV

1. **Infer:** In Act IV, Scene i, Antony expresses his opinion of Lepidus. Why is Octavius surprised to hear this opinion?

_____

_____

2. **Compare and Contrast:** In Act IV, Scene ii, Brutus and Cassius argue. What difference in their characters does the argument emphasize?

_____

_____

3. **Literary Analysis:** Use the center box in the diagram below to identify two **external conflicts** in Act IV. Also, identify two **internal conflicts** that Brutus has in Act IV. List the opposing forces of each conflict in the outer boxes.

Force 1	Conflict: External/Internal	Force 2
→		←
→		←
→		←
→		←

4. **Reading Skill:** Read what Cassius says in Scene iii, lines 92–98. Now, **read between the lines** to explain the unspoken significance of his words.

_____

_____

SUPPORT FOR WRITING AND EXTEND YOUR LEARNING

Writing: Newspaper Editorial

Imagine that you are a journalist at the time of Caesar's murder. Write an **editorial** to express your opinion of Rome's future. Take notes for your editorial by filling out the chart below. Consider the whole play, not just Act IV.

Editorial on Rome's Future		
Events: What has happened?	**Issues: What problems must be solved?**	**Results: What is the best outcome for Rome?**

Listening and Speaking: Profile

Create a **profile** of Brutus for a magazine-style TV news show. Include interviews with Brutus' friends and family. Use this list to help you take notes for your profile.

- Describe Brutus in his public life:

  _____

  _____

- Describe Brutus in his private life:

  _____

  _____

- Describe his relationship with Caesar:

  _____

  _____

- Describe his goals:

  _____

  _____

The Tragedy of Julius Caesar, Act V

LITERARY ANALYSIS

Traditionally, a **tragic hero** is a person, usually of noble birth, who suffers a catastrophe. The hero's choices leading to the catastrophe may reflect a personal shortcoming, such as pride, called a **tragic flaw**. While **Shakespeare's tragic heroes** incorporate these traditional elements, he develops them in new ways:

- He adds complexity to his heroes, who may have opposing desires and who may suffer hesitation and doubt before acting.
- He presents a character's inner turmoil directly, through devices like the *soliloquy*, a speech in which a character thinks aloud.
- He focuses on the choices characters make rather than on fate.
- His characters' problems often concern the difference between the reasons for an action and its outcome. For example, Brutus acts for reasons of honor—the right reasons—but in a world of men who are less than honorable, the results are disastrous.

READING SKILL

Shakespeare may emphasize the important qualities of one character by presenting another character with contrasting qualities. When **reading Shakespearean drama**, you can often gain understanding by **comparing and contrasting characters**. Look for similarities and differences in the characters' personalities, situations, behavior, and attitudes. Use the chart below to compare and contrast characters as you read Act V.

Brutus	Cassius
nobleman	nobleman
idealistic	practical

The Tragedy of Julius Caesar, Act V

William Shakespeare

Summary Brutus and Cassius meet Antony and Octavius on the battlefield. Cassius thinks that his best friend, Titinius, has been captured. Cassius kills himself as a result. Brutus kills himself when he sees that Antony is winning the battle at the end.

Note-taking Guide

Use this cause-and-effect chart to record events and their results in Act V.

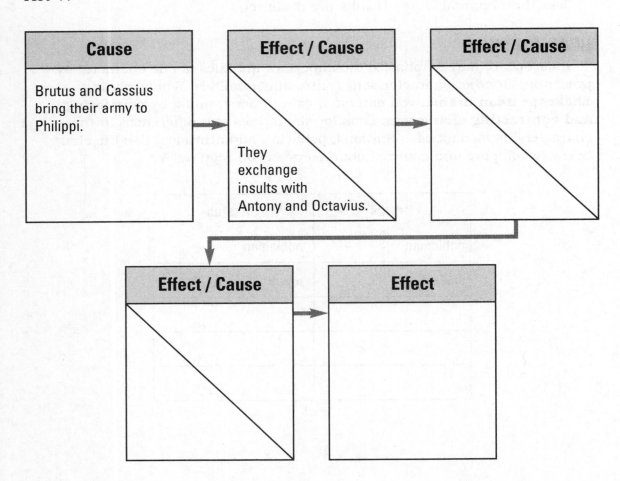

Cause
Brutus and Cassius bring their army to Philippi.

Effect / Cause
They exchange insults with Antony and Octavius.

Effect / Cause

Effect / Cause

Effect

The Tragedy of Julius Caesar, Act V

1. **Draw Conclusions:** Cassius and Brutus make plans in case they lose the battle. What do their plans show about their values?

   _____

   _____

2. **Make a Judgment:** Brutus says, "My heart doth joy that yet in all my life / I found no man but he was true to me." Brutus means that no one he has known has ever betrayed him. Do these lines express a positive attitude or a blindness toward others? Explain.

   _____

   _____

3. **Literary Analysis:** Use this chart to give examples that show that Brutus and Caesar have the qualities of traditional **tragic heroes**.

	Noble Birth	Suffers Catastrophe	Tragic Flaw
Brutus			
Caesar			

4. **Reading Skill: Compare and contrast** Brutus and Cassius. Give specific examples to support your points.

   _____

   _____

   _____

   _____

SUPPORT FOR WRITING AND EXTEND YOUR LEARNING

Writing: Obituary

Write an **obituary** for a character who dies in *Julius Caesar*. Use these questions to prepare for writing.

- How was the character an inspiration to others?

  _____

  _____

- How did this character respond to difficult times?

  _____

  _____

- What friends and family members survive this character?

  _____

  Funeral service information:

  _____

Research and Technology: Research Note

Write a **research note** to the play. In the note, explain what took place in Rome after the events in the play. Record the information in this chart.

What happened in Rome after the death of Julius Caesar?
Information source:
Notes:
Information source:
Notes:
Information source:
Notes:

Signs

ABOUT SIGNS

Signs give information to the public. They may be posters, placards, or other markers. Signs present information so that people can see it at any time. For example, you may see a sign that reads "open" or "closed" when you approach a store. You have taken in important information without opening a book or asking a question. The sign tells you whether you can enter the store. Signs can provide the following types of information:

- Rules
- Warnings
- Hours of operation
- Information that identifies things, such as the animals in a zoo
- Background information, such as that found in museum exhibits

The signs you will read here are from the Folger Shakespeare Library in Washington, D.C. The first sign appears at the visitor entrance. The second sign tells visitors about Queen Elizabeth I. She ruled England at the time when Shakespeare's plays were written and first performed.

READING SKILL

You usually have a specific purpose for reading a sign. You read it because you need certain information. You may want to use **signs as research aids** when you visit a museum. First, find your purpose. Then, you can use the appearance of the text on signs to find the information you need. **Use text format** to help you locate information quickly. Text format is the size, color, and arrangement of different parts of the text.

Practice connecting your purpose to your reading of signs. Use the K-W-L chart below as you read the signs in this lesson. Your purpose is to answer the questions you ask in the "What I Want to Know" column.

What I **K**now	What I **W**ant to Know	What I **L**earned
This is a museum.		

VISITOR ENTRANCE

ELIZABETHAN THEATRE
BOX OFFICE OPENS
ONE HOUR BEFORE EVENTS

EXHIBITIONS

◀ELIZABETHAN GARDEN

MONDAY–SATURDAY
10:00 A.M. – 4:00 P.M.

RESEARCH ENTRANCE ▶
READING ROOM • MUSEUM SHOP
ADMINISTRATIVE OFFICES

CLOSED ALL FEDERAL HOLIDAYS

Elizabeth I

"TO BE A KING AND WEAR A CROWN is a thing more glorious to them that see it than it is pleasant to them that bear it." These words, spoken by Elizabeth I to her Parliament in 1601, might just as well be echoed by any head of state today. All the perks of office—the fine clothes, jewels, servants, and now, private planes and media attention—are there to be enjoyed, but they come with the high price of responsibility to the people and the nation. Elizabeth was not elected, she inherited this responsibility from her father, Henry VIII, but she took it seriously and was educated to be a prince. In 1558 after the death of her Catholic sister Mary, Elizabeth came to the throne and reigned for forty-four years. Though she restored the Protestant church to England, she resisted extremes in religion as well as policy. She also resisted pressure by her male council and Parliament to marry, turning the many offers for her hand into a game of political chess. She was a true "career woman" long before the term was coined; her job was her life.

Now, four hundred years after Elizabeth's death in March of 1603, the Folger Library honors her memory and her reign. Because Emily and Henry Folger focused their collecting on the age of Shakespeare, when Elizabeth was queen, the Folger Library has the largest collection of artifacts relating to Elizabeth in America. She has never really gone out of style. Every generation has re-read her through their own ideas of womanhood, and today perhaps we can appreciate her political skills more than did any other era. In her "Golden Speech" quoted above, she also said: "though you have had and may have many princes more mighty and wise sitting in this seat, yet you never had or shall have any that will be more careful and loving."

Major support for this exhibition comes from the Winton and Carolyn Blount Exhibition Fund of the Folger Shakespeare Library.

THINKING ABOUT THE SIGN

1. The first sign says that the library is closed on all federal holidays. Name three holidays on which the library would be closed.

   _____

   _____

   _____

2. Three facilities are listed under the heading "Research Entrance." Which of these would be most important for someone doing a research project? Explain.

   _____

   _____

READING SKILL

3. Study the arrangement and size of text of the visitor-entrance sign. What piece of information did the designer of the sign think was most important?

   _____

4. Study the sign that introduces Elizabeth I. Describe one possible research topic on which the sign gives information.

   _____

TIMED WRITING: DESCRIPTION (35 minutes)

Write an essay describing a topic for a research project. The project could be completed by using the Folger Shakespeare Library. Include the following in your essay:

- A detailed explanation of the research topic
- Why the Folger Shakespeare Library would be a good resource

To help you get started, first write your idea for a topic. Then make a few notes about how each sign would help someone find information about that topic.

_____

_____

from Places Left Unfinished at the Time of Creation

Long before it was written down, literature was passed by word of mouth. People exchanged tales while doing chores or resting from them. This type of communication of stories is known as the **oral tradition**. These stories explore **universal themes**—ideas about life that are similar, regardless of time and place. For example, many different stories show the value of friendship or the need for courage.

In telling their tales, people naturally used **archetypes**. These repeated characters, situations, images, and symbols appear in the narratives of many different cultures. The presentation of these archetypes may change based on the **historical context**, or social and cultural background, of the storyteller and the audience. Here are some common **archetypical characters and ideas**.

Archetypical Characters and Ideas	Definition	Example
Wise and virtuous king	A great ruler whose reign brings in a **golden age**, or time of peace and prosperity	King Arthur and Camelot
Dreamer	A character who imagines new possibilities and defies danger to bring an important gift to society	Long Arrow
Hero	An unpromising youth who blossoms into a wise, strong, and courageous leader	Rama
Protagonist	The main character in a story	Wart
Antagonist	A person or a force that opposes the protagonist	Queen Mother

Historically, anonymous storytellers developed different forms to express archetypes. Because these early forms were oral, tales might change with every telling. Later in history, stories were written down, and individual authors emerged. Archetypes are often found in the following types of stories:

- **Myths** explain the action of gods and the humans who interact with them. They may also explain the causes of natural phenomena.

- **Legends** are traditional stories about the past. They are usually based on historical fact.

- **Epics** are long narrative poems about a larger-than-life **epic hero**. The epic hero's career is important to the history of a group.

- **Folk tales** focus on human or animal heroes.

- **Fairy tales** are folk tales that recount the adventures of spirits who appear as very small humans.

Each of these forms express the **values**, or model behaviors, of a society. Some ideas are **shared values**, which are held by many societies. Others are **culturally distinct values**, which are specific to a group. **Cultural details** in a narrative illustrate the beliefs and customs that give a particular group its **identity**, or sense of self.

Modern fiction, written by individuals rather than created by a group, can also express universal themes. It can also express a **parody**, or humorous mockery, of an archetypal pattern.

from Places Left Unfinished at the Time of Creation

John Phillip Santos

Summary John Phillip Santos uses objects collected from the past to reflect on the meaning of ordinary events. He explores the past and blends the history of his family with the spirit of his Mexican ancestors. Family photographs, Christmas cards, and even a grocery receipt show his relationship to those who came before him.

Note-taking Guide

Use this cluster diagram to record the small stories that appear within this excerpt from Santos's book.

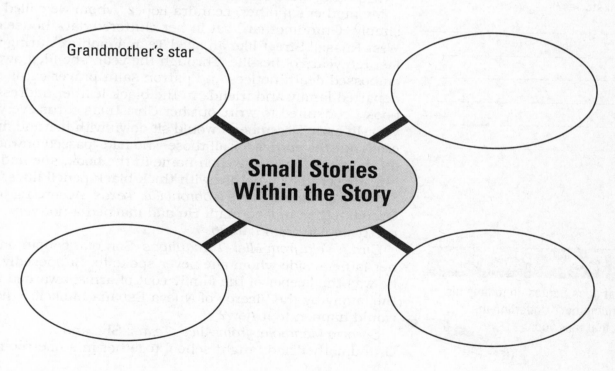

Name a custom or holiday that you will observe when you have your own home. Explain your choice.

_____

_____

_____

_____

_____

Themes in Literature

Oral tradition means stories were passed on verbally instead of being written down. Were many keepsakes handed down in Santos's family? How might this effect each family member's ability to tell stories?

_____

_____

_____

_____

_____

_____

Reading Check

What does Santos do to help his grandmother? Underline the text that tells you.

from Places Left Unfinished at the Time of Creation
John Phillip Santos

. . . The past can be difficult to conjure again when so little has been left behind. A few photographs, a golden medal, a pair of eyeglasses as delicate as eggshells, an old Bible, a letter or two. Some families in Mexico have troves of their ancestors' belongings, from pottery of the ancients and exquisite paintings of Mexico City in the eighteenth century to helmets and shields of the Spaniards, and even hundred-year-old parrots and maguey plants[1] that have been handed down, from the great-grandparents who first tended them.

By comparison, the Santos are traveling light through time. In my family, virtually nothing has been handed down, not because there was nothing to give, but after leaving Mexico to come to Texas—so many loved ones left behind, cherished places and things abandoned—the antepasados[2] ceased to regard anything as a keepsake. Everything was given away. Or they may have secretly clung so closely to their treasured objects that they were never passed on.

Then they were lost.

My mother's mother, Leandra Lopez, whom we called simply "Grandmother," sat in her cluttered dark house on West Russell Street like an aged Tejana[3] sphinx during the last ten years of her life. Through the year, she filed away embossed death notices and patron saint prayer cards of departed family and friends in the black leather address book I consulted to write out her Christmas cards every year. In early December, I would sit down with her and first cross out the entries for all those who had "passed onward," as she used to say. By each name in the book, she had already scratched a cross with thick black pencil lines.

Memo Montalvo from Hebbronville, Texas. According to Grandmother, a good man. He had married a not-very-pretty cousin from Laredo.

Efraín Vela from Mier, Tamaulipas. Son of a cousin on her father's side whom she never spoke to. Supposedly, he was the keeper of the family coat of arms, awarded to the family by the Viceroy of Nueva España himself. What would happen to it now?

Socorro Mendiola, from Alice, Texas. She and Grandmother had taught school together in a one-room

---

1. **maguey** (MAG way) **plants** *n.* fleshy-leaved plants common to Mexico, Central America, and the southwestern United States; used for making rope and tequila.
2. **antepasados** (ahn tah pah SAH dohs) *n.* forebears, ancestors.
3. **Tejana** (tay HAH nah) *adj.* Texan.

schoolhouse in Cotulla in 1910. Then Socorro became a Franciscan nun, breaking the heart of Grandmother's cousin, Emeterio Vela, whom, she noted with a sigh, had died just last year.

And every year, by the degrees of each ended life, as the world grew older, our addressing marathons grew shorter—though Grandmother would change the subject if I pointed out this mortal ratio.

Inside her rolltop writing desk, she kept a mysterious wooden polygonal[4] star that had a different swatch of old Mexican fabrics glued on each facet. The multicolored curiosity smelled like Mexico, all cumin, wild honey, and smoky rose, and when you shook it, a small solitary object rattled inside. A stone? A marble? A gem? To me, it seemed like some magician's puzzle, and locked inside were all of the secrets of old Mexico.

During one of our annual Christmas-card sessions, I asked her if I could have that star, instead of the customary reward of a box of animal crackers and five dollars in change, which she laboriously fished out of her zippered, yellowing plastic coin purse. Grandmother was almost completely blind by then, so I put her hand to the last of the Hallmark Christmas cards in the place for her to sign her name. She slowly scratched out Leandra Vela Lopez, and told me no, I could not have the star.

I never saw it again.

My uncle, Lico Lopez, her son, ferreted out the past as a passionate genealogist who used research, fantasy, and spells of breathless diabetic madness to craft his ancestral charts of the Lopez and Vela families. Some are elaborate discs, in which each outward concentric ring represents a new generation. In these, as you delve closer to the center, you also go deeper into the past. In others, quickly dashed off as notes to himself, ragged trees and jagged lines are drawn between names like Evaristo, Viviano, Blas, and Hermenegilda. In one, going back to 1763, the capstone slot contains the cryptic entry,

"King of Spain"

from whom, presumably, he believed we were descended. Subtle faculties and proclivities[5] were passed, speechlessly, through the flesh of successive generations. The ghosts of Spanish royalty mingled with Indios, Negros, and people from every part of the world—in Uncle Lico's

---

Vocabulary Development: facet (FAS it) *n.* any of a number of sides or aspects

---

4. **polygonal** (pah LIG ah nuhl) *adj.* many-sided.
5. **proclivities** (proh KLIV uh tees) *n.* natural or habitual inclinations.

TAKE NOTES

Themes in Literature

Cultural details illustrate the beliefs and customs of a group. Underline the words and groups of words that create a mental picture of the star.

Stop to Reflect

Why do you think Santos wanted the star?

_____

_____

Why do you think Santos's grandmother would not give him the star?

_____

_____

Themes in Literature

Why does Santos call his uncle's work madness?

_____

_____

Identity, or sense of self, is often linked with the past. What does his uncle's work have to do with the family's identity?

_____

_____

_____

_____

Why do you think the family preserved the grocery receipt?

_____

_____

_____

What does it reveal about the family's **identity**?

_____

_____

_____

_____

Why do you think Santos goes into so much detail about the one photograph?

_____

_____

_____

_____

What happened to the family photographs when Madrina moved out of her old house? Underline the text that tells you.

secret genealogy of Mexico. Yet, despite the uninterest and ridicule of many, he managed to recover numerous family names and stories.

Lico knew I had some of the same magnetic attraction to the past that fueled his manic genealogies, as if the molecules of our bodies were <u>polarized</u> in a way that drew us both back in time, back, <u>inexorably</u>, toward the ancestors. Before he died, suddenly, in San Antonio, of a heart attack, he sent me all of the notes and charts accumulated in his forty years of digging in the family root cellars. He also gave me a receipt, dated May 25, 1928, laminated and mounted on wood, from my grandfather's grocery store, Leonides Lopez Groceries, in Cotulla, Texas. In my grandfather's filigreed wrought iron pencil script, it details a sale on that day of *harina* (flour), *azúcar* (sugar), *fideos* (vermicelli), *manteca* (lard), *papas* (potatoes), and other assorted dry goods, for a total of $5.05.

A relic like this is the exception, though. A trunkful of the Santos family photographs disappeared when Madrina moved out of the old house on Cincinnati Street. She swears she remembers seeing it fall off the truck near the corner of Zarzamora Street, where La Poblanita bakery was located. It was a pine box the size of a shipping trunk, stuffed with heirloom photographs. She can't remember why she said nothing at the time. It fell off a truck onto the dusty streets of old San Antonio de Bejar one day and was left behind, abandoned, lost.

In one photo that survived it is 1960, and the whole Santos tribe is standing on the porch of my grandmother's house, in early evening shadows. It must have been Easter because my many cousins and I are in church clothes, standing in the yard around the trunk of a great sycamore tree. My aunts and uncles are there, partly old Mexican, partly new American, looking handsome, hopeful, proud of the brood standing in front of them. In the very middle of the scene, *las Ancianas*, Grandmother Santos, whom we called "Uela," short for *abuela*, and Madrina, her sister, are standing regally in a perfect moment, radiating the indelible light of Mexico. On the porch, Mother and an aunt have my newborn twin brothers, George and Charles, wrapped in blankets in their arms. My father looks serious, with a distant gaze, in a dark suit and silky tie. To one side, standing apart from us, is one of my eldest cousins, René, who would be killed in Vietnam just seven years later.

Vocabulary Development: polarized (POH luh ryzd) *adj.* divided into two opposing groups
inexorably (in EKS uh ruhb lee) *adv.* unrelentingly

These are the memento mori[6] of the Santos. There are a few photographs, rosary chains of half-remembered stories, carried out of another time by the old Mexicans I grew up with. In dreams, the ancestors who have passed on visit with me, in this world, and in a world that lies perhaps within, amidst, and still beyond this world—a mystical limbo dimension that the descendants of the Aztecs call *el Inframundo*. In the *Inframundo*, all that has been forgotten still lives. Nothing is lost. All remembrance is redeemed from oblivion.

These ancestors, living and dead, have asked me the questions they were once asked: Where did our forebears come from and what have we amounted to in this world? Where have we come to in the span of all time, and where are we headed, like an arrow shot long ago into infinite empty space? What messages and markings of the ancient past do we carry in these handed-down bodies we live in today?

With these questions swirling inside me, I have rediscovered some stories of the family past in the landscapes of Texas and Mexico, in the timeless language of stone, river, wind, and trees. Tío Abrán, twin brother to my great-grandfather Jacobo, was a master of making charcoal. He lived in the hill country, where the cedars needed to make charcoal were planted a century ago to supply the industry. Today, long after he worked there, walking in that central Texas landscape crowded with deep green cedar, I feel old Abrán's presence, like the whisper of a tale still waiting to be told, wondering whether my intuition and the family's history are implicitly intertwined. Even if everything else had been lost—photographs, stories, rumors, and suspicions—if nothing at all from the past remained for us, the land remains, as the original book of the family.

It was always meant to be handed down.

Once they arrived in Texas during the revolution, maybe the Santos and Garcia families simply wanted to forget their past in Mexico—the dusty streets, broken-down houses, and hunger. They wanted to burn away the memory of when the families came north across the Rio Grande. Northern Mexico became one of the most violent and chaotic battlefields of *la Revolución* of 1910, a revolution that was to last eleven years. But for the first years, the revolution was only distant thunder, more of a concern to Mexicans well to the south of Coahuila in states such as Guerrero, Puebla, and Mexico City. The family's flight from Coahuila was in 1914, the year Pancho Villa, along with a myriad of other revolutionary bands, rose up to occupy

---

6. **memento mori** (muh MEN toh MORI ee) *n.* reminder of death.

from Places Left Unfinished at the Time of Creation **389**

TAKE NOTES

Stop to Reflect

Do you think Santos expects solutions to the mysteries of his family's past? Why or why not?

_____

_____

Themes in Literature

Historical context is the social and cultural background of the story-teller and the audience. Read the underlined sentence. What can you tell about Santos's cultural background from this sentence?

_____

_____

_____

Themes in Literature

Underline where the Santos family went in 1914. Circle what drove them from Mexico. How do these details add to your understanding of the Santos's family **identity**?

_____

_____

Reading Check

What is the Inframundo? Bracket the text that tells you.

Underline the reasons why the family felt out of place in the Gringo world of San Antonio. How did these experiences affect the **cultural details** to which the family had to adjust?

_____

_____

_____

_____

_____

_____

Imagine that you had to move to a new town. What adjustments would you have to make? What would be difficult about the move?

_____

_____

_____

How does Santos describe his home in San Antonio? Circle the text that tells you.

the bare constellation of towns across the parched high Norteño desert where they had made their homes. San Antonio provided them a convenient escape from the fighting, and—despite other intentions—a shelter for memory, instead of its negation.

For my cousins, as for my brothers and me, the homes of *las Viejitas*[7] were sanctuaries where Coahuila was still alive, and places where the inhibitions and proprieties of the Gringo world of San Antonio, Texas, outside did not apply. Those were days when the taco and the tamal[8] were stigmatized in public, and Spanish was seldom heard on downtown streets. The old tíos[9] had to speak English, often haltingly, to get along in the working world. Most of *las Viejitas*, staying in their homes, spoke only Spanish, or at least pretended not to speak English. When Uela spoke Spanish, her sentences moved in one steady arc, like a bow across a violin, and her words were delicately pronounced, so that you could hear every tinkle of an old chandelier, every gust of a Coahuila wind falling to a hush, and the grain of a rustling squash blossom.

The migrations continued through the century. In the 1960s, my parents moved us from one of the old neighborhoods of the city to a new suburb at the city's northwestern edge, in order to get us into the better public schools in San Antonio. We were the first Mexicans in the neighborhood, in a two-floor house with a two-car garage, a built-in dishwasher, central air-conditioning, and intercom consoles in every room. We spoke English to each other, and Spanish to the old ones in the family. When the mariachis played in our backyard, the rapid plucking of the bajo sexto[10] and the shimmering trumpet lines echoed off the neighbors' houses and drew them out to listen. Out there in that virgin neighborhood, it always felt as if we were closer to the iridescent Texas sky, stripped of the protective canopy of sycamore, wisteria, china berry, and live oak that arched over so many of the streets of our old, secret Mexican city, San Antonio de Bejar.

That old San Antonio was part of the hoary earth of the ancestors. Out there in the suburb at the edge of the city, following the early Gemini and Apollo space missions, I read books about space and prepared for the day in the future, which would undoubtedly come, when I would leave this planet in a rocket of my own.

---

7. **las Viejitas** (lahs bee ay HAY tahs) *n.* literally, "little old ladies." Santos is using this as a term of endearment for his elderly women relatives.
8. **tamal** (TAH mahl) *n.* tamale, a steamed corn husk filled with meat and cornmeal.
9. **tíos** (TI ohs) *n.* uncles.
10. **bajo sexto** (BAH hoh SEKS toh) *n.* six-string bass.

Today, in New York City, I live in a world *las Viejitas* never visited, very far from the land they knew well. I have been to places they never imagined, like England, Europe, Turkey, Peru, and the Sudan. Yet, wherever I go, there is a ribbon of primordial Mexican night, the color of obsidian,[11] snaking in a dream through the skies high over my head. Sometimes it is easily visible to me, like a burning galaxy, sometimes it is not. Sometimes it drizzles a fine rain of voices, images, and stories. And *las Viejitas* are here now, too, as they have always been, invisible yet abiding. They are keeping a vigil over the stories they told to me as if they are a *compromiso*, a promise that has been handed on. I have always felt connected, oriented, and imparted to by them, but unsure how I fit into a story that was never meant to be told.

---

11. **obsidian** (uhb SID ee uhn) *n.* dark or black volcanic glass.

Reader's Response: How important do you think it is for a family to actively preserve its history and traditions? Explain your answer.

_____

_____

_____

Stop to Reflect

What do you think Santos means by calling the stories of *las Viejitas* a promise but saying that they were never meant to be told?

_____

_____

_____

_____

Themes in Literature

1. **Analyze Cause and Effect:** Why might the move from Mexico to San Antonio have affected the Santos family's desire to remember the past?

   _____

   _____

   _____

2. **Interpret:** What does Santos mean when he says his family is "traveling light through time"?

   _____

   _____

   _____

3. **Themes in Literature:** Use the chart below to identify passages containing **cultural details**. Also, show why these details were important to help the Santos family maintain its **identity**.

Passage	Cultural Detail	Why It Is Important

4. **Themes in Literature:** What role does the **oral tradition** play in helping Santos understand his family's past?

   _____

   _____

   _____

RESEARCH THE AUTHOR

Annotated Map

Create an **annotated map** of the places where Santos and his family settled in Mexico and Texas. Use your notes from the following prompts to create your map.

- Use library and Internet sources to study each place Santos mentions in the text. Use phrases such as "San Antonio history" and "Cotulla, Texas history" during your search. Take notes on the information you want to include on your map.

_____

_____

_____

- For each location, write a brief note about important events that occurred while the family or Santos himself lived there.

_____

_____

_____

_____

- Watch the video interview with John Phillip Santos. Add any new information that Santos presents about the settlements of his family.

_____

_____

_____

_____

_____

_____

_____

_____

_____

Prometheus and the First People •
The Orphan Boy and the Elk Dog

LITERARY ANALYSIS

Myths are stories that are part of an oral tradition: Before being written, they were told and retold from one generation to the next. Myths reflect the culture of the people who originated and shared them.

- Some myths explain a natural phenomenon or specific custom by telling of its **origins**—how it came to be. These myths reveal the beliefs of ancient cultures.
- Myths include characters with exceptional characteristics. These characteristics emphasize qualities that the culture admired or feared.
- Some myths tell of a **quest**, or search, for knowledge or some important object. These myths reveal what was important to the culture.
- Other myths tell of a **transgression**, or the violation of a rule. These myths teach the values of the culture.

READING SKILL

To understand myth, **analyze cultural context**, or determine ways in which the myth reflects the lives and concerns of those who told it. **Generate questions** about the cultural context before you read. Ask yourself one question about each element shown in the chart. Then, note details in the myth that help you answer your questions.

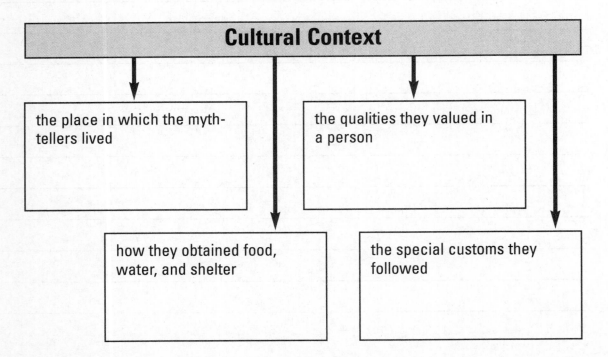

Cultural Context

the place in which the myth-tellers lived

the qualities they valued in a person

how they obtained food, water, and shelter

the special customs they followed

Prometheus and the First People

Olivia Coolidge

Summary This myth tells the story of the god Prometheus. He gave humans the abilities to think and to understand. He also gave humans fire, but he stole the fire from the gods. Zeus became angry and punished Prometheus. Zeus wanted to take revenge on the humans. He created Pandora to bring humans sorrow.

Reading/Writing Connection

Complete each sentence to describe inventions people use for comfort and protection.

1. Manufacturers <u>assemble</u> cars that _____.

2. People can watch television to <u>anticipate</u> _____.

3. A student can use the computer to <u>study</u> _____.

Note-taking Guide

Use this diagram to note the actions in the myths and the things that happen as a result of those actions.

Action	What happens
Prometheus gave humans fire.	Zeus chained Prometheus to a rock where the sun burned him all day.

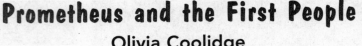
TAKE NOTES

Activate Prior Knowledge

Have you ever heard a story from a different culture about how humans came to be? How did humans come to be according to the story?

_____

_____

_____

Literary Analysis

Myths are stories that are told and retold from one generation to the next. Some myths explain **origins**, or how something came to be. Underline details in the bracketed text that show you that this myth will explain the origins of something.

Reading Skill

To understand a myth, **analyze cultural context**. Find ways in which the myth reflects the lives and concerns of those who told it. Underline details on this page that tell you about the region where the Greeks lived.

Reading Check

To what animals did Epimetheus give strength? Underline the text that tells you.

HUMANITY'S BEGINNINGS

The Greeks have several stories about how man came to be. One declares that he was created in the age of Kronos,[1] or Saturn, who ruled before Zeus [zoos]. At that time, the legend says, there was no sorrow, toil, sickness, or age. Men lived their lives in plenty and died as though they went to sleep. They tilled[2] no ground, built no cities, killed no living thing, and among them war was unknown. The earth brought forth strawberries, cherries, and ears of wheat for them. Even on the bramble bushes grew berries good to eat. Milk and sweet nectar flowed in rivers for men to drink, and honey dripped from hollow trees. Men lived in caves and thickets, needing little shelter, for the season was always spring.

Another legend declares that Zeus conceived of animals first and he entrusted their creation to Prometheus [proh MEE thee uhs] and Epimetheus [ep uh MEE thee uhsz], his brother. First, Epimetheus undertook to order all things, but he was a heedless person and soon got into trouble. Finally he was forced to appeal to Prometheus.

"What have you done?" asked Prometheus.

"Down on the earth," answered his brother, "there is a green, grassy clearing, ringed by tall oak trees and shaded by steep slopes from all but the midday sun. There I sat and the animals came to me, while I gave to each the gifts which should be his from this time forward. Air I gave to the birds, seas to the fishes, land to four-footed creatures and the creeping insects, and to some, like the moles, I gave burrows beneath the earth."

"That was well done," answered Prometheus. "What else did you do?"

"Strength," said Epimetheus, "I gave to lions and tigers, and the fierce animals of the woods. Size I gave to others like the great whales of the sea. The deer I made swift and timid, and the insects I made tiny that they might escape from sight. I gave warm fur to the great bears and the little squirrels, keen eyes and sharp talons[3] to the birds of prey, tusks to the elephant, hide to the wild boar, sweet songs

---

Vocabulary Development: toil (toyl) *n.* hard, tiring work
heedless (heed) *adj.* careless; thoughtless

---

1. **Kronos** (KROH nuhs) *n.* son of the sky and Earth; father of Zeus.
2. **tilled** *v.* cultivated; plowed or hoed.
3. **talons** (TAHL uns) *n.* claws (of birds of prey).

and bright feathers to the birds. To each I gave some special excellence, that whether large or small, kind or terrible, each might live in his own place, find food, escape enemies, and enjoy the wide world which is his to inhabit."

"All this is very good," said his brother, Prometheus. "You have done well. Wherein lies your trouble?"

"Because I did not think it out beforehand," said the heedless brother sadly, "I did not count how many animals there were to be before I started giving. Now when I have given all, there comes one last animal for whom I have neither skill nor shape, nor any place to dwell in. Everything has been given already."

"What is this animal," said Prometheus, "who has been forgotten?"

"His name," said Epimetheus, "is Man."

Thus it was that the future of man was left to Prometheus, who was forced to make man different from all other creatures. Therefore he gave him the shape of the gods themselves and the privilege of walking upright as they do. He gave him no special home, but made him ruler over the whole earth, and over the sea and air. Finally, he gave him no special strength or swiftness, but stole a spark from heaven and lighted a heavenly fire within his mind which should teach him to understand, to count, to speak, to remember. Man learned from it how to build cities, tame animals, raise crops, build boats, and do all the things that animals cannot. Prometheus also kindled fire on earth that man might smelt[4] metals and make tools. In fact, from this heavenly fire of Prometheus all man's greatness comes.

Before this time fire was a divine thing and belonged only to the gods. It was one of their greatest treasures, and Zeus would never have given Prometheus permission to use it in the creation of man. Therefore when Prometheus stole it, Zeus was furious indeed. He chained Prometheus to a great, lofty rock, where the sun scorched him by day and the cruel frost tortured him by night. Not content with that, he sent an eagle to tear him, so that, though he could not die, he lived in agony. For many centuries Prometheus hung in torment, but he was wiser than Zeus, and by reason of a secret he had, he forced Zeus in later ages to set him free. By then, also, Zeus had learned that there is more in ruling than power and cruelty. Thus, the two at last were friends.

THE COMING OF EVIL

After the punishment of Prometheus, Zeus planned to take his revenge on man. He could not recall the gift of fire, since it had been given by one of the immortals,[5] but

---

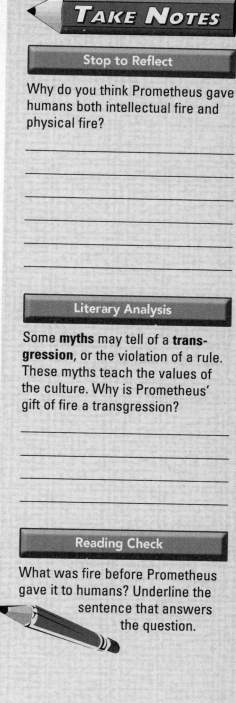

TAKE NOTES

Stop to Reflect

Why do you think Prometheus gave humans both intellectual fire and physical fire?

_____

_____

_____

_____

_____

Literary Analysis

Some **myths** may tell of a **transgression**, or the violation of a rule. These myths teach the values of the culture. Why is Prometheus' gift of fire a transgression?

_____

_____

_____

_____

Reading Check

What was fire before Prometheus gave it to humans? Underline the sentence that answers the question.

---

4. **smelt** v. purified metal by melting it.
5. **immortals** (i MOR tuhlz) n. those who do not die.

Read the bracketed text. **Generate questions** about the ancient Greeks' view of women.

_____

_____

_____

_____

_____

_____

What **transgression** does Pandora carry out? What is the effect of her transgression?

_____

_____

_____

_____

Who gave women beauty? Underline the text that tells you.

he was not content that man should possess this treasure in peace and become perhaps as great as were the gods themselves. He therefore took <u>counsel</u> with the other gods, and together they made for man a woman. All the gods gave gifts to this new creation. Aphrodite [af ruh DYT ee] gave her fresh beauty like the spring itself. The goddess Athene [uh THEE nee] dressed her and put on her a garland of flowers and green leaves. She had also a golden diadem[6] beautifully decorated with figures of animals. In her heart Hermes [HER meez] put cunning, deceit, and curiosity. She was named Pandora [pan DAWR uh], which means All-Gifted, since each of the gods had given her something. The last gift was a chest in which there was supposed to be great treasure, but which Pandora was instructed never to open. Then Hermes, the Messenger, took the girl and brought her to Epimetheus.

Epimetheus had been warned by his brother to receive no gifts from Zeus, but he was a heedless person, as ever, and Pandora was very lovely. He accepted her, therefore, and for a while they lived together in happiness, for Pandora besides her beauty had been given both wit and charm. Eventually, however, her curiosity got the better of her, and she determined to see for herself what treasure it was that the gods had given her. One day when she was alone, she went over to the corner where her chest lay and cautiously lifted the lid for a peep. The lid flew up out of her hands and knocked her aside, while before her frightened eyes dreadful, shadowy shapes flew out of the box in an endless stream. There were hunger, disease, war, greed, anger, jealousy, toil, and all the griefs and hardships to which man from that day has been subject. Each was terrible in appearance, and as it passed, Pandora saw something of the misery that her thoughtless action had brought on her descendants. At last the stream slackened,[7] and Pandora, who had been paralyzed with fear and horror, found strength to shut her box. The only thing left in it now, however, was the one good gift the gods had put in among so many evil ones. This was hope, and since that time the hope that is in man's heart is the only thing which has made him able to bear the sorrows that Pandora brought upon him.

Vocabulary Development: counsel (KOWN suhl) *n.* advice; discussion

6. **diadem** (DY uh dem) *n.* crown
7. **slackened** (SLAK end) *v.* diminished; became less active.

THE GREAT FLOOD

When evil first came among mankind, people became very wicked. War, robbery, treachery, and murder prevailed throughout the world. Even the worship of the gods, the laws of truth and honor, reverence[8] for parents and brotherly love were neglected.

Finally, Zeus determined to destroy the race of men altogether, and the other gods agreed. All the winds were therefore shut up in a cave except the South Wind, the wet one. He raced over the earth with water streaming from his beard and long, white hair. Clouds gathered around his head, and dew dripped from his wings and the ends of his garments. With him went Iris, the rainbow goddess, while below Poseidon [poh SY duhn] smote the earth with his trident until it shook and gaped open, so that the waters of the sea rushed up over the land.

Fields and farmhouses were buried. Fish swam in the tops of the trees. Sea beasts were quietly feeding where flocks and herds had grazed before. On the surface of the water, boars, stags, lions, and tigers struggled desperately to keep afloat. Wolves swam in the midst of flocks of sheep, but the sheep were not frightened by them, and the wolves never thought of their natural prey. Each fought for his own life and forgot the others. Over them wheeled countless birds, winging far and wide in the hope of finding something to rest upon. Eventually they too fell into the water and were drowned.

All over the water were men in small boats or makeshift rafts. Some even had oars which they tried to use, but the waters were fierce and stormy, and there was nowhere to go. In time all were drowned, until at last there was no one left but an old man and his wife, Deucalion [doo KAYL ee uhn] and Pyrrha [PIR uh]. These two people had lived in truth and justice, unlike the rest of mankind. They had been warned of the coming of the flood and had built a boat and stocked it. For nine days and nights they floated until Zeus took pity on them and they came to the top of Mount Parnassus, the sacred home of the Muses.[9] There they found land and <u>disembarked</u> to wait while the gods recalled the water they had unloosed.

When the waters fell, Deucalion and Pyrrha looked over the land, despairing. Mud and sea slime covered the

8. **reverence** (REV uh rens) *n.* feeling or display of great respect.
9. **Muses** (MYOOZ ez) *n.* nine goddesses who rule over literature and the arts and sciences.

TAKE NOTES

Stop to Reflect

According to the myth about the Great Flood, what is the relationship between the gods and humans like?

_____

_____

_____

_____

Literary Analysis

Myths include characters with exceptional characteristics. These characteristics emphasize qualities that the culture admired or feared. Underline details about Deucalion and his wife. What do these characteristics say about traits that the ancient Greeks admired?

_____

_____

_____

Reading Check

What happened when evil came among humankind? Underline the text that answers the question.

Read the bracketed passage to **analyze the cultural context**. What does it suggest about the values of the ancient Greeks?

_____

_____

_____

_____

What fact of life does the **myth** of Deucalion and Pyrrha explain?

_____

_____

_____

_____

Why do Deucalion and Pyrrha go to the temple? Underline the text that tells you.

earth; all living things had been swept away. Slowly and sadly they made their way down the mountain until they came to a temple where there had been an oracle.[10] Black seaweed dripped from the pillars now, and the mud was over all. Nevertheless the two knelt down and kissed the temple steps while Deucalion prayed to the goddess to tell them what they should do. All men were dead but themselves, and they were old. It was impossible that they should have children to people the earth again. Out of the temple a great voice was heard speaking strange words.

"Depart," it said, "with veiled heads and loosened robes, and throw behind you as you go the bones of your mother."

Pyrrha was in despair when she heard this saying. "The bones of our mother!" she cried. "How can we tell now where they lie? Even if we knew, we could never do such a dreadful thing as to disturb their resting place and scatter them over the earth like an armful of stones."

"Stones!" said Deucalion quickly. "That must be what the goddess means. After all Earth is our mother, and the other thing is too horrible for us to suppose that a goddess would ever command it."

Accordingly both picked up armfuls of stones, and as they went away from the temple with faces veiled, they cast the stones behind them. From each of those Deucalion cast sprang up a man, and from Pyrrha's stones sprang women. Thus the earth was repeopled, and in the course of time it brought forth again animals from itself, and all was as before. Only from that time men have been less sensitive and have found it easier to endure toil, and sorrow, and pain, since now they are descended from stones.

_____

10. **oracle** (AWR uh kuhl) *n.* person who, when consulted on a matter, revealed the will of the gods.

Reader's Response: What questions would you like to ask Zeus? Explain.

_____

_____

_____

_____

Prometheus and the First People

1. **Contrast:** Contrast the gifts Prometheus gives people with the gifts Epimetheus gives the animals.

   _____

   _____

2. **Connect:** Pandora opened the box the gods gave to her. How does this solve the problem Prometheus caused for the gods?

   _____

   _____

3. **Literary Analysis:** Use the chart below to identify which characteristics of **myths** are found in "Prometheus and the First People." Support your choices by providing examples from the text.

What the Story Explains	Exceptional or Fantastic Characteristics	Quest	Transgression

4. **Reading Skill:** What are two questions you might ask to **analyze the cultural context** of the myth?

   _____

   _____

   _____

SUPPORT FOR WRITING AND EXTEND YOUR LEARNING

Writing: Myth

Write a **myth** about the origin of some aspect of human life, such as how gossip or forgiveness entered the world. Answer the following questions to help you write your myth.

- What aspect of human life will the myth explain?

  _____

  _____

- What values will the myth teach?

  _____

  _____

- How will the main character learn or display these values?

  _____

  _____

Use your notes to help you write your myth.

Listening and Speaking: Retelling

Find another Greek myth about the gods and humans. Present a **retelling** of the story to your class. Fill in the chart below to organize information for the retelling.

What the story explains	Characters	Lesson or Moral

Use your notes to prepare your retelling.

The Orphan Boy and the Elk Dog

(from the Blackfeet)

Summary This myth examines the life of Long Arrow. He is a young man who is mistreated by his Blackfeet tribe. Long Arrow takes a dangerous journey to prove that he is valuable. Along the journey, he finds a mythic animal that will change the lives of his people.

Reading/Writing Connection

Complete this paragraph. Write about a kind of transportation other than walking.

Some people <u>rely</u> on _____. They can <u>depend</u> on it because _____. It can <u>transport</u> them _____.

Note-taking Guide

Use this chart to recall how the orphan boy solves his problem.

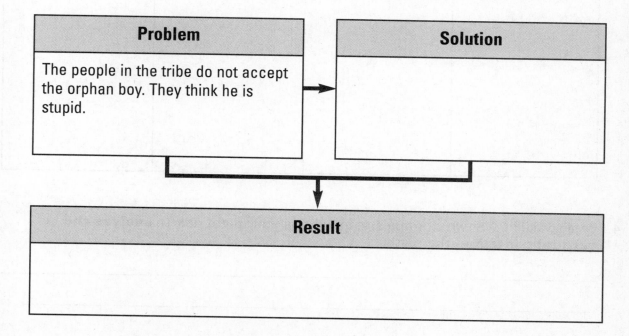

Problem	Solution
The people in the tribe do not accept the orphan boy. They think he is stupid.	

Result

The Orphan Boy and the Elk Dog

1. **Analyze:** What did you learn about the villagers from their treatment of Long Arrow at the beginning of the story?

   _____

   _____

2. **Infer:** Long Arrow sets out on his journey to make his grandfather proud. What does this show about his feelings for Good Running?

   _____

   _____

3. **Literary Analysis:** Use the chart below to identify which characteristics of **myths** are found in "The Orphan Boy and the Elk Dog."

What the Story Explains	Special Characters	Quest	Transgression

4. **Reading Skill:** Give two examples of questions you might ask to **analyze the cultural context** of the myth.

   _____

   _____

SUPPORT FOR WRITING AND EXTEND YOUR LEARNING

Writing: Myth

Write a **myth** about the origin of some part of your everyday world. Answer the following questions to help you prepare. Use your notes to create your myth.

- Who are the characters? What is the setting?

_____

_____

- Will your myth include a quest? What will it be?

_____

_____

_____

- What special qualities will the main character have? What do these qualities say about the values of your culture?

_____

_____

_____

Listening and Speaking: Retelling

Present a **retelling** of a Native American myth. Write the main events in order in the boxes below. Use your notes as you write your myth.

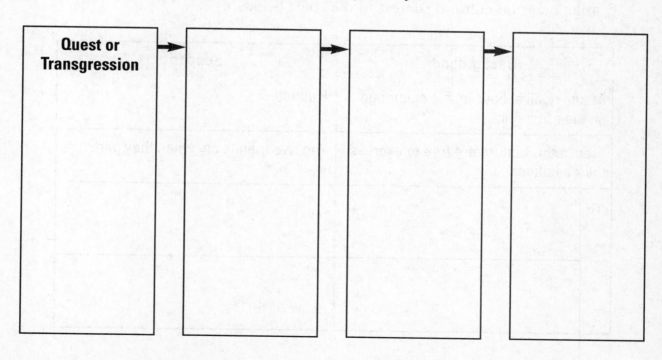

Quest or Transgression			

from Sundiata: An Epic of Old Mali •
Rama's Initiation from Ramayana

LITERARY ANALYSIS

An **epic** is an extended narrative poem about the actions of heroes. The typical **epic hero** is a male warrior. His character may be based on a historic or a legendary figure. In a number of epics, the hero strives to win immortality or undying fame through great deeds, especially in combat. The typical hero has the following characteristics:

- He has a high position in society and the virtues of a warrior, such as strength, courage, and perseverance.
- He defends his family's honor, and he acts ethically, fighting evil and striving for justice.
- He may be marked by the gods or by fate and so may benefit from special blessings or suffer from special burdens.

READING SKILL

To understand an epic, **analyze cultural context**, or determine ways in which the epic reflects the culture in which it was composed. You can **acquire background knowledge** about the culture in these ways:

- Read introductory sections, footnotes, and other text aids.
- Draw conclusions from the details in the selection.

Take notes on cultural context in the chart below.

Background	Support
At age twelve, boys in this culture go on their first hunt.	Footnote 2
Men in this culture are free to express their emotions.	The two friends cry when they part.

from Sundiata:
An Epic of Old Mali

D. T. Niane

Summary The young child Mari Djata has a large head and cannot walk. His father, the king, believes Mari Djata will be the next king. When the king dies, a different son becomes king. Mari Djata's mother is humiliated by the new king's mother. Mari Djata must prove that he is the true king.

Reading/Writing Connection

Complete the sentences below. Describe why a culture might value strength.

1. To <u>attain</u> strength requires _____.

2. A person can <u>acquire</u> strength by _____.

3. Strength can allow a person to <u>dominate</u> _____.

Note-taking Guide

Use this diagram to record the key characteristics of each character.

Character	Key Characteristics
Mari Djata	calm, quiet
Sogolon	
Sassouma Bérété	
Balla Fasséké	

TAKE NOTES

Activate Prior Knowledge

How would you react if someone did something to embarrass your friend or relative?

_____

_____

_____

Reading Skill

To understand an epic, **analyze cultural context**. Find ways in which the epic reflects the culture in which it was written. Look at the list of characters in Sundiata. What can you conclude about the culture in which the epic was written?

_____

_____

_____

_____

Literary Analysis

Characteristics of an **epic hero** include a high position in society, strength, courage, and perseverance. He defends his family's honor, fights evil, and works for justice. He may be marked by the gods or fate. He may benefit from special blessings or suffer from special burdens. What quality of an epic hero does Sogolon's son show as a child?

_____

_____

_____

_____

from Sundiata:
An Epic of Old Mali

D. T. Niane

Characters in Sundiata

BALLA FASSÉKÉ (BAH lah fah SAY kah): Griot and counselor of Sundiata

BOUKARI (boo KAH ree): Son of the king and Namandjé, one of his wives; also called Manding (MAHN din) Boukari

DANKARAN TOUMAN (DAHN kah rahn TOO mahn): Son of the king and his first wife, Sassouma, who is also called Sassouma Bérété

DJAMAROU (jah MAH roo): Daughter of Sogolon and the king; sister of Sundiata and Kolonkan

FARAKOUROU (fah rah KOO roo): Master of the forges

GNANKOUMAN DOUA (nahn KOO mahn DOO uh) The king's griot; also called simply, Doua

KOLONKAN (koh LOHN kuhn): Sundiata's eldest sister

NAMANDJÉ (nah MAHN jee): One of the king's wives

NARÉ MAGHAN (NAH ray MAHG hahn): Sundiata's father

NOUNFAÏRI (NOON fah ee ree): Soothsayer and smith; father of Farakourou

SASSOUMA BÉRÉTÉ (sah SOO mah BE re te): The king's first wife

SOGOLON (su gu LOHN): Sundiata's mother; also called Sogolon Kedjou (KAY joo)

SUNDIATA (soon DYAH tah): Legendary king of Mali; referred to as Djata (DYAH tah) and Sogolon Djata ("son of Sogolon"), and Mari (MAH ree) Djata.

CHILDHOOD

God has his mysteries which none can <u>fathom</u>. You, perhaps, will be a king. You can do nothing about it. You, on the other hand, will be unlucky, but you can do nothing about that either. Each man finds his way already marked out for him and he can change nothing of it.

Sogolon's son had a slow and difficult childhood. At the age of three he still crawled along on all-fours while children of the same age were already walking. He had nothing of the great beauty of his father Naré Maghan. He had a head so big that he seemed unable to support it; he also had large eyes which would open wide whenever anyone entered his mother's house. He was taciturn[1] and

---

Vocabulary Development: fathom (FATH uhm) *v.* understand thoroughly

---

1. **taciturn** (TAS i tern) *adj.* almost always silent; not liking to talk.

used to spend the whole day just sitting in the middle of the house. Whenever his mother went out he would crawl on all-fours to rummage about in the calabashes[2] in search of food, for he was very greedy.

Malicious tongues began to blab. What three-year-old has not yet taken his first steps? What three-year-old is not the despair of his parents through his whims and shifts of mood? What three-year-old is not the joy of his circle through his backwardness in talking? Sogolon Djata (for it was thus that they called him, prefixing his mother's name to his), Sogolon Djata, then, was very different from others of his own age. He spoke little and his severe face never relaxed into a smile. You would have thought that he was already thinking, and what amused children of his age bored him. Often Sogolon would make some of them come to him to keep him company. These children were already walking and she hoped that Djata, seeing his companions walking, would be tempted to do likewise. But nothing came of it. Besides, Sogolon Djata would brain the poor little things with his already strong arms and none of them would come near him any more.

The king's first wife was the first to rejoice at Sogolon Djata's infirmity. Her own son, Dankaran Touman, was already eleven. He was a fine and lively boy, who spent the day running about the village with those of his own age. He had even begun his initiation into the bush.[3] The king had had a bow made for him and he used to go behind the town to practice archery with his companions. Sassouma was quite happy and snapped her fingers at Sogolon, whose child was still crawling on the ground. Whenever the latter happened to pass by her house, she would say, "Come, my son, walk, jump, leap about. The jinn didn't promise you anything out of the ordinary,[4] but I prefer a son who walks on his two legs to a lion that crawls on the ground." She spoke thus whenever Sogolon went by her door. The <u>innuendo</u> would go straight home and then she would burst into laughter, that diabolical laughter which a jealous woman knows how to use so well.

Her son's infirmity weighed heavily upon Sogolon Kedjou; she had resorted to all her talent as a sorceress to

---

Vocabulary Development: innuendo (in yoo EN doh) *n.* indirect insult or accusation; insinuation

---

2. **calabashes** (KAL uh bash iz) *n.* dried, hollow shells of gourds, (squash-like fruits), used as bowls, cups, and so on.
3. **initiation in the bush** education in tribal lore given to twelve-year-old West African boys so they can become full members of the tribe.
4. **the jinn . . . ordinary** Jinn are supernatural beings that influence human affairs. They promised that the son of Sogolon would make Mali a great empire.

TAKE NOTES

Reading Skill

You can **acquire background knowledge** about the culture by reading introductory sections, footnotes, and other text aids. You can also draw conclusions from details in the selection. Circle footnote 2 in the text. What detail does the background information in footnote 2 help you understand?

_____
_____
_____
_____

Stop to Reflect

Read the bracketed paragraph. Why might Sassouma be the "first to rejoice" at Sogolon Djata's condition?

_____
_____
_____
_____

Reading Check

What did Djata spend the whole day doing? Underline the text that tells you.

To understand an epic, **acquire background knowledge** from details in the text. What traits of Mali culture are suggested by the king's conversations with Doua and Nounfaïri?

_____

_____

_____

_____

What quality of an **epic hero** do the king's conversations suggest Sogolon Djata has?

_____

_____

Read the underlined text to **analyze the cultural context** of the epic. What does the image of the seed germinating suggest about Mali society?

_____

_____

_____

What did the soothsayers predict Namandjé's child would do when he was older? Underline the text that tells you.

give strength to her son's legs, but the rarest herbs had been useless. The king himself lost hope.

How impatient man is! Naré Maghan became imperceptibly estranged but Gnankouman Doua never ceased reminding him of the hunter's words. Sogolon became pregnant again. The king hoped for a son, but it was a daughter called Kolonkan. She resembled her mother and had nothing of her father's beauty. The disheartened king debarred Sogolon from his house and she lived in semi-disgrace for a while. Naré Maghan married the daughter of one of his allies, the king of the Kamaras. She was called Namandjé and her beauty was legendary. A year later she brought a boy into the world. When the king consulted soothsayers[5] on the destiny of this son he received the reply that Namandjé's child would be the right hand of some mighty king. The king gave the newly-born the name of Boukari. He was to be called Manding Boukari or Manding Bory later on.

Naré Maghan was very perplexed. Could it be that the stiff-jointed son of Sogolon was the one the hunter soothsayer had foretold?

"The Almighty has his mysteries," Gnankouman Doua would say and, taking up the hunter's words, added, "The silk-cotton tree emerges from a tiny seed."

One day Naré Maghan came along to the house of Nounfaïri, the blacksmith seer of Niani. He was an old, blind man. He received the king in the anteroom which served as his workshop. To the king's question he replied, "When the seed germinates growth is not always easy; great trees grow slowly but they plunge their roots deep into the ground."

"But has the seed really germinated?" said the king.

"Of course," replied the blind seer. "Only the growth is not as quick as you would like it; how impatient man is."

This interview and Doua's confidence gave the king some assurance. To the great displeasure of Sassouma Bérété the king restored Sogolon to favor and soon another daughter was born to her. She was given the name of Djamarou.

However, all Niani talked of nothing else but the stiff-legged son of Sogolon. He was now seven and he still crawled to get about. In spite of all the king's affection, Sogolon was in despair. Naré Maghan aged and he felt

Vocabulary Development: estranged (e STRAYNJD) *adj.* kept apart; in the condition of having had affection turn into indifference or hostility

5. **soothsayers** (SOOTH say uhrz) *n.* people who profess to foretell the future.

his time coming to an end. Dankaran Touman, the son of Sassouma Bérété, was now a fine youth.

One day Naré Maghan made Mari Djata come to him and he spoke to the child as one speaks to an adult. "Mari Djata, I am growing old and soon I shall be no more among you, but before death takes me off I am going to give you the present each king gives his successor. In Mali every prince has his own griot. Doua's father was my father's griot, Doua is mine and the son of Doua, Balla Fasséké here, will be your griot. Be inseparable friends from this day forward. From his mouth you will hear the history of your ancestors, you will learn the art of governing Mali according to the principles which our ancestors have bequeathed to us. I have served my term and done my duty too. I have done everything which a king of Mali ought to do. I am handing an enlarged kingdom over to you and I leave you sure allies. May your destiny be accomplished, but never forget that Niani is your capital and Mali the cradle of your ancestors."

The child, as if he had understood the whole meaning of the king's words, beckoned Balla Fasséké to approach. He made room for him on the hide he was sitting on and then said, "Balla, you will be my griot."

"Yes, son of Sogolon, if it pleases God," replied Balla Fasséké.

The king and Doua exchanged glances that radiated confidence.

THE LION'S AWAKENING

A short while after this interview between Naré Maghan and his son the king died. Sogolon's son was no more than seven years old. The council of elders met in the king's palace. It was no use Doua's defending the king's will which reserved the throne for Mari Djata, for the council took no account of Naré Maghan's wish. With the help of Sassouma Bérété's intrigues, Dankaran Touman was proclaimed king and a regency council[6] was formed in which the queen mother was all-powerful. A short time after, Doua died.

As men have short memories, Sogolon's son was spoken of with nothing but irony and scorn. People had seen one-eyed kings, one-armed kings, and lame kings, but a stiff-legged king had never been heard tell of. No matter how great the destiny promised for Mari Djata might be, the throne could not be given to someone who had no power in his legs; if the jinn loved him, let them begin by giving him the use of his legs. Such were the remarks that Sogolon heard every day. The queen mother, Sassouma Bérété, was the source of all this gossip.

---

6. **regency** (REE juhn see) **council** group who rule instead of the king or queen when the king or queen is still a child or is otherwise incapable of ruling.

TAKE NOTES

Stop to Reflect

Read the underlined text. What is significant about the text?

_____

_____

_____

Reading Skill

Acquire background knowledge from details from the text. What do the details in the bracketed text tell about the way in which West African society was ruled?

_____

_____

_____

Reading Check

Who is the king's griot? Underline the sentence that answers the question.

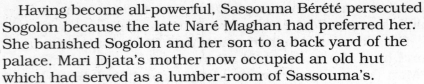

Literary Analysis

In what way is the honor of Mari Djata's family threatened?

_____

_____

_____

How is this characteristic of an **epic hero**?

_____

_____

_____

Reading Skill

Read the bracketed text to **analyze the cultural context** of the epic. What do the details tell about food in the Mali culture?

_____

_____

_____

Literary Analysis

Underline the text that describes how Mari Djata responds when his mother hits him. Why is Mari Djata's response one of an **epic hero**?

_____

_____

_____

Reading Check

How did Kolonkan help Sologon? Circle the text that tells you.

Having become all-powerful, Sassouma Bérété persecuted Sogolon because the late Naré Maghan had preferred her. She banished Sogolon and her son to a back yard of the palace. Mari Djata's mother now occupied an old hut which had served as a lumber-room of Sassouma's.

The wicked queen mother allowed free passage to all those inquisitive people who wanted to see the child that still crawled at the age of seven. Nearly all the inhabitants of Niani filed into the palace and the poor Sogolon wept to see herself thus given over to public ridicule. Mari Djata took on a ferocious look in front of the crowd of sightseers. Sogolon found a little consolation only in the love of her eldest daughter, Kolonkan. She was four and she could walk. She seemed to understand all her mother's miseries and already she helped her with the housework. Sometimes, when Sogolon was attending to the chores, it was she who stayed beside her sister Djamarou, quite small as yet.

Sogolon Kedjou and her children lived on the queen mother's leftovers, but she kept a little garden in the open ground behind the village. It was there that she passed her brightest moments looking after her onions and gnougous.[7] One day she happened to be short of condiments and went to the queen mother to beg a little baobab leaf.[8]

"Look you," said the malicious Sassouma, "I have a calabash full. Help yourself, you poor woman. As for me, my son knew how to walk at seven and it was he who went and picked these baobab leaves. Take them then, since your son is unequal to mine." Then she laughed derisively with that fierce laughter which cuts through your flesh and penetrates right to the bone.

Sogolon Kedjou was dumbfounded. She had never imagined that hate could be so strong in a human being. With a lump in her throat she left Sassouma's. Outside her hut Mari Djata, sitting on his useless legs, was blandly eating out of a calabash. Unable to contain herself any longer, Sogolon burst into sobs and seizing a piece of wood, hit her son.

"Oh son of misfortune, will you never walk? Through your fault I have just suffered the greatest affront of my life! What have I done, God, for you to punish me in this way?"

Mari Djata seized the piece of wood and, looking at his mother, said, "Mother, what's the matter?"

Vocabulary Development: affront (uh FRUNT) *n.* open insult

---

7. **gnougous** (NOO gooz) *n.* root vegetables.
8. **baobab** (BAY oh bab) **leaf** The baobab is a thick-trunked tree; its leaves are used to flavor foods.

"Shut up, nothing can ever wash me clean of this insult."

"But what then?"

"Sassouma has just humiliated me over a matter of a baobab leaf. At your age her own son could walk and used to bring his mother baobab leaves."

"Cheer up, Mother, cheer up."

"No. It's too much. I can't."

"Very well then, I am going to walk today," said Mari Djata. "Go and tell my father's smiths to make me the heaviest possible iron rod. Mother, do you want just the leaves of the baobab or would you rather I brought you the whole tree?"

"Ah, my son, to wipe out this insult I want the tree and its roots at my feet outside my hut."

Balla Fasséké, who was present, ran to the master smith, Farakourou, to order an iron rod.

Sogolon had sat down in front of her hut. She was weeping softly and holding her head between her two hands. Mari Djata went calmly back to his calabash of rice and began eating again as if nothing had happened. From time to time he looked up discreetly at his mother who was murmuring in a low voice, "I want the whole tree, in front of my hut, the whole tree."

All of a sudden a voice burst into laughter behind the hut. It was the wicked Sassouma telling one of her serving women about the scene of humiliation and she was laughing loudly so that Sogolon could hear. Sogolon fled into the hut and hid her face under the blankets so as not to have before her eyes this heedless boy, who was more preoccupied with eating than with anything else. With her head buried in the bedclothes Sogolon wept and her body shook violently. Her daughter, Sogolon Djamarou, had come and sat down beside her and she said, "Mother, Mother, don't cry. Why are you crying?"

Mari Djata had finished eating and, dragging himself along on his legs, he came and sat under the wall of the hut for the sun was scorching. What was he thinking about? He alone knew.

The royal forges were situated outside the walls and over a hundred smiths worked there. The bows, spears, arrows and shields of Niani's warriors came from there. When Balla Fasséké came to order the iron rod, Farakourou said to him, "The great day has arrived then?"

"Yes. Today is a day like any other, but it will see what no other day has seen."

The master of the forges, Farakourou, was the son of the old Nounfaïri, and he was a soothsayer like his father. In his workshops there was an enormous iron bar wrought by his father Nounfaïri. Everybody wondered what this bar was destined to be used for. Farakourou

TAKE NOTES

Stop to Reflect

Why do you think Mari Djata goes back to eating while his mother weeps?

_____

_____

_____

Reading Skill

Read the bracketed paragraph to **analyze the cultural context** of the epic. What do the details tell about the role of blacksmiths and warriors in West African culture?

_____

_____

_____

_____

Reading Check

What does Mari Djata ask of his father's smiths? Underline the text that tells you.

Analyze the cultural context of the first bracketed paragraph. What does the passage tell about the relationship between griots and those they serve in Mali culture?

_____

_____

_____

_____

Read the second bracketed paragraph. What qualities of an **epic hero** does Mari Djata show here?

_____

_____

_____

_____

How does Sogolon respond to seeing her son walk? Underline the text that tells you.

called six of his apprentices and told them to carry the iron bar to Sogolon's house.

When the smiths put the gigantic iron bar down in front of the hut the noise was so frightening that Sogolon, who was lying down, jumped up with a start. Then Balla Fasséké, son of Gnankouman Doua, spoke.

"Here is the great day, Mari Djata. I am speaking to you, Maghan, son of Sogolon. The waters of the Niger can efface the stain from the body, but they cannot wipe out an insult. Arise, young lion, roar, and may the bush know that from henceforth it has a master."

The apprentice smiths were still there, Sogolon had come out and everyone was watching Mari Djata. He crept on all-fours and came to the iron bar. Supporting himself on his knees and one hand, with the other hand he picked up the iron bar without any effort and stood it up vertically. Now he was resting on nothing but his knees and held the bar with both his hands. A deathly silence had gripped all those present. Sogolon Djata closed his eyes, held tight, the muscles in his arms tensed. With a violent jerk he threw his weight on to it and his knees left the ground. Sogolon Kedjou was all eyes and watched her son's legs which were trembling as though from an electric shock. Djata was sweating and the sweat ran from his brow. In a great effort he straightened up and was on his feet at one go—but the great bar of iron was twisted and had taken the form of a bow!

Then Balla Fasséké sang out the "Hymn to the Bow," striking up with his powerful voice:

"Take your bow, Simbon,
Take your bow and let us go.
Take your bow, Sogolon Djata."

When Sogolon saw her son standing she stood dumb for a moment, then suddenly she sang these words of thanks to God who had given her son the use of his legs:

"Oh day, what a beautiful day,
Oh day, day of joy;
Allah[9] Almighty, you never created a finer day.
So my son is going to walk!"

Standing in the position of a soldier at ease, Sogolon Djata, supported by his enormous rod, was sweating great beads of sweat. Balla Fasséké's song had alerted the whole palace and people came running from all over to see what had happened, and each stood bewildered before Sogolon's son. The queen mother had rushed there and when she saw Mari Djata standing up she trembled from head to foot. After recovering his breath Sogolon's son dropped the

---

9. **Allah** (AHL uh) Muslim name for God.

bar and the crowd stood to one side. His first steps were those of a giant. Balla Fasséké fell into step and pointing his finger at Djata, he cried:

"Room, room, make room!
The lion has walked;
Hide antelopes,
Get out of his way."

Behind Niani there was a young baobab tree and it was there that the children of the town came to pick leaves for their mothers. With all his might the son of Sogolon tore up the tree and put it on his shoulders and went back to his mother. He threw the tree in front of the hut and said, "Mother, here are some baobab leaves for you. From henceforth it will be outside your hut that the women of Niani will come to stock up."

Reader's Response: How does Mari Djata's triumph make you feel? Explain.

_____

_____

_____

_____

Reading Skill

Analyze the cultural context of the epic. What do the images in the griot's song tell about the region in which the storytellers live?

_____

_____

_____

_____

Reading Check

How does the author describe Sogolon Djata's first steps? Underline the sentence that tells you.

from Sundiata: An Epic of Old Mali

1. **Infer:** How do Mari Djata's difficulties affect the way people treat his mother?

   _____

2. **Analyze Cause and Effect:** How do the soothsayers' predictions about Namandjé's son help prompt the king's wishes?

   _____

   _____

   _____

3. **Literary Analysis:** Use the chart below to list specific examples that show which qualities of an **epic hero** Mari Djata possesses.

Nobel Birth	Warrior Virtues	Acts Honorably	Chosen by the Gods or Fate

4. **Reading Skill:** List two things you learned about West African **cultural context** from the selection.

   _____

   _____

SUPPORT FOR WRITING AND EXTEND YOUR LEARNING

Writing: Newspaper Report

Write a **newspaper report** of events at the end of the story. Complete this sequence chart to help you organize the events. Use your notes to help you write your report.

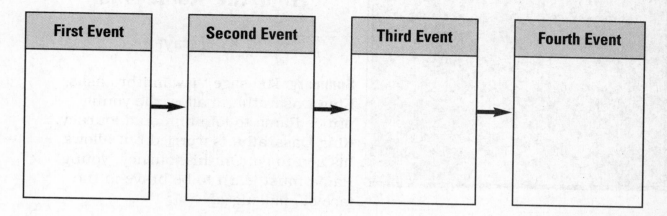

First Event	Second Event	Third Event	Fourth Event

Research and Technology: Summary of Research Notes

Find audiovisual resources about culture and history in Old Mali. Write a **summary of research notes** about what you learn. Use the outline below to help you write your summary.

- Resource _____

    1. Information and facts I learned

    _____

    _____

    _____

    2. Summary of information

    _____

    _____

    _____

- Resource _____

    1. Information and facts I learned

    _____

    _____

    _____

    2. Summary of information

    _____

    _____

    _____

Rama's Initiation
from the Ramayana

R. K. Narayan

Summary The sage Viswamithra asks King Dasaratha to allow the young prince Rama to join him on a journey. King Dasaratha is worried but allows his son to go. On this journey, young Rama must learn to be brave in the face of challenges.

Reading/Writing Connection

Complete the following paragraph. Write about the qualities of superheroes.

Superheroes <u>embody</u> _____. They sometimes

<u>intervene</u> in _____. Superheroes <u>prevail</u>

because _____.

Note-taking Guide

Use this chart to record Rama's traits and actions.

What he says   **What he does**

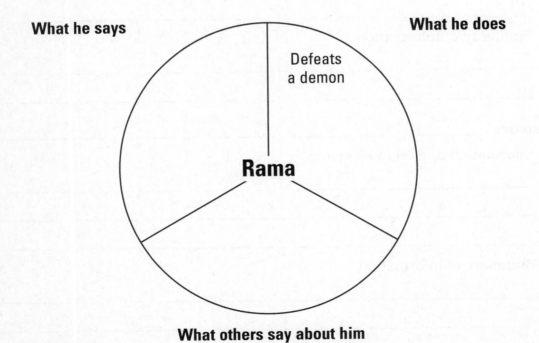

Defeats
a demon

Rama

What others say about him

Rama's Initiation from the Ramayana

1. **Hypothesize:** Why does Viswamithra want Rama, rather than King Dasaratha, to join him on the journey?

   _____

   _____

   _____

2. **Make a Judgment:** Was Viswamithra a good or bad teacher for Rama? Why or why not?

   _____

   _____

3. **Literary Analysis:** Use the chart to give examples that show which qualities of an **epic hero** Rama possesses.

Noble Birth	Warrior Virtues	Acts Honorably	Chosen by the Gods or Fate

4. **Reading Skill:** Describe two things from this story that help you understand Hindu **cultural context**.

   _____

   _____

   _____

SUPPORT FOR WRITING AND EXTEND YOUR LEARNING

Writing: Newspaper Report

Write a **newspaper report** of events at the end of the selection. Use the questions below to prepare you to write your report. Use your notes to write your newspaper report.

- What events happen at the end of the story?

_____

_____

_____

_____

- How are each of these events significant?

_____

_____

_____

_____

_____

Research and Technology: Summary of Research Notes

Write a **summary of research notes** about the culture and history of classical India. Use the chart below to help you organize your research for the different parts of Indian culture and history. Use your notes to write the summary of research notes.

Music	Art	Architecture	Religion

Research Sources

ABOUT RESEARCH SOURCES

Research sources are texts that present information. They include encyclopedias, atlases, and some Web sites. Many research sources will have the following features:

- heads and subheads to help you locate information quickly
- statements of fact rather than opinion
- statistics, or information using numbers
- visual aids, such as maps, graphs, diagrams, charts, icons, and symbols

READING SKILL

Research sources can help you understand the cultural setting of literary works. You can use research sources to **make generalizations** about a topic you are studying. Generalizations are statements that explain, connect, or sum up the facts that you find in your research sources.

- First, ask a general question about your topic. Then, identify the facts that help answer your question. Finally, state the answer to your question in a sentence. Your answer will be a generalization.

Question	Facts	Generalization
What is the standard of living in Mali?	Poverty is a main political issue.	The standard of living is probably not high.

- Look for connections or patterns that join the facts about your topic. Brainstorm general words that describe these connections or patterns. These words should be nouns, like *influence*, or adjectives, like *warlike*. Use these words in a sentence to make a generalization.

Facts	Pattern	General Words	Generalization
Language: French Currency: franc	French things in Malinese life.	*influence* *relationship*	Mali has been influenced by the French.

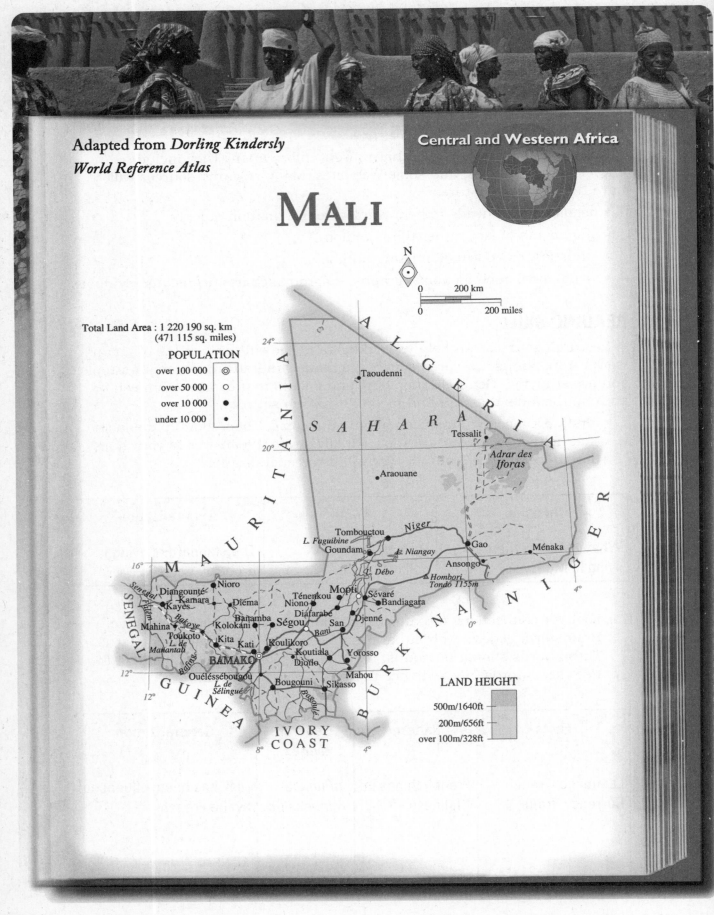

Adapted from *Dorling Kindersly World Reference Atlas*

MALI

N

0   200 km
0   200 miles

Total Land Area : 1 220 190 sq. km
(471 115 sq. miles)

POPULATION

over 100 000   ◎
over 50 000   ○
over 10 000   ●
under 10 000   ·

ALGERIA

24°

Taoudenni

SAHARA

20°

Tessalit

Adrar des
Iforas

Araouane

MAURITANIA

Tombouctou   Niger
L. Faguibine
Goundam   L. Niangay   Gao   Ménaka

16°   Ansongo

L. Débo

Nioro   ▲ Hombori
Diangounté   Tondó 1155m
Senegal Kamara   Ténenkou   Mopti   Sévaré
Fulem Kayes   Diéma   Niono   Bandiagara
SENEGAL Bakoye   Diafarabe
Mahina Banamba Ségou   San   Djenné
Toukoto Kolokani   Bani
L. de   Kita Kati Koulikoro
Manantali   Koutiala   Yorosso
Bafins BAMAKO   Diofo

12°   Ouéléssébougou Bougouni Mahou
L. de   Sikasso
Sélingué
12°
GUINEA   BURKINA   NIGER

IVORY
COAST

LAND HEIGHT

500m/1640ft
200m/656ft
over 100m/328ft

4°

0°

Mali

Official Name: Republic of Mali
Capital: Bamako
Population: 10.8 million
Currency: CFA franc
Official Language: French

Mali is landlocked in the heart of West Africa. Its mostly flat terrain comprises virtually uninhabited Saharan plains in the north and more fertile savanna land in the south, where most of the population live. The River Niger irrigates the central and southwestern regions of the country. Following independence in 1960, Mali experienced a long period of largely single-party rule. It became a multiparty democracy in 1992.

CLIMATE

In the south, intensely hot, dry weather precedes the westerly rains. Mali's northern half is almost rainless.

TRANSPORTATION

 Has no fleet  Bamako-Senou

Mali is linked by rail with the port of Dakar in Senegal, and by good roads to the port of Abidjan in Ivory Coast.

TOURISM

 16,000 visitors Down 33% in 1994

Tourism is largely safari-oriented, although the historic cities of Djénné, Gao and Mopti, lying on the banks of the River Niger, also attract visitors. A national domestic airline began operating in 1990.

PEOPLE

 Bambara, Fulani, Senufo, Soninke, French 24 people per sq. mile

Mali's most significant ethnic group, the Bambara, is also politically dominant. The Bambara speak the lingua franca of the River Niger, which is shared with other groups including the Malinke. The relationship between the Bambara–Malinke majority and the Tuareg nomads of the Saharan north is often tense and sometimes violent. As with elsewhere in Africa, the extended family, often based around the village, is a vital social security system and a link between the urban and rural poor. There are a few powerful women in Mali but, in general, women have little status.

POLITICS

The successful transition to multiparty politics in 1992 followed the overthrow in the previous year of Moussa Traoré, Mali's dictator for 23 years. The army's role was crucial in leading the coup, while Colonel Touré, who acted as interim president, was responsible for the swift return to civilian rule in less than a year. The change marks Mali's first experience of multipartyism. Maintaining good relations with the Tuaregs, after a peace agreement in 1991, is a key issue. However, the main challenge facing President Alpha Oumar Konaré's government is to alleviate poverty while placating the opposition, which feels that the luxury of multipartyism is something that Mali cannot afford.

APPLY THE SKILLS

THINKING ABOUT THE RESEARCH SOURCES

1. Does the city of Taoudenni receive much rain? Explain.

   _____

   _____

2. What important change occurred to the political system of Mali in the 1990s?

   _____

   _____

READING SKILL

3. What **generalization** can you make using the population information on the map of Mali?

   _____

4. Identify two facts from the atlas entry that support the **generalization**, "The people of Mali practice many European ways of life."

   _____

   _____

TIMED WRITING: RESEARCH (45 minutes)

Write a **research plan** based on an interesting fact or detail from the Mali atlas entry.

Review the Mali atlas entry to find a topic. Then, write your list of questions on the lines below. Next to each question, make a note of the specific research source you could use to find the answer.

   _____

   _____

   _____

   _____

Morte d'Arthur • Arthur Becomes King of Britain

LITERARY ANALYSIS

Legends are popular stories about the past that have been handed down for generations. Most legends have some basis in historical fact. Legends share the following characteristics:

- A focus on the life and adventures of **legendary heroes,** or characters who are human yet "larger than life"
- A deep concern with right and wrong
- Support for feelings of national pride

Legends help shape a people's cultural identity and reflect the values of a community or nation.

READING SKILL

A **worldview** consists of values and beliefs held by a culture. When a writer retells a legend, the retelling may reflect two worldviews—that of the writer and that of the original tale. To understand a retelling, **compare and contrast** worldviews.

- **Identify details** that indicate characters' beliefs and their reasons for acting or feeling as they do. In addition, identify details that are clues to the writer's attitudes.

- **Draw a conclusion** from these details about the values and basic beliefs of each character and of the writer.

Use this chart to compare and contrast worldviews.

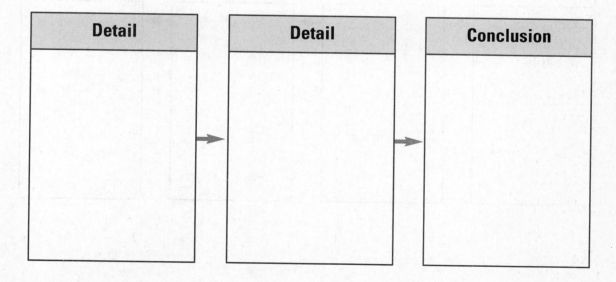

Detail	Detail	Conclusion

Morte d'Arthur

Alfred, Lord Tennyson

Summary A group of friends persuades a poet to tell the legend of King Arthur. As the poet's story opens, King Arthur is near death. He commands his knight Sir Bedivere to throw the king's prized sword, Excalibur, into the lake. When Sir Bedivere does so, a mysterious hand catches the sword in mid-air, and the legend of Excalibur is born.

Reading/Writing Connection

Complete the following paragraph to describe why the past may sometimes seem better than the present.

The past has more <u>appeal</u> because it _____.

People sometimes <u>repress</u> _____.

Memories of the past may <u>diminish</u> because _____.

Note-taking Guide

Use the following chart to record the sequence of events that leads to the end of King Arthur's life.

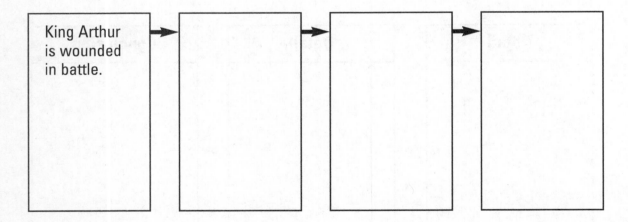

King Arthur is wounded in battle. →　　　 →　　　 →

Morte d'Arthur

1. **Interpret:** Why does Bedivere fear that if he obeys Arthur's request, "much honor and much fame were lost"?

   _____

   _____

2. **Evaluate:** Find a passage in the poem that describes what life might be like after Arthur is gone. What does this passage suggest?

   _____

   _____

   _____

3. **Literary Analysis:** Which features of **legends** are present in this poem? Fill in the chart with examples from the selection.

Life Story of Legendary Hero	Concern with Right and Wrong	Reflections of National Pride

4. **Reading Skill:** The narrator dreams that Arthur returns. What do you think the dream represents about Tennyson's **worldview**?

   _____

   _____

SUPPORT FOR WRITING AND EXTEND YOUR LEARNING

Writing: Script for a Television News Report

Write a brief **script for a television news report** on the death of King Arthur. Answer the following questions in the way that you feel Bedivere might answer them in a news interview. Use your notes to create your script.

- How did you feel when King Arthur grew angry with you shortly before he died?

_____

_____

- What message did King Arthur leave behind for his subjects?

_____

_____

- What will you and the other Knights of the Round Table do now that King Arthur is gone?

_____

_____

Research and Technology: Technical Report

Write a brief **technical report** in which you explain, in step-by-step form, one of the technological processes used by people of King Arthur's era. Use the following questions to gather information for your report.

- What is the technology?

_____

- What was its purpose?

_____

_____

- What materials are necessary to create this technology?

_____

- How did people use the materials to create this technology?

_____

_____

Arthur Becomes King of Britain

T. H. White

Summary A sword sits in an anvil on a stone in front of a church. The person who is able to pull out the sword will become king. When Sir Kay forgets his sword, he sends his squire to fetch it. The inn where the sword lies is locked, so the squire takes the sword from the anvil in front of the church.

Reading/Writing Connection

Complete the sentences below to explain whether you think people can learn to become heroic.

A hero must <u>respond</u> to _____. He or she must <u>rely</u>

on _____. Heroes <u>focus</u> on _____.

Note-taking Guide

Use this diagram to summarize the six most important events of the story.

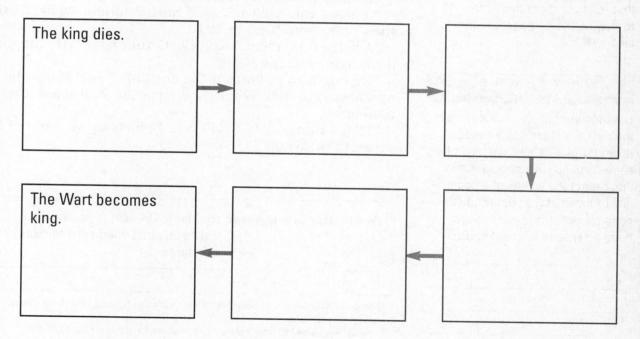

The king dies.

The Wart becomes king.

Activate Prior Knowledge

In the story, an unexpected person becomes king. Has someone whom you least expected to do so received an award or honor or done well in a sport? Describe what happened.

_____

_____

_____

_____

_____

Reading Skill

A **worldview** consists of values and beliefs held by a culture. **Compare and contrast** worldviews to understand a retelling of a story. Read the bracketed text. Circle the details in the nurse's speech that reflect a modern outlook. Underline the details that reflect medieval life.

Literary Analysis

Legends are popular stories about the past that have been handed down for generations. Legends help shape a people's cultural identity and reflect the values of a community or nation. What details on this page show that the characters have a sense of national pride?

_____

_____

_____

_____

_____

Arthur Becomes King of Britain
T. H. White

King Pellinore arrived for the important weekend in a high state of flurry.

"I say," he exclaimed, "do you know? Have you heard? Is it a secret, what?"

"Is what a secret, what?" they asked him.

"Why, the King," cried his majesty. "You know, about the King?"

"What's the matter with the King?" inquired Sir Ector. "You don't say he's comin' down to hunt with those darned hounds of his or anythin' like that?"

"He's dead," cried King Pellinore tragically. "He's dead, poor fellah, and can't hunt any more."

Sir Grummore stood up respectfully and took off his cap of maintenance.

"The King is dead," he said. "Long live the King."

Everybody else felt they ought to stand up too, and the boys' nurse burst into tears.

"There, there," she sobbed. "His loyal highness dead and gone, and him such a respectful gentleman. Many's the illuminated picture I've cut out of him, from the Illustrated Missals,[1] aye, and stuck up over the mantel. From the time when he was in swaddling bands,[2] right through them world towers till he was a-visiting the dispersed areas as the world's Prince Charming, there wasn't a picture of 'im but I had it out, aye, and give 'im a last thought o' nights."

"Compose yourself, Nannie," said Sir Ector.

"It is solemn, isn't it?" said King Pellinore, "what? Uther the Conqueror, 1066 to 1216."

"A solemn moment," said Sir Grummore. "The King is dead. Long live the King."

"We ought to pull down the curtains," said Kay, who was always a <u>stickler</u> for good form, "or half-mast[3] the banners."

"That's right," said Sir Ector. "Somebody go and tell the sergeant-at-arms."

Vocabulary Development: stickler (STIK luhr) *n.* person who insists on strict obedience to rules or standards

---

1. **Missals** (MIS uhlz) *n.* books produced by the Roman Catholic Church for solemn religious purposes.
2. **swaddling** (SWAHD ling) **bands** in former times, long, narrow bands of cloth wrapped around a newborn baby.
3. **half-mast** *v.* lower a flag halfway down a pole as a sign of mourning.

It was obviously the Wart's duty to execute this command, for he was now the junior nobleman present, so he ran out cheerfully to find the sergeant. Soon those who were left in the solar[4] could hear a voice crying out, "Nah then, one-two, special mourning fer 'is lite majesty, lower awai on the command Two!" and then the flapping of all the standards, banners, pennons, pennoncells, banderolls, guidons, streamers and cognizances[5] which made gay the snowy turrets of the Forest Sauvage.

"How did you hear?" asked Sir Ector.

"I was pricking through the purlieus[6] of the forest after that Beast, you know, when I met with a solemn friar of orders gray, and he told me. It's the very latest news."

"Poor old Pendragon," said Sir Ector.

"The King is dead," said Sir Grummore solemnly. "Long live the King."

"It is all very well for you to keep on mentioning that, my dear Grummore," exclaimed King Pellinore <u>petulantly</u>, "but who is this King, what, that is to live so long, what, accordin' to you?"

"Well, his heir," said Sir Grummore, rather taken aback.

"Our blessed monarch," said the Nurse tearfully, "never had no hair. Anybody that studied the loyal family knowed that."

"Good gracious!" exclaimed Sir Ector. "But he must have had a next-of-kin?"

"That's just it," cried King Pellinore in high excitement. "That's the excitin' part of it, what? No hair and no next of skin, and who's to succeed to the throne? That's what my friar was so excited about, what, and why he was asking who could succeed to what, what? What?"

"Do you mean to tell me," exclaimed Sir Grummore indignantly, "that there ain't no King of Gramarye?"

"Not a scrap of one," cried King Pellinore, feeling important. "And there have been signs and wonders of no mean might."

"I think it's a scandal," said Sir Grummore. "God knows what the dear old country is comin' to. Due to these lollards and communists, no doubt."

"What sort of signs and wonders?" asked Sir Ector.

"Well, there has appeared a sort of sword in a stone, what, in a sort of a church. Not in the church, if you see

---

Vocabulary Development: petulantly (PECH uh luhnt lee) *adv.* in a manner that expresses impatience or irritation

---

4. **solar** (SOH luhr) *n.* sun room.
5. **standards . . . cognizances** (KAHG nuh zuhn suhz) banners or flags.
6. **purlieus** (PERL yooz) *n.* here, the outlying part of a forest, in which forest laws were not enforced.

TAKE NOTES

Reading Skill

To help you understand a retelling of a story, **identify details** that tell about the writer's thoughts. What does the humor in the story tell you about the writer's **worldview**?

_____

_____

_____

_____

Literary Analysis

Read the bracketed text. Why is humor like this surprising in a retelling of a **legend**?

_____

_____

_____

_____

Reading Check

Who tells the sergeant-at-arms that the king is dead? Circle the answer in the text.

To learn about a character's **world-view**, identify details that tell why a character behaves the way he or she does. Why does Sir Ector tell King Pellinore, "You have a bit of rest, old boy"?

_____

_____

_____

_____

Why is the image of the sword in the stone something you would find in a **legend**?

_____

_____

_____

Where is the stone containing the sword? Underline the sentence that tells you the answer.

---

what I mean, and not in the stone, but that sort of thing, what, like you might say."

"I don't know what the Church is coming to," said Sir Grummore.

"It's in an anvil,"[7] explained the King.

"The Church?"

"No, the sword."

"But I thought you said the sword was in the stone?"

"No," said King Pellinore. "The stone is outside the church."

"Look here, Pellinore," said Sir Ector. "You have a bit of a rest, old boy, and start again. Here, drink up this horn of mead[8] and take it easy."

"The sword," said King Pellinore, "is stuck through an anvil which stands on a stone. It goes right through the anvil and into the stone. The anvil is stuck to the stone. The stone stands outside a church. Give me some more mead."

"I don't think that's much of a wonder," remarked Sir Grummore. "What I wonder at is that they should allow such things to happen. But you can't tell nowadays, what with all these Saxon agitators."[9]

"My dear fellah," cried Pellinore, getting excited again, "it's not where the stone is, what, that I'm trying to tell you, but what is written on it, what, where it is."

"What?"

"Why, on its pommel."[10]

"Come on, Pellinore," said Sir Ector. "You just sit quite still with your face to the wall for a minute, and then tell us what you are talkin' about. Take it easy, old boy. No need for hurryin'. You sit still and look at the wall, there's a good chap, and talk as slow as you can."

"There are words written on this sword in this stone outside this church," cried King Pellinore piteously, "and these words are as follows. Oh, do try to listen to me, you two, instead of interruptin' all the time about nothing for it makes a man's head go ever so."

"What are these words?" asked Kay.

"These words say this," said King Pellinore, "so far as I can understand from that old friar of orders gray."

"Go on, do," said Kay, for the King had come to a halt.

"Go on," said Sir Ector, "what do these words on this sword in this anvil in this stone outside this church, say?"

"Some red propaganda, no doubt," remarked Sir Grummore.

King Pellinore closed his eyes tight, extended his arms in both directions, and announced in capital letters,

---

7 **anvil** (AN vuhl) *n.* iron or steel block on which a blacksmith rests metal to hammer it into shape.

8. **mead** (meed) *n.* drink made of fermented honey and water.

9. **Saxon** (SAK suhn) **agitators** (AJ i tayt uhrz) The Saxons were a Germanic people who conquered parts of England in ancient times. Agitators are those who stir up people for a cause.

10. **pommel** (PAHM uhl) n. knob at the end of the hilt of some swords.

"Whoso Pulleth Out This Sword of this Stone and Anvil, is Rightwise King Born of All England."

"Who said that?" asked Sir Grummore.

"But the sword said it, like I tell you."

"Talkative weapon," remarked Sir Grummore skeptically.

"It was written on it," cried the King angrily. "Written on it in letters of gold."

"Why didn't you pull it out then?" asked Sir Grummore.

"But I tell you that I wasn't there. All this that I am telling you was told to me by that friar I was telling you of, like I tell you."

"Has this sword with this inscription been pulled out?" inquired Sir Ector.

"No," whispered King Pellinore dramatically. "That's where the whole excitement comes in. They can't pull this sword out at all, although they have all been tryin' like fun, and so they have had to proclaim a tournament all over England, for New Year's Day, so that the man who comes to the tournament and pulls out the sword can be King of all England forever, what, I say?"

"Oh, father," cried Kay. "The man who pulls the sword out of the stone will be the King of England. Can't we go to the tournament, father, and have a shot?"

"Couldn't think of it," said Sir Ector.

"Long way to London," said Sir Grummore, shaking his head.

"My father went there once," said King Pellinore.

Kay said, "Oh, surely we could go? When I am knighted I shall have to go to a tournament somewhere, and this one happens at just the right date. All the best people will be there, and we should see the famous knights and great kings. It does not matter about the sword, of course, but think of the tournament, probably the greatest there has ever been in Gramarye, and all the things we should see and do. Dear father, let me go to this tourney, if you love me, so that I may bear away the prize of all, in my maiden fight."

"But, Kay," said Sir Ector, "I have never been to London."

"All the more reason to go. I believe that anybody who does not go for a tournament like this will be proving that he has no noble blood in his veins. Think what people will say about us, if we do not go and have a shot at that sword. They will say that Sir Ector's family was too vulgar and knew it had no chance."

"We all know the family has no chance," said Sir Ector, "that is, for the sword."

"Lot of people in London," remarked Sir Grummore, with a wild surmise. "So they say."

Vocabulary Development: surmise (suhr MYZ) n. guess; idea based on evidence that is not conclusive

TAKE NOTES

Literary Analysis

Read the underlined text. Why are these words suitable for a **legend**?

_____

_____

_____

Reading Skill

Details about a character's beliefs and behavior can help you **draw a conclusion** about his or her **worldview**. How do details about the choosing of the next king suggest a belief in mysterious powers that guide humans?

_____

_____

_____

Stop to Reflect

To which character do you most closely relate? Explain.

_____

_____

_____

_____

Stop to Reflect

Read the bracketed paragraph. What modern values are reflected in Kay's request to go to London?

_____

_____

_____

The Wart enters the room during a comic scene, but he is on the verge of tears. What effect does this have on the reader's sense of his character in this **legend**?

_____

_____

_____

_____

Read Sir Ector's response to Merlyn's reason for leaving in the bracketed passage. How does Sir Ector's **worldview** differ from Merlyn's worldview?

_____

_____

_____

_____

_____

What do you think Merlyn means by "We shall all meet again"?

_____

_____

_____

Why is Merlyn leaving Sir Ector's household? Underline the text that answers the question.

He took a deep breath and goggled at his host with eyes like marbles.

"And shops," added King Pellinore suddenly, also beginning to breathe heavily.

"Dang it!" cried Sir Ector, bumping his horn mug on the table so that it spilled. "Let's all go to London, then, and see the new King!"

They rose up as one man.

"Why shouldn't I be as good a man as my father?" exclaimed King Pellinore.

"Dash it all," cried Sir Grummore. "After all, it is the capital!"

"Hurray!" shouted Kay.

"Lord have mercy," said the nurse.

At this moment the Wart came in with Merlyn, and everybody was too excited to notice that, if he had not been grown up now, he would have been on the verge of tears.

"Oh, Wart," cried Kay, forgetting for the moment that he was only addressing his squire, and slipping back into the familiarity of their boyhood. "What do you think? We are all going to London for a great tournament on New Year's Day!"

"Are we?"

"Yes, and you will carry my shield and spears for the jousts, and I shall win the palm[11] of everybody and be a great knight!"

"Well, I am glad we are going," said the Wart, "for Merlyn is leaving us too."

"Oh, we shan't need Merlyn."

"He is leaving us," repeated the Wart.

"Leavin' us?" asked Sir Ector. "I thought it was we that were leavin'?"

"He is going away from the Forest Sauvage."

Sir Ector said, "Come now, Merlyn, what's all this about? I don't understand all this a bit."

"I have come to say Goodbye, Sir Ector," said the old magician. "Tomorrow my pupil Kay will be knighted, and the next week my other pupil will go away as his squire. I have outlived my usefulness here, and it is time to go."

"Now, now, don't say that," said Sir Ector. "I think you're a jolly useful chap whatever happens. You just stay and teach me, or be the librarian or something. Don't you leave an old man alone, after the children have flown."

"We shall all meet again," said Merlyn. "There is no cause to be sad."

"Don't go," said Kay.

"I must go," replied their tutor. "We have had a good time while we were young, but it is in the nature of Time

---

11. **win the palm** be the winner. A palm leaf is a symbol of victory.

to fly. There are many things in other parts of the kingdom which I ought to be attending to just now, and it is a specially busy time for me. Come, Archimedes,[12] say Goodbye to the company."

"Goodbye," said Archimedes tenderly to the Wart.

"Goodbye," said the Wart without looking up at all.

"But you can't go," cried Sir Ector, "not without a month's notice."

"Can't I?" replied Merlyn, taking up the position always used by philosophers who propose to dematerialize. He stood on his toes, while Archimedes held tight to his shoulder—began to spin on them slowly like a top—spun faster and faster till he was only a blur of grayish light—and in a few seconds there was no one there at all.

"Goodbye, Wart," cried two faint voices outside the solar window.

"Goodbye," said the Wart for the last time—and the poor fellow went quickly out of the room.

The knighting took place in a whirl of preparations. Kay's sumptuous bath had to be set up in the box room, between two towel-horses and an old box of selected games which contained a worn-out straw dart-board—it was called fléchette in those days—because all the other rooms were full of packing. The nurse spent the whole time constructing new warm pants for everybody, on the principle that the climate of any place outside the Forest Sauvage must be treacherous to the extreme, and, as for the sergeant, he polished all the armor till it was quite brittle and sharpened the swords till they were almost worn away.

At last it was time to set out.

Perhaps, if you happen not to have lived in the Old England of the twelfth century, or whenever it was, and in a remote castle on the borders of the Marches at that, you will find it difficult to imagine the wonders of their journey.

The road, or track, ran most of the time along the high ridges of the hills or downs, and they could look down on either side of them upon the desolate marshes where the snowy reeds sighed, and the ice crackled, and the duck in the red sunsets quacked loud on the winter air. The whole country was like that. Perhaps there would be a moory marsh on one side of the ridge, and a forest of a hundred thousand acres on the other, with all the great branches weighted in white. They could sometimes see a wisp of smoke among the trees, or a huddle of buildings far out among the impassable reeds, and twice they came to quite respectable towns which had several inns to boast of, but on the whole it was an England without civilization. The

---

12. **Archimedes** (ahr kuh MEE deez) Merlin's owl, who is able to talk.

TAKE NOTES

Literary Analysis

Which character is more of a **legendary hero**—Sir Ector or Merlyn? Explain.

_____

_____

_____

Reading Skill

Read the bracketed paragraph. How does the writer's attitude connect past and present **worldviews**?

_____

_____

_____

Reading Check

Why does the nurse make warm pants for everyone? Circle the text that tells the answer.

Reading Skill

Read the bracketed paragraph. Which detail in the paragraph reflects a modern **worldview**? Why?

_____

_____

_____

_____

Stop to Reflect

Why is Kay unable to sleep the night before the tournament?

_____

_____

_____

Reading Skill

Reread the narrator's description of the jousting area. Circle the details that reflect the narrator's modern **worldview**.

better roads were cleared of cover for a bow-shot on either side of them, lest the traveler should be slain by hidden thieves.

They slept where they could, sometimes in the hut of some cottager who was prepared to welcome them, sometimes in the castle of a brother knight who invited them to refresh themselves, sometimes in the firelight and fleas of a dirty little hovel with a bush tied to a pole outside it—this was the signboard used at that time by inns—and once or twice on the open ground, all huddled together for warmth between their grazing chargers. Wherever they went and wherever they slept, the east wind whistled in the reeds, and the geese went over high in the starlight, honking at the stars.

London was full to the brim. If Sir Ector had not been lucky enough to own a little land in Pie Street, on which there stood a respectable inn, they would have been hard put to it to find a lodging. But he did own it, and as a matter of fact drew most of his dividends from that source, so they were able to get three beds between the five of them. They thought themselves fortunate.

On the first day of the tournament, Sir Kay managed to get them on the way to the lists at least an hour before the jousts could possibly begin. He had lain awake all night, imagining how he was going to beat the best barons in England, and he had not been able to eat his breakfast. Now he rode at the front of the cavalcade, with pale cheeks, and Wart wished there was something he could do to calm him down.

For country people, who only knew the dismantled tilting ground[13] of Sir Ector's castle, the scene which met their eyes was ravishing. It was a huge green pit in the earth, about as big as the arena at a football match. It lay ten feet lower than the surrounding country, with sloping banks, and the snow had been swept off it. It had been kept warm with straw, which had been cleared off that morning, and now the close-worn grass sparkled green in the white landscape. Round the arena there was a world of color so dazzling and moving and twinkling as to make one blink one's eyes. The wooden grandstands were painted in scarlet and white. The silk pavilions of famous people, pitched on every side, were azure and green and saffron and checkered. The pennons and pennoncells which floated everywhere in the sharp wind were flapping with every color of the rainbow, as they strained and slapped at their flagpoles, and the barrier down the middle of the arena itself was done in chessboard squares of black and white. Most of the combatants and their friends had not yet arrived, but one could see from those

---

13. **tilting ground** ground on which a joust takes place.

few who had come how the very people would turn the scene into a bank of flowers, and how the armor would flash, and the scalloped sleeves of the heralds jig in the wind, as they raised their brazen trumpets to their lips to shake the fleecy clouds of winter with joyances[14] and fanfares.

"Good heavens!" cried Sir Kay. "I have left my sword at home."

"Can't joust without a sword," said Sir Grummore. "Quite irregular."

"Better go and fetch it," said Sir Ector. "You have time."

"My squire will do," said Sir Kay. "What an awful mistake to make! Here, squire, ride hard back to the inn and fetch my sword. You shall have a shilling[15] if you fetch it in time."

The Wart went as pale as Sir Kay was, and looked as if he were going to strike him. Then he said, "It shall be done, master," and turned his ambling palfrey[16] against the stream of newcomers. He began to push his way toward their hostelry[17] as best he might.

"To offer me money!" cried the Wart to himself. "To look down at this beastly little donkey-affair off his great charger and to call me Squire! Oh, Merlyn, give me patience with the brute, and stop me from throwing his filthy shilling in his face."

When he got to the inn it was closed. Everybody had thronged to see the famous tournament, and the entire household had followed after the mob. Those were lawless days and it was not safe to leave your house—or even to go to sleep in it—unless you were certain that it was impregnable.[18] The wooden shutters bolted over the downstairs windows were two inches thick, and the doors were double-barred.

"Now what do I do," asked the Wart, "to earn my shilling?"

He looked ruefully at the blind little inn, and began to laugh.

"Poor Kay," he said. "All that shilling stuff was only because he was scared and miserable, and now he has good cause to be. Well, he shall have a sword of some sort if I have to break into the Tower of London.

"How does one get hold of a sword?" he continued. "Where can I steal one? Could I waylay some knight, even if I am mounted on an ambling pad, and take his weapons by force? There must be some swordsmith or

---

14. **joyances** (JOY uhns iz) *n.* old word meaning "rejoicing."
15. **shilling** (SHIL ing) *n.* British silver coin.
16. **palfrey** (PAWL free) *n.* old term for a saddle horse, especially one for women.
17. **hostelry** (HAHS tuhl ree) *n.* inn.
18. **impregnable** (im PREG nuh buhl) *adj.* not capable of being captured or entered by force.

TAKE NOTES

Literary Analysis

Underline the Wart's response to Sir Kay when Kay tells him to fetch the sword for a shilling. What does the Wart's reaction have in common with the reaction that a **legendary hero** might have in this situation?

_____

_____

_____

_____

_____

Reading Skill

Compare and contrast the Wart's and the author's **worldview**. Which details of the Wart's behavior reflect modern attitudes? Which reflect the world of legend?

_____

_____

_____

_____

_____

Reading Check

Why is the Wart unable to enter the inn? Underline the text that contains the answer.

Read the bracketed text. How do the Wart's experiences add to the **legendary quality** of events?

_____

_____

_____

_____

_____

_____

What does the underlined text reveal about the writer's **world-view**?

_____

_____

_____

_____

What purpose does the Wart believe the sword in the stone serves? Circle the text that contains the answer.

armorer in a great town like this, whose shop would be still open."

He turned his mount and cantered off along the street. There was a quiet churchyard at the end of it, with a kind of square in front of the church door. In the middle of the square there was a heavy stone with an anvil on it, and a fine new sword was stuck through the anvil.

"Well," said the Wart, "I suppose it is some sort of war memorial, but it will have to do. I am sure nobody would grudge Kay a war memorial, if they knew his desperate straits."

He tied his reins round a post of the lych gate,[19] strode up the gravel path, and took hold of the sword.

"Come, sword," he said. "I must cry your mercy and take you for a better cause.

"This is extraordinary," said the Wart. "I feel strange when I have hold of this sword, and I notice everything much more clearly. Look at the beautiful gargoyles[20] of the church, and of the monastery which it belongs to. See how splendidly all the famous banners in the aisle are waving. How nobly that yew[21] holds up the red flakes of its timbers to worship God. How clean the snow is. I can smell something like fether few and sweet briar—and is it music that I hear?"

It was music, whether of pan-pipes or of recorders, and the light in the churchyard was so clear, without being dazzling, that one could have picked a pin out twenty yards away.

"There is something in this place," said the Wart. "There are people. Oh, people, what do you want?"

Nobody answered him, but the music was loud and the light beautiful.

"People," cried the Wart, "I must take this sword. It is not for me, but for Kay. I will bring it back."

There was still no answer, and Wart turned back to the anvil. He saw the golden letters, which he did not read, and the jewels on the pommel, flashing in the lovely light.

"Come, sword," said the Wart.

He took hold of the handles with both hands, and strained against the stone. There was a melodious consort[22] on the recorders, but nothing moved.

The Wart let go of the handles, when they were beginning to bite into the palms of his hands, and stepped back, seeing stars.

"It is well fixed," he said.

---

19. **lych** (lich) **gate** roofed gate at the entrance to a churchyard.
20. **gargoyles** (GAHR goylz) _n._ grotesque sculptures of animals or fantastic creatures decorating a building.
21. **yew** (yoo) _n._ type of evergreen tree with red cones.
22. **consort** (KAHN sawrt) _n._ piece of music composed for a small group.

He took hold of it again and pulled with all his might. The music played more strongly, and the light all about the churchyard glowed like amethysts; but the sword still stuck.

"Oh, Merlyn," cried the Wart, "help me to get this weapon."

There was a kind of rushing noise, and a long chord played along with it. All round the churchyard there were hundreds of old friends. They rose over the church wall all together, like the Punch-and-Judy[23] ghosts of remembered days, and there were badgers and nightingales and vulgar crows and hares and wild geese and falcons and fishes and dogs and dainty unicorns and solitary wasps and corkindrills and hedgehogs and griffins and the thousand other animals he had met. They loomed round the church wall, the lovers and helpers of the Wart, and they all spoke solemnly in turn. Some of them had come from the banners in the church, where they were painted in heraldry, some from the waters and the sky and the fields about—but all, down to the smallest shrew mouse, had come to help on account of love. Wart felt his power grow.

"Put your back into it," said a luce (or pike) off one of the heraldic banners, "as you once did when I was going to snap you up. Remember that power springs from the nape of the neck."

"What about those forearms," asked a badger gravely, "that are held together by a chest? Come along, my dear embryo,[24] and find your tool."

A merlin sitting at the top of the yew tree cried out, "Now then, Captain Wart, what is the first law of the foot? I thought I once heard something about never letting go."

"Don't work like a stalling woodpecker," urged a tawny owl affectionately. "Keep up a steady effort, my duck, and you will have it yet."

A white-front said. "Now, Wart, if you were once able to fly the great North Sea, surely you can coordinate a few little wing-muscles here and there? Fold your powers together, with the spirit of your mind, and it will come out like butter. Come along, Homo sapiens,[25] for all we humble friends of yours are waiting here to cheer."

The Wart walked up to the great sword for the third time. He put out his right hand softly and drew it out as gently as from a scabbard.

There was a lot of cheering, a noise like a hurdy-gurdy[26] which went on and on. In the middle of this noise, after a long time, he saw Kay and gave him the sword. The people at the tournament were making a frightful row.

---

23. **Punch-and-Judy** puppets of the quarrelsome Punch and his wife, Judy, who fight constantly in a comical way.
24. **embryo** (EM bree oh) *n.* anything in an early stage of development.
25. **Homo sapiens** (HOH moh SAY pee uhnz) scientific name for human beings.
26. **hurdy-gurdy** (HER dee GER dee) *n.* musical instrument played by turning a crank.

TAKE NOTES

Reading Skill

Read the first bracketed paragraph. Which details in this paragraph suggest the **worldview** of people who lived during legendary times?

_____

_____

Stop to Reflect

Read the second bracketed paragraph. What is the significance of the merlin's speaking to the Wart?

_____

_____

_____

_____

Reading Check

Who does the Wart ask for help to pull out the sword? Underline the text that contains the answer.

Read the conversation between Sir Ector and Kay. **Identify details** that reflect both modern and medieval values.

_____

_____

_____

_____

_____

Read the bracketed text. How does what happens contradict a **legend's** characteristic of a deep concern for right and wrong?

_____

_____

_____

_____

When Sir Kay finds Sir Ector, what does Kay tell him about the sword? Underline the answer in the text.

"But this is not my sword," said Sir Kay.

"It was the only one I could get," said the Wart. "The inn was locked."

"It is a nice-looking sword. Where did you get it?"

"I found it stuck in a stone, outside a church."

Sir Kay had been watching the tilting nervously, waiting for his turn. He had not paid much attention to his squire.

"That is a funny place to find one," he said.

"Yes, it was stuck through an anvil."

"What?" cried Sir Kay, suddenly rounding upon him. "Did you just say this sword was stuck in a stone?"

"It was," said the Wart. "It was a sort of war memorial."

Sir Kay stared at him for several seconds in amazement, opened his mouth, shut it again, licked his lips, then turned his back and plunged through the crowd. He was looking for Sir Ector, and the Wart followed after him.

"Father," cried Sir Kay, "come here a moment."

"Yes, my boy," said Sir Ector. "Splendid falls these professional chaps do manage. Why, what's the matter, Kay? You look as white as a sheet."

"Do you remember that sword which the King of England would pull out?"

"Yes."

"Well, here it is. I have it. It is in my hand. I pulled it out."

Sir Ector did not say anything silly. He looked at Kay and he looked at the Wart. Then he stared at Kay again, long and lovingly, and said, "We will go back to the church."

"Now then, Kay," he said, when they were at the church door. He looked at his firstborn kindly, but straight between the eyes. "Here is the stone, and you have the sword. It will make you the King of England. You are my son that I am proud of, and always will be, whatever you do. Will you promise me that you took it out by your own might?"

Kay looked at his father. He also looked at the Wart and at the sword.

Then he handed the sword to the Wart quite quietly.

He said, "I am a liar. Wart pulled it out."

As far as the Wart was concerned, there was a time after this in which Sir Ector kept telling him to put the sword back into the stone—which he did—and in which Sir Ector and Kay then vainly tried to take it out. The Wart took it out for them, and stuck it back again once or twice. After this, there was another time which was more painful.

He saw that his dear guardian was looking quite old and powerless, and that he was kneeling down with difficulty on a gouty[27] knee.

"Sir," said Sir Ector, without looking up, although he was speaking to his own boy.

"Please do not do this, father," said the Wart, kneeling down also. "Let me help you up, Sir Ector, because you are making me unhappy."

"Nay, nay, my lord," said Sir Ector, with some very feeble old tears. "I was never your father nor of your blood, but I wote[28] well ye are of an higher blood than I wend[29] ye were."

"Plenty of people have told me you are not my father," said the Wart, "but it does not matter a bit."

"Sir," said Sir Ector humbly, "will ye be my good and gracious lord when ye are King?"

"Don't!" said the Wart.

"Sir," said Sir Ector, "I will ask no more of you but that you will make my son, your foster-brother, Sir Kay, seneschal[30] of all your lands."

Kay was kneeling down too, and it was more than the Wart could bear.

"Oh, do stop," he cried. "Of course he can be seneschal, if I have got to be this King, and, oh, father, don't kneel down like that, because it breaks my heart. Please get up, Sir Ector, and don't make everything so horrible. Oh, dear, oh, dear, I wish I had never seen that filthy sword at all."

And the Wart also burst into tears.

---

27. **gouty** (GOWT ee) *adj.* having gout, a disease causing swelling and severe pain in the joints.
28. **wote** (woht) *v.* old word meaning "know."
29. **wend** (wend) *v.* thought (past tense of *ween*, an old word meaning "think.")
30. **seneschal** (SEN uh shuhl) *n.* steward, or manager, in the house of a medieval noble.

Literary Analysis

Sir Ector changes the tone of his words when he realizes that the Wart will be king. How does this behavior emphasize the legendary importance of the event?

_____

_____

_____

_____

Reading Check

How are the Wart and Sir Ector related? Underline the text that contains the answer.

Reader's Response: Who is your favorite character in this retelling of the Arthur legend? Explain your answer.

_____

_____

_____

_____

Arthur Becomes King of Britain

1. **Draw Conclusions:** The new king of England is to be chosen by pulling a sword from a stone. What does this method tell you about the reason that men become kings in the world of the story?

_____

_____

2. **Interpret:** When Wart pulls the sword from the stone, he is surrounded by animals offering advice. How does this add to the sense of the importance of Wart's action?

_____

_____

3. **Literary Analysis:** Which features of **legends** are present in this story? Use the chart below to gather examples from the text.

Life Story of Legendary Hero	Concern with Right and Wrong	Reflections of National Pride

4. **Reading Skill:** Characters in this story often speak casually or in slang. What might this speech suggest about the differences between the author's **worldview** and the worldview of those who originally told the legend of Arthur?

_____

_____

SUPPORT FOR WRITING AND EXTEND YOUR LEARNING

Writing: Script for a Television News Report

Write a **script for a television news report** to present the discovery that the Wart will be king of England. Take notes to help you write your report.

- How did the Wart become King?

  _____

  _____

- Who was involved?

  _____

  _____

- Why is this event important?

  _____

  _____

- What are people saying about the event?

  _____

  _____

Listening and Speaking: "Influences" Chart

Watch a movie based on the legends of King Arthur. Make an **"influences" chart**.

- List actions or behaviors that reflect Arthur's world.

  _____

  _____

  _____

- List actions or behaviors that reflect the modern world.

  _____

  _____

  _____

Use your lists to help you complete a chart.

from A Connecticut Yankee in King Arthur's Court • from Don Quixote

LITERARY ANALYSIS

A **parody** is a work in which the author imitates the style or ideas of other works, using exaggeration and humor. For example, the following passage is a parody of the style, conflict, characters, and themes typical of sports stories:

> John was tense as he flipped the final peanut into the air. Then, he exploded into action. In one flawless move, he snapped his head back, and the peanut dropped neatly into his mouth.

The drama of the passage is exaggerated because of the silliness of the topic. As you read each selection, consider which styles or ideas the author of the parody imitates.

READING SKILL

A work of literature reflects the writer's **worldview**, or basic beliefs and values. The writer of a parody, however, may portray that worldview as an illusion.

As you read, notice how characters' beliefs and actions reveal what is illusion and what is reality. Then, use this chart to **compare and contrast** how writers use characters to reveal illusion and reality.

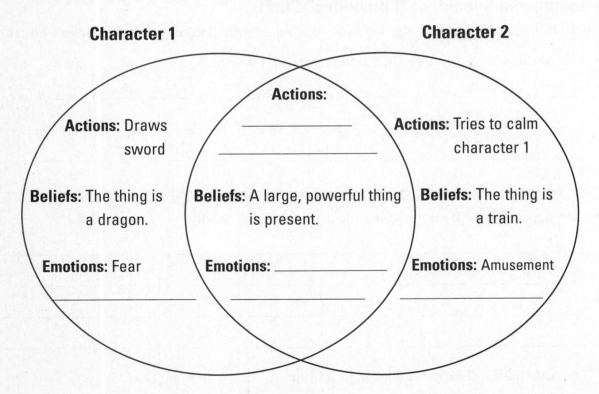

Character 1

Actions: Draws sword

Beliefs: The thing is a dragon.

Emotions: Fear

_____

Actions:
_____
_____

Beliefs: A large, powerful thing is present.

Emotions: _____

_____

Character 2

Actions: Tries to calm character 1

Beliefs: The thing is a train.

Emotions: Amusement

_____

from A Connecticut Yankee in King Arthur's Court

Mark Twain

Summary Hank Morgan is knocked unconscious in 1879. He wakes up in 528. He is waiting to be executed in King Arthur's court. He makes a plan to save himself by pretending that he is a magician. The problem is that Hank's plan does not work as well as he wants it to.

Reading/Writing Connection

Complete the paragraph below. Tell why someone might want to travel in time. Describe difficulties that the person may face.

A person may want to travel in time to <u>withdraw</u> _____.

A time traveler might <u>violate</u> _____. Many

people would <u>react</u> to such a traveler by _____.

Note-taking Guide

Use this diagram to summarize the five most important events of the story.

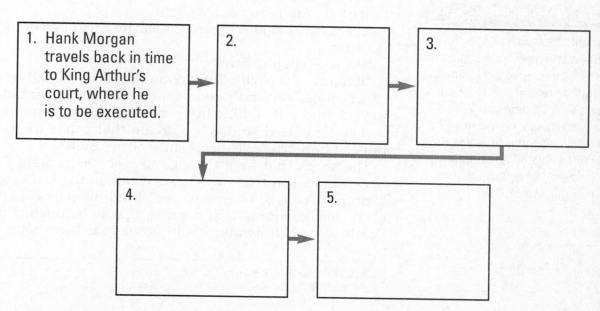

1. Hank Morgan travels back in time to King Arthur's court, where he is to be executed.

2.

3.

4.

5.

Have you ever thought about traveling in time? Where would you go? What year would it be?

_____

_____

_____

A **parody** is a work in which the author imitates the style of another work, using exaggeration and humor. A story may be a parody of the style, conflict, characters and themes of another story. Read the bracketed text. What details of a medieval story are exaggerated here?

_____

_____

_____

_____

A work of literature reflects the writer's **worldview**, or the basic beliefs and values of a person. A writer may present this worldview in an illusion. To help you understand worldviews, **compare and contrast** illusion and reality in the story. What illusion does Hank think he has? What illusion does Clarence think Hank has?

_____

_____

_____

_____

from a Connecticut Yankee in King Arthur's Court
Mark Twain

The practical Hank Morgan is manager of an arms factory in Connecticut in 1879. One day, in a fight with an employee named Hercules, he is knocked unconscious. Awakening in a strange place, he finds himself the prisoner of a knight in armor, Sir Kay. On their way to King Arthur's court, Hank meets Clarence, a friendly young page. Hank is unsure of where he is, and he is astonished when Clarence tells him that it is June 19 in the year 528. Hank knows that a solar eclipse occurred at noon on June 21 in the year 528 but that no eclipse is predicted for his own year. If an eclipse occurs, he reasons, it will confirm that he has traveled in time. In the meantime, he is taken to a dungeon to await execution.

CHAPTER V—AN INSPIRATION

I was so tired that even my fears were not able to keep me awake long.

When I next came to myself, I seemed to have been asleep a very long time. My first thought was, "Well, what an astonishing dream I've had! I reckon I've waked only just in time to keep from being hanged or drowned or burned or something. . . . I'll nap again till the whistle blows, and then I'll go down to the arms factory and have it out with Hercules."

But just then I heard the harsh music of rusty chains and bolts, a light flashed in my eyes, and that butterfly,[1] Clarence, stood before me! I gasped with surprise; my breath almost got away from me.

"What!" I said, "you here yet? Go along with the rest of the dream! scatter!"

But he only laughed, in his light-hearted way, and fell to making fun of my sorry plight.

"All right," I said resignedly, "let the dream go on; I'm in no hurry."

"Prithee[2] what dream?"

"What dream? Why, the dream that I am in Arthur's court—a person who never existed; and that I am talking to you, who are nothing but a work of the imagination."

"Oh, la, indeed! and is it a dream that you're to be burned to-morrow? Ho-Ho—answer me that!"

The shock that went through me was distressing. I now began to reason that my situation was in the last degree serious, dream or no dream; for I knew by past experience of the lifelike intensity of dreams, that to be burned to death, even in a dream, would be very far from being a

---

1. **butterfly** *n.* sociable, lighthearted person.
2. **Prithee** (PRITH ee) *interjection* old term for "please."

jest, and was a thing to be avoided, by any means, fair or
foul, that I could contrive. So I said beseechingly:

"Ah, Clarence, good boy, only friend I've got—for you are
my friend, aren't you?—don't fail me; help me to devise
some way of escaping from this place!"

"Now do but hear thyself! Escape? Why, man, the
corridors are in guard and keep of men-at-arms."

"No doubt, no doubt. But how many, Clarence? Not
many, I hope?"

"Full a score.³ One may not hope to escape." After a
pause—hesitatingly: "and there be other reasons—and
weightier."

"Other ones? What are they?"

"Well, they say—oh, but I daren't, indeed and indeed, I
daren't!"

"Why, poor lad, what is the matter? Why do you
blench? Why do you tremble so?"

"Oh, in sooth, there is need! I do want to tell you, but—"

"Come, come, be brave, be a man—speak out, there's a
good lad!"

He hesitated, pulled one way by desire, the other way
by fear; then he stole to the door and peeped out,
listening; and finally crept close to me and put his mouth
to my ear and told me his fearful news in a whisper, and
with all the cowering apprehension of one who was
venturing upon awful ground and speaking of things
whose very mention might be freighted with death.

"Merlin, in his malice, has woven a spell about this
dungeon, and there bides not the man in these kingdoms
that would be desperate enough to essay to cross its lines
with you! Now God pity me, I have told it! Ah, be kind to
me, be merciful to a poor boy who means thee well; for an
thou betray me I am lost!"

I laughed the only really refreshing laugh I had had for
some time; and shouted:

"Merlin has wrought a spell! Merlin, forsooth! That
cheap old humbug,⁴ that maundering old ass? Bosh, pure
bosh, the silliest bosh in the world! Why, it does seem to
me that of all the childish, idiotic, chuckleheaded,
chicken-livered superstitions that ev—oh, [curse] Merlin!"

But Clarence had slumped to his knees before I had half
finished, and he was like to go out of his mind with fright.

"Oh, beware! These are awful words! Any moment these
walls may crumble upon us if you say such things. Oh,
call them back before it is too late!"

Now this strange exhibition gave me a good idea and set
me to thinking. If everybody about here was so honestly
and sincerely afraid of Merlin's pretended magic as

---

3. **a score** twenty.
4. **humbug** *n.* con artist; impostor; one who misrepresents himself or herself in order
   to take advantage of others.

TAKE NOTES

Stop to Reflect

Do you believe that Hank is dreaming? Explain.

_____

_____

_____

_____

Reading Skill

Read the dialogue between Hank
and Clarence. How does each of
their attitudes reflect the **worldviews** of their cultures?

_____

_____

_____

_____

Literary Analysis

Read the bracketed text. What
language in Clarence's speech
imitates the style of medieval
tales?

_____

_____

_____

_____

Reading Check

What does Hank ask Clarence to
help him do? Underline
the sentence that
tells you.

Read the underlined text. What does this passage reveal about Hank's **worldview**?

_____

_____

_____

_____

Circle the paragraph in which Hank asks Clarence to tell the king that he (Hank) is a magician. Explain why Hank's language is a **parody** of the speech of a medieval sorcerer.

_____

_____

_____

_____

What does Hank claim to be? Underline the text that answers the question.

Clarence was, certainly a superior man like me ought to be shrewd enough to contrive some way to take advantage of such a state of things. I went on thinking, and worked out a plan. Then I said:

"Get up. Pull yourself together; look me in the eye. Do you know why I laughed?"

"No—but for our blessed Lady's sake, do it no more."

"Well, I'll tell you why I laughed. Because I'm a magician myself."

"Thou!" The boy recoiled a step, and caught his breath, for the thing hit him rather sudden; but the aspect which he took on was very, very respectful. I took quick note of that; it indicated that a humbug didn't need to have a reputation in this asylum; people stood ready to take him at his word, without that. I resumed.

"I've known Merlin seven hundred years, and he—"

"Seven hun—"

"Don't interrupt me. He has died and come alive again thirteen times, and traveled under a new name every time: Smith, Jones, Robinson, Jackson, Peters, Haskins, Merlin—a new alias every time he turns up. I knew him in Egypt three hundred years ago; I knew him in India five hundred years ago—he is always bletering around in my way, everywhere I go; he makes me tired. He don't amount to shucks, as a magician; knows some of the old common tricks, but has never got beyond the rudiments, and never will. He is well enough for the provinces[5]—one-night stands and that sort of thing, you know—but dear me, he ought'nt to set up for an expert—anyway not where there's a real artist. Now look here, Clarence, I am going to stand your friend, right along, and in return you must be mine. I want you to do me a favor. I want you to get word to the king that I am a magician myself—and the Supreme Grand High-yu-Muckamuck and head of the tribe, at that; and I want him to be made to understand that I am just quietly arranging a little calamity here that will make the fur fly in these realms if Sir Kay's project is carried out and any harm comes to me. Will you get that to the king for me?"

The poor boy was in such a state that he could hardly answer me. It was pitiful to see a creature so terrified, so unnerved, so demoralized. But he promised everything; and on my side he made me promise over and over again

Vocabulary Development: rudiments (ROO duh muhnts) *n.* basics; slight beginning
calamity (kuh LAM uh tee) *n.* terrible misfortune; disaster

5. **for the provinces** (PRAHV ins iz) for unsophisticated audiences in places far from a big city.

that I would remain his friend, and never turn against him or cast any enchantments upon him. Then he worked his way out, staying himself with his hand along the wall, like a sick person.

Presently this thought occurred to me: how heedless I have been! When the boy gets calm, he will wonder why a great magician like me should have begged a boy like him to help me get out of this place; he will put this and that together, and will see that I am a humbug.

I worried over that heedless blunder for an hour, and called myself a great many hard names, meantime. But finally it occurred to me all of a sudden that these animals didn't reason; that they never put this and that together; that all their talk showed that they didn't know a discrepancy when they saw it. I was at rest, then.

But as soon as one is at rest, in this world, off he goes on something else to worry about. It occured to me that I had made another blunder: I had sent the boy off to alarm his betters with a threat—I intending to invent a calamity at my leisure; now the people who are the readiest and eagerest and willingest to swallow miracles are the very ones who are hungriest to see you perform them; suppose I should be called on for a sample? Suppose I should be asked to name my calamity? Yes, I had made a blunder; I ought to have invented my calamity first. "What shall I do? what can I say, to gain a little time?" I was in trouble again; in the deepest kind of trouble: . . . "There's a footstep!—they're coming. If I had only just a moment to think. . . . Good, I've got it. I'm all right."

You see, it was the eclipse. It came into my mind, in the nick of time, how Columbus, or Cortez, or one of those people, played an eclipse as a saving trump once, on some savages, and I saw my chance. I could play it myself, now; and it wouldn't be any plagiarism, either, because I should get it in nearly a thousand years ahead of those parties.

Clarence came in, subdued, distressed, and said:

"I hasted the message to our liege the king, and straightway he had me to his presence. He was frighted even to the marrow, and was minded to give order for your instant enlargement,[6] and that you be clothed in fine raiment and lodged as befitted one so great; but then came Merlin and spoiled all; for he persuaded the king that you are mad, and know not whereof you speak; and said your threat is but foolishness and idle vaporing. They disputed long, but in the end, Merlin, scoffing, said, 'Wherefore hath he not named his brave calamity? Verily it is because he cannot.' This thrust did in a most sudden sort close the king's mouth, and he could offer naught to turn the argument; and so, reluctant, and full loth to do

---

6. **enlargement** *n.* old term for "release."

© Pearson Education, Inc., publishing as Pearson Prentice Hall.   from A Connecticut Yankee in King Arthur's Court **449**

TAKE NOTES

Reading Skill

How does Hank take advantage of Clarence's **worldview**?

_____

_____

_____

_____

Reading Check

How do the king and Merlin respond to Hank's threat of a "calamity"? Underline details that answer the question.

Literary Analysis

Clarence describes to Hank the argument between Merlin and the king. Why does the formality of the words Clarence uses seem exaggerated?

_____

_____

_____

_____

How does Clarence's speech make you feel about Hank's situation?

_____

_____

_____

_____

Think about Hank's situation in this **parody**. How does his situation make his imitation of a magician's speech seem comical?

_____

_____

_____

_____

At what time will Hank be burned at the stake? Underline the text that answers the question.

you the discourtesy, he yet prayeth you to consider his perplexed case, as noting how the matter stands, and name the calamity—if so be you have determined the nature of it and the time of its coming. Oh, prithee delay not; to delay at such a time were to double and treble the perils that already compass thee about. Oh, be thou wise—name the calamity!"

I allowed silence to accumulate while I got my impressiveness together, and then said:

"How long have I been shut up in this hole?"

"Ye were shut up when yesterday was well spent. It is nine of the morning now."

"No! Then I have slept well, sure enough. Nine in the morning now! And yet it is the very complexion of midnight, to a shade. This is the 20th, then?"

"The 20th—yes."

"And I am to be burned alive tomorrow." The boy shuddered.

"At what hour?"

"At high noon."

"Now then, I will tell you what to say." I paused, and stood over that cowering lad a whole minute in awful silence; then, in a voice deep, measured, charged with doom, I began, and rose by dramatically graded stages to my colossal climax, which I delivered in as sublime and noble a way as ever I did such a thing in my life: "Go back and tell the king that at that hour I will smother the whole world in the dead blackness of midnight; I will blot out the sun, and he shall never shine again; the fruits of the earth shall rot for lack of light and warmth, and the peoples of the earth shall famish and die, to the last man!"

I had to carry the boy out myself, he sunk into such a collapse. I handed him over to the soldiers, and went back.

CHAPTER VI—THE ECLIPSE

In the stillness and the darkness, realization soon began to supplement knowledge. The mere knowledge of a fact is pale; but when you come to realize your fact, it takes on color. It is all the difference between hearing of a man being stabbed to the heart, and seeing it done. In the stillness and the darkness, the knowledge that I was in deadly danger took to itself deeper and deeper meaning all the time; a something which was realization crept inch by inch through my veins and turned me cold.

But it is a blessed provision of nature that at times like these, as soon as a man's mercury[7] has got down to a certain point there comes a revulsion, and he rallies. Hope springs up, and cheerfulness along with it, and then he is

---

7. **mercury** referring to the liquid metal used in a thermometer; the mercury rises and falls in the thermometer with the temperature.

in good shape to do something for himself, if anything can be done. When my rally came, it came with a bound. I said to myself that my eclipse would be sure to save me, and make me the greatest man in the kingdom besides; and straightway my mercury went up to the top of the tube, and my solicitudes all vanished. I was as happy a man as there was in the world. I was even impatient for tomorrow to come, I so wanted to gather in that great triumph and be the center of all of the nation's wonder and reverence. Besides, in a business way it would be the making of me; I knew that.

Meantime there was one thing which had got pushed into the background of my mind. That was the half-conviction that when the nature of my proposed calamity should be reported to those superstitious people, it would have such an effect that they would want to compromise. So, by and by when I heard footsteps coming, that thought was recalled to me, and I said to myself, "As sure as anything, it's the compromise. Well, if it is good, all right, I will accept; but if it isn't, I mean to stand my ground and play my hand for all it is worth."

The door opened, and some men-at-arms appeared. The leader said:

"The stake is ready. Come!"

The stake! The strength went out of me, and I almost fell down. It is hard to get one's breath at such a time, such lumps come into one's throat, and such gaspings; but as soon as I could speak, I said:

"But this is a mistake—the execution is to-morrow."

"Order changed; been set forward a day. Haste thee!"

I was lost. There was no help for me. I was dazed, stupefied; I had no command over myself; I only wandered purposelessly about, like one out of his mind; so the soldiers took hold of me, and pulled me along with them, out of the cell and along the maze of underground corridors, and finally into the fierce glare of daylight and the upper world. As we stepped into the vast inclosed court of the castle I got a shock; for the first thing I saw was the stake, standing in the center, and near it the piled fagots[8] and a monk. On all four sides of the court the seated multitudes rose rank above rank, forming sloping terraces that were rich with color. The king and the queen sat in their thrones, the most conspicuous figures there, of course.

Vocabulary Development: multitudes (MUL tuh toodz) *n.* crowds; large numbers of people or things

---

8. **fagots** (FAG uhts) *n.* bundles of sticks used as fuel.

TAKE NOTES

Reading Skill

Read the underlined text. What do Hank's thoughts indicate about his values?

_____

_____

_____

Reading Skill

What type of reasoning does Hank follow to determine that he will not succeed in creating his illusion? What does this reveal about his **worldview**?

_____

_____

_____

Reading Check

Which event has been set forward one day? Underline the text that answers the question.

Read the bracketed paragraph. In what way does Clarence's scheming develop **parody**?

_____

_____

_____

_____

Compare and contrast illusion and reality as you read. What illusion does Clarence believe in when he changes the date of the execution? What is the reality?

_____

_____

_____

_____

_____

How does the crowd react as Hank is led to the stake? Underline details that answer the question.

To note all this, occupied but a second. The next second Clarence had slipped from some place of concealment and was pouring news into my ear, his eyes beaming with triumph and gladness. He said:

"'Tis through *me* the change was wrought! And main hard have I worked to do it, too. But when I revealed to them the calamity in store, and saw how mighty was the terror it did engender, then saw I also that this was the time to strike! Wherefore I diligently pretended, unto this and that and the other one, that your power against the sun could not reach its full until the morrow; and so if any would save the sun and the world, you must be slain to-day, while your enchantments are but in the weaving and lack potency. Odsbodikins, it was but a dull lie, a most indifferent invention, but you should have seen them seize it and swallow it, in the frenzy of their fright, as it were salvation sent from heaven; and all the while was I laughing in my sleeve the one moment, to see them so cheaply deceived, and glorifying God the next, that He was content to let the meanest[9] of His creatures be His instrument to the saving of thy life. Ah, how happy has the matter sped! You will not need to do the sun a real hurt—ah, forget not that, on your soul forget it not! Only make a little darkness—only the littlest little darkness, mind, and cease with that. It will be sufficient. They will see that I spoke falsely—being ignorant, as they will fancy—and with the falling of the first shadow of that darkness you shall see them go mad with fear; and they will set you free and make you great! Go to thy triumph, now! But remember—ah, good friend, I implore thee remember my supplication, and do the blessed sun no hurt. For *my* sake, thy true friend."

I choked out some words through my grief and misery; as much as to say I would spare the sun; for which the lad's eyes paid me back with such deep and loving gratitude that I had not the heart to tell him his good-hearted foolishness had ruined me and sent me to my death.

As the soldiers assisted me across the court the stillness was so profound that if I had been blindfold I should have supposed I was in a solitude instead of walled in by four thousand people. There was not a movement perceptible in those masses of humanity; they were as rigid as stone images, and as pale; and dread sat upon every countenance. This hush continued while I was being chained to the stake; it still continued while the fagots were carefully and tediously piled about my ankles, my knees, my thighs, my body. Then there was a pause, and a deeper hush, if possible, and a man knelt down at my feet with a blazing torch; the multitude strained

---

9. **meanest** *adj.* lowest; least significant.

forward, gazing, and parting slightly from their seats without knowing it; the monk raised his hands above my head, and his eyes toward the blue sky, and began some words in Latin; in this attitude he droned on and on, a little while, and then stopped. I waited two or three moments; then looked up; he was standing there petrified. With a common impulse the multitude rose slowly up and stared into the sky. I followed their eyes; as sure as guns, there was my eclipse beginning! The life went boiling through my veins; I was a new man! The rim of black spread slowly into the sun's disk, my heart beat higher and higher, and still the assemblage and the priest stared into the sky, motionless. I knew that this gaze would be turned upon me, next. When it was, I was ready. I was in one of the most grand attitudes I ever struck, with my arm stretched up pointing to the sun. It was a noble effect. You could see the shudder sweep the mass like a wave. Two shouts rang out, one close upon the heels of the other:

"Apply the torch!"

"I forbid it!"

The one was from Merlin, the other from the king. Merlin started from his place—to apply the torch himself, I judged. I said:

"Stay where you are. If any man moves—even the king—before I give him leave, I will blast him with thunder, I will consume him with lightnings!"

The multitude sank meekly into their seats, and I was just expecting they would. Merlin hesitated a moment or two, and I was on pins and needles that little while. Then he sat down, and I took a good breath; for I knew I was master of the situation now. The king said:

"Be merciful, fair sir, and essay no further in this perilous matter, lest disaster follow. It was reported to us that your powers could not attain unto their full strength until the morrow; but—"

"Your Majesty thinks the report may have been a lie? It *was* a lie."

That made an immense effect; up went appealing hands everywhere, and the king was assailed with a storm of supplications that I might be bought off at any price, and the calamity stayed.

The king was eager to comply. He said:

"Name any terms, reverend sir, even to the halving of my kingdom; but banish this calamity, spare the sun!"

My fortune was made, I would have taken him up in a minute, but I couldn't stop an eclipse; the thing was out of the question. So I asked time to consider. The king said:

"How long—ah, how long, good sir? Be merciful; look, it groweth darker, moment. Prithee how long?"

Literary Analysis

Read the underlined text. How is this a **parody** of a medieval magician's actions?

_____

_____

_____

Reading Skill

How does Hank react to the eclipse? How does the crowd react? How do their reactions show their different **worldviews**?

_____

_____

_____

_____

Reading Check

What event happens just before Hank is to be burned? Underline the text that contains the answer.

Reading Skill

How does Hank answer the question of whether he is suffering from an illusion of his own?

_____
_____
_____
_____

Literary Analysis

Read the bracketed text. What two types of language does Hank mix in this speech? Underline an example of one type. Circle an example of the other type. How do these two types of language show the two different **worldviews** of the characters in the story?

_____
_____
_____
_____

Reading Check

What position in the kingdom does Hank ask the king to grant him? Underline the text that answers the question.

"Not long. Half an hour—maybe an hour."

There were a thousand pathetic protests, but I couldn't shorten up any, for I couldn't remember how long a total eclipse lasts. I was in a puzzled condition, anyway, and wanted to think. Something was wrong about that eclipse, and the fact was very unsettling. If this wasn't the one I was after, how was I to tell whether this was the sixth century, or nothing but a dream? Dear me, if I could only prove it was the latter! Here was a glad new hope. If the boy was right about the date, and this was surely the 20th, it wasn't the sixth century. I reached for the monk's sleeve, in considerable excitement, and asked him what day of the month it was.

Hang him, he said it was the *twenty-first!* It made me turn cold to hear him. I begged him not to make any mistake about it; but he was sure; he knew it was the 21st. So, that feather-headed boy had botched things again! The time of the day was right for the eclipse; I had seen that for myself, in the beginning, by the dial[10] that was near by. Yes, I *was* in King Arthur's court, and I might as well make the most of it I could.

The darkness was steadily growing, the people becoming more and more distressed. I now said:

"I have reflected, Sir King. For a lesson, I will let this darkness proceed, and spread night in the world; but whether I blot out the sun for good, or restore it shall rest with you. These are the terms, to wit: You shall remain king over all your dominions, and receive all the glories and honors that belong to the kingship; but you shall appoint me your perpetual minister and executive, and give me for my services one per cent. of such actual increase of revenue[11] over and above its present amount as I may succeed in creating for the state. If I can't live on that, I sha'n't ask anybody to give me a lift. Is it satisfactory?"

There was a prodigious roar of applause, and out of the midst of it the king's voice rose, saying:

"Away with his bonds, and set him free! and do him homage, high and low, rich and poor, for he is become the king's right hand, is clothed with power and authority, and his seat is upon the highest step of the throne! Now sweep away this creeping night, and bring the light and cheer again, that all the world may bless thee."

But I said:

Vocabulary Development: homage (AHM ij) *n.* public act of respect; tribute

---

10. **dial** *n.* sundial, or device used to measure time by the position of the sun in the sky.
11. **revenue** (REV uh noo) *n.* money taken in by a government in the form of taxes, fees, and penalties.

"That a common man should be shamed before the world, is nothing; but it were dishonor to the *king* if any that saw his minister naked should not also see him delivered from his shame. If I might ask that my clothes be brought again—"

"They are not meet," the king broke in. "Fetch raiment of another sort; clothe him like a prince!"

My idea worked. I wanted to keep things as they were till the eclipse was total, otherwise they would be trying again to get me to dismiss the darkness, and of course I couldn't do it. Sending for the clothes gained some delay, but not enough. So I had to make another excuse. I said it would be but natural if the king should change his mind and repent to some extent of what he had done under excitement; therefore I would let the darkness grow awhile, and if at the end of a reasonable time the king had kept his mind the same, the darkness should be dismissed. Neither the king nor anybody else was satisfied with that arrangement, but I had to stick to my point.

It grew darker and darker and blacker and blacker, while I struggled with those awkward sixth-century clothes. It got to be pitch-dark, at last, and the multitude groaned with horror to feel the cold uncanny night breezes fan through the place and see the stars come out and twinkle in the sky. At last the eclipse was total, and I was very glad of it, but everybody else was in misery; which was quite natural. I said:

"The king, by his silence, still stands to the terms." Then I lifted up my hand—stood just so a moment—then I said, with the most awful solemnity: "Let the enchantment dissolve and pass harmless away!"

There was no response, for a moment, in that deep darkness and that graveyard hush. But when the silver rim of the sun pushed itself out, a moment or two later, the assemblage broke loose with a vast shout and came pouring down like a deluge to smother me with blessings and gratitude.

And Clarence was not the last of the wash, to be sure.

Reader's Response: If you traveled back to another time as Hank Morgan did, what would you miss most about the time you live in now?

_____

_____

_____

_____

© Pearson Education, Inc., publishing as Pearson Prentice Hall.

from A Connecticut Yankee in King Arthur's Court **455**

TAKE NOTES

Stop to Reflect

If you were Hank, what would you ask of the king in return for bringing the sun back?

_____

_____

_____

_____

Reading Skill

Think about the differing **worldviews** of Hank and the crowd of people. How do two different ideas about one event lead both Hank and the crowd to feel relieved?

_____

_____

_____

_____

Reading Check

How does the crowd react when the sun returns? Underline the text that contains the answer.

from a Connecticut Yankee in King Arthur's Court

1. **Interpret:** What does the deal Hank strikes with King Arthur show about Hank's character?

   _____

   _____

2. **Speculate:** King Arthur makes Hank a minister at his court. Name one difficulty that Hank may face as a minister at King Arthur's court.

   _____

   _____

3. **Literary Analysis:** Use the chart below to give examples of ways in which Hank is a **parody** of a heroic figure.

Arthurian Hero	Hank Morgan
1. wins with great strength or supernatural power	1. wins through trickery
2. desires glory	
3. serves his king out of loyalty	

4. **Reading Skill: Compare and contrast** the reaction of Hank and Clarence to a particular danger. What does the contrast suggest about common illusions in Arthur's day?

   _____

   _____

   _____

   _____

SUPPORT FOR WRITING AND EXTEND YOUR LEARNING

Writing: Parody

Write a **parody** in which a twenty-first century time traveler lands in King Arthur's world. Complete the outline below.

I. What situation does the time traveler face? _____

   1. What is reality? _____

   2. What is an illusion? _____

II. What are the major events?

   1. Reality _____

      Illusion _____

   2. Reality _____

      Illusion _____

III. How is the major event resolved?

_____

_____

IV. How does the story end?

_____

_____

Research and Technology: Biographical Brochure

Conduct research for a **biographical brochure** on Mark Twain. Answer the following questions to help you begin your research.

How did he become a writer? _____

_____

Did he have other jobs? What were they? _____

_____

Give an example of how an event in his life influenced what he wrote. _____

_____

from Don Quixote

Miguel de Cervantes

Summary An old gentleman escapes reality by reading stories about knights, battles, and love. He imagines himself as a knight. He takes the name Don Quixote. He puts on rusty armor, mounts a tired old horse, and sets out in search of adventure.

Reading/Writing Connection

Complete the following paragraph about a character from a book whose life you might like to lead.

_____ lived a life dedicated to _____

_____. This character could appreciate _____

_____. The character tried to achieve _____.

Note-taking Guide

Use this chart to record the differences between Don Quixote's real life and his fantasy.

Don Quixote's Reality	Don Quixote's Fantasy

from Don Quixote

1. **Analyze Cause and Effect:** Why does Don Quixote become a knight?

_____

_____

2. **Hypothesize:** What would happen to Don Quixote's dreams of knightly adventure if he were to admit the truth about the windmills?

_____

_____

3. **Literary Analysis:** Use this chart to give examples of ways in which Don Quixote is a **parody** of a heroic knight.

Legendary Knight	Don Quixote
1. wears shining armor	1.
2. rides a great steed	2.
3. pledges love to a lady	3.
4. conquers giants	4.

4. **Reading Skill:** How does Don Quixote's life at the beginning of the selection **compare and contrast** with his life at the end?

_____

_____

_____

_____

SUPPORT FOR WRITING AND EXTEND YOUR LEARNING

Writing: Parody

Write a **parody** of an adventure in which Don Quixote takes on a twenty-first century challenge. Use the word web below to gather ideas for your parody.

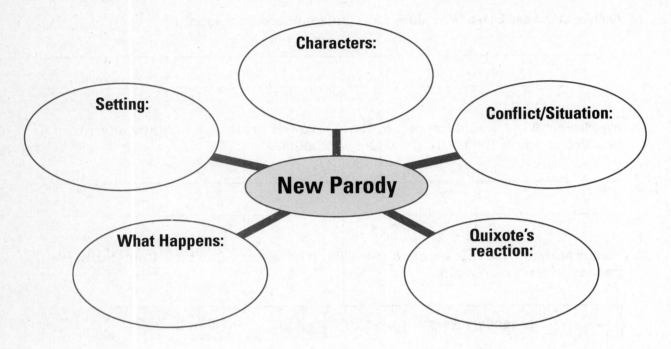

Research and Technology: Biographical Brochure

Find information on the life of Miguel de Cervantes. Then, create a **biographical brochure** for people who want to know more about this writer. Use these questions to guide your research:

- Where and when was Cervantes born? _____

- What adventures did he have in Italy and on his way home to Spain?

  _____

  _____

- Did Cervantes have other jobs? What were they? _____

  _____

  _____

- Give an example of how an event in his life influenced what he wrote.

  _____

  _____

Position Statements

ABOUT POSITION STATEMENTS

A **position statement** is a written presentation of a person's or an organization's opinion on a specific topic. For example, a group might publish a position statement about a new law that affects the environment. Most position statements include the following:

- background information on the issue
- a clear statement of the person's or organization's opinion
- facts and details that support the opinion
- a call for action, or steps to take to resolve the issue

READING SKILL

You can evaluate position statements by **comparing and contrasting the writers' purposes**. Some common purposes of position statements include these:

- to persuade readers to think in a certain way or to take a specific action.
- to inform an audience
- to honor an important person
- to entertain readers or to win their interest

Use the chart below to compare and contrast position statements.

DETAILS GIVEN
1.
2.

GENERAL PURPOSE THAT DETAIL SUPPORTS
Detail 1. ❑ Inform ❑ Persuade ❑ Entertain
Detail 2. ❑ Inform ❑ Persuade ❑ Entertain

SPECIFIC PURPOSE OR POSITION

SPECIAL EXHIBITIONS

- Home
- Special Exhibitions

Christo and Jeanne-Claude: *The Gates*, Central Park, New York

More about this Exhibition

The evolution of the widely anticipated outdoor work of art for New York City initiated in 1979 by the husband-and-wife collaborators Christo and Jeane-Claude is the subject of the exhibition "Christo and Jeanne-Claude: *The Gates*, Central Park, New York," on view at The Metropolitan Museum of Art through July 25, 2004. Fifty-one preparatory drawings and collages by Christo, sixty-four photographs, and eleven maps and technical diagrams document the soon-to-be-realized work of art, which when completed will consist of 7,500 saffron-colored gates placed at twelve-foot intervals throughout twenty-three miles of pedestrian walkways lacing Central Park from 59th Street to 110th Street and from Central Park West to Fifth Avenue.

"*The Gates*, Central Park, New York City, 1979–2005" will be on view in Central Park for sixteen days in February 2005. This outdoor project—in which 193 gates will surround the Metropolitan Museum in the park, all the way to the glass wall of The American Wing—will be entirely financed by Christo and Jeanne-Claude.

The exhibition is made possible by an anonymous donor.

Philippe de Montebello, director, The Metropolitan Museum of Art, commented: "We are delighted to present the blueprints, if you will, of this far-reaching project, which the public will be able to preview here at the Museum. At long last Christo and Jeanne-Claude's project will see fruition, and our exhibition will trace the full course of its evolution. This work of massive scope, when realized, will surely constitute a tribute to the grandeur of Central Park and New York City, and reaffirm the continuity of culture and the centrality of art to the life of our city and all cities."

• Current Exhibitions • Upcoming Exhibitions • Past Exhibitions • Traveling Exhibitions • Printing Instructions

http://www.christojeanneclaude.net

Welcome Page | Artworks in Progress | Exhibitions/Collections | Bibliography | About the Artists | Contact

Christo and Jeanne-Claude

The Gates
Project for Central Park, New York City

© 2005 Christo and Jeanne-Claude

Photo: Wolfgang Volz/laif/Redux

As Christo and Jeanne-Claude have always done for their projects, *The Gates* will be entirely financed by the artists with the sale of preparatory studies, drawings, collages, and scale models, earlier works of the fifties and sixties, and original lithographs on other subjects.

The artists do not accept sponsorship or donations. All materials used in the project will be recycled.

> The artists responsible for *The Gates* use both facts and colorful descriptive language such as *bloom* to give readers a sense of their project.

The final installation of the 7,503 gates will be done, in five days, simultaneously by hundreds of workers. The unfurling of the fabric panels will bloom in one day.

A written contract has been drafted between the City of New York and the Department of Parks and Recreation and the artists.

The contract requires the artists to provide, among other terms and conditions:

> Details about the artists' contract with the city may reassure critical readers about the cost and consequences of the project.

- Personal and property liability insurance holding harmless the City, the Department of Parks and Recreation and the Central Park Conservancy.
- Restoration Bond providing funds for complete removal.
- Clearance for the usual activities in the park and access of Rangers, maintenance, clean-up, police and emergency vehicles.
- The artists shall pay all costs of the Park's supervision directly related to the project.

- Neither vegetation nor rock formations shall be disturbed.
- *The Gates* will be clear of rocks, tree roots and low branches.
- The people of New York will continue to use Central Park as usual.
- After the removal, the site shall be inspected by the Department of Parks and Recreation, which will be holding the security until satisfaction.

For those who will walk through *The Gates*, following the walkways, and staying away from the grass, *The Gates* will be a golden ceiling creating warm shadows. When seen from the buildings surrounding Central Park, *The Gates* will seem like a golden river appearing and disappearing through the bare branches of the trees and will highlight the shape of the footpaths.

The 16-day-duration work of art, free to all, will be a long-to-be-remembered joyous experience for every New Yorker, as a democratic expression that Olmsted[1] invoked when he conceived a "central" park. The luminous moving fabric will underline the organic design of the park, while the rectangular poles will be a reminder of the geometric grid pattern of the city blocks around the park. *The Gates* will harmonize with the beauty of Central Park.

> Here the artists use descriptive details and historical facts to express their position: The work of art will give spectators pleasure while affirming the beauty of the park.

> A preliminary sketch for the project, incorporating a map of the park, helps bring the project to life for readers.

Christo: *The Gates, Project for Central Park, New York City.* Collage, 2002.
In two parts. 12" x 30 1/2" and 26 1/4" x 30 1/2".

©2002 Christo   Photo: Wolfgang Volz/laif/Redux

---

1. Olmsted (1822–1903) Frederick Law Olmsted, landscape architect and social thinker who helped to design Central Park, New York City, the nation's first large urban park. Olmsted intended his designs to make beauty available to everyone.

Forgotten Delights

Send comments

Who's in charge of this site

What's on this site

Christo's *Gates*: Art in Individual Minds and Public Places
Copyright © Dianne L. Durante 2004.

A great work of art [. . .] transforms the artist's message into an unforgettable image. Such a work is not merely pretty décor: it gives you a guide to living your life.

At its best, art can literally help you keep your goals in sight. A work of visual art condenses a whole view of the world. You can hold it in your mind as a single, concrete image of what sort of person you'd like to become: a person with the pride of Michelangelo's *David*, or the elegance of *Madame Récamier*.[1] You can use it to recall the sort of world you want to live in: the peace of a Constable landscape, the bustle and energy of Canaletto's Venice, the drama of a Delacroix. . . .[2]

What message will *The Gates* convey? None at all. If you examine every fiber of the million square feet of fabric, you won't be a nanometer closer to knowing what sort of person you'd like to be, what you should focus on, what sort of world you'd like to live in. Prominent art historians and critics at the Whitney, the Museum of Modern Art and *The New York Times* haven't even tried to proclaim any meaning in *The Gates*. They merely assert that it will draw attention to Central Park. . . .

If you want to enjoy art in Central Park, do your best to avoid Christo's giant slalom poles. Instead, seek out the dozens of figurative sculptures scattered through the Park, from *Duke Ellington* to the Delacorte Clock, from the Maine Monument to *Samuel Morse*, from *Still Hunt* to the Untermeyer Fountain. Like genuine works of art ever since the caveman's time, these have the potential to speak to you.

---

1. Michelangelo's (mǐ´ kəl an´ jə loz´) ***David. . . Madame Récamier*** (rā kà myā´) Sculptor and painter Michelangelo (1475–1564) chiseled a famous sculpture depicting the Biblical hero David, who killed Goliath. The beautiful, witty, socially successful Frenchwoman Madame Récamier (1777–1849) was the subject of a number of paintings by nineteenth-century artists.
2. Constable. . . Delacroix (də là krwàl´) Englishman John Constable (1776–1837) is famous for his paintings of the English countryside. Italian Antonio Canaletto (1697–1768) is noted for his paintings of Venice, Italy. Frenchman Eugène Delacroix (1798–1863) painted battles and life in other cultures.

THINKING ABOUT THE POSITION STATEMENT

1. Why does the Forgotten Delights Web site oppose *The Gates*?

_____

_____

2. What response might Christo and Jeanne-Claude make to the *Forgotten Delights* article?

_____

_____

READING SKILL

3. Give an example of a detail from one of the Web sites that is meant to persuade readers.

_____

_____

4. Give an example of a detail from one of the Web sites that is meant to inform readers.

_____

_____

TIMED WRITING: PERSUASION (45 minutes)

Write a **position statement** that explains your opinion of *The Gates*. Summarize the reasons that other people are for and against *The Gates*. Use details or quotations from at least one position statement to support your points.

To help you get started, list one reason that people are for *The Gates* and one reason that people are against the exhibition.

_____

_____

_____

PART 2: TURBO VOCABULARY

The exercises and tools presented here are designed to help you increase your vocabulary. Review the instruction and complete the exercises to build your vocabulary knowledge. Throughout the year, you can apply these skills and strategies to improve your reading, writing, speaking, and listening vocabulary.

WORD ROOTS

The following list contains common word roots with meanings and examples. On the blank lines, write other words you know that have the same roots. Write the meanings of the new words.

Root	Meaning	Example and Meaning	Your Words	Meanings
-cred-	believe	*credible:* able to be believed; believable		
-dict-	speak or say	*contradictory:* describing things that say the opposite of each other		
-doc-	teach	*documentary:* a movie or television program that teaches or gives information		
-form-	shape	*formation:* the process by which something develops into a particular thing or shape		
-loqu-	speak	*eloquent:* speaking out with force or clarity		
-nov-	new	*innovative:* new, different, and better		
-sequi-	follow	*sequence:* an arrangement in which one follows another		
-sign-	signal; meaning	*significant:* important; full of meaning		

Root	Meaning	Example and Meaning	Your Words	Meanings
-spec-	look; see	*perspective:* a way of looking at or thinking about something, which is influenced by the kind of person you are		
-spont(e)-	free will	*spontaneous:* done freely and impulsively		
-tempor-	of time	*temporary:* lasting for a time only; not permanent		
-tri-	three	*tripod:* a three-legged stool or table		
-val-	courage or strength	*valid:* having a strong foundation in logic		
-ver-	truth	*verify:* prove something true		
-vinc-/-vict-	conquer	*convince:* overcome doubts; persuade		
-vis-/-vid-	see	*vision:* the act of seeing		
-vit-	life	*vital:* necessary for life		
-volve-	roll	*involve:* roll in or include		

PREFIXES

The following list contains common prefixes with meanings and examples. On the blank lines, write other words you know that begin with the same prefixes. Write the meanings of the new words.

Prefix	Meaning	Example and Meaning	Your Words	Meanings
ante-	before; prior to	*anticipate:* expect something		
con-/com-	with; together	*concur:* agree with		
contra-	against	*controversy:* a discussion over opposing viewpoints; a dispute		
en-/em-	in, into, within	*enlighten:* to give the light of fact and knowledge to; to make clear to		
dis-	not, the opposite of, apart from	*dishonest:* not honest; lying and cheating		
in-/ir-	without; not	*incapable:* not able *irresistible:* not able to be resisted; too fascinating to be withstood		
inter-	between; among; or within	*internal:* on the inside		

Prefix	Meaning	Example and Meaning	Your Words	Meanings
mis-	wrong; bad	*misspell:* spell incorrectly		
multi-	many	*multicolored:* having many colors		
non-	without; not	*nonfiction:* writing that is about real people or events, not imagined ones		
ob-	against	*obstacle:* something that makes it difficult for you to succeed		
post-	after	*postpone:* change an event to a later time or date		
pre-	before	*preview:* look before		
re-	again	*remake:* make again		
sub-	below, under	*submarine:* under the ocean		
super-	above; over	*superior:* better than another		
un-/an-/a-	not	*unbelievable:* not believable		

SUFFIXES

The following list contains common suffixes with meanings and examples. On the blank lines, write other words you know that have the same suffixes. Write the meanings of the new words.

Suffix	Meaning	Example and Meaning	Your Words	Meanings
-able	capable of being; or having the quality of	*usable:* capable of being used		
-age	that which relates to the act of or the condition of	*usage:* way of using something		
-al	having the form or character of; relating to	*seasonal:* relating to a season		
-ance/-ence	act of; state of; quality of	*assistance:* act of giving help		
-ate	make	*motivate:* make someone feel eager to do something		
-er/-or	one who	*painter:* person who paints		
-ful	filled with	*joyful:* filled with happiness		
-hood	state or quality of	*brotherhood:* the state of being brothers; a feeling of unity and cooperation among people		

Suffix	Meaning	Example and Meaning	Your Words	Meanings
-ism	a condition of being; the result of	*mechanism:* system or means of doing something; working parts of a machine		
-ist	one who	*pianist:* person who plays the piano		
-ize	to engage in; to cause to be	*emphasize:* stress		
-less	without	*powerless:* without power		
-logy	field of study	*biology:* study of living things		
-ment	act or quality of	*contentment:* the state of being contented, or happy enough with what one has		
-ness	state or quality of	*quietness:* the state of being quiet or silent		
-ous	having; full of	*courageous:* brave; having courage		
-tion	the act of; the state of being	*deliberation:* the act of carefully thinking about an issue		

Use a **dictionary** to find the correct spelling, the meaning, the pronunciation, and the part of speech of a word. The dictionary will show you how the plural is formed if it is irregular. You can also find the word's history, or *etymology*, in a dictionary. Etymology explains how words change, how they are borrowed from other languages, and how new words are invented, or "coined."

Here is a sample entry from a dictionary. Notice what it tells about the word. Then, follow the instructions.

> **lemon** (lem´ ən) *n.* [ME *lymon* < MFr *limon* < Ar *laimūn* < Pers *līmūn*] **1** a small, egg-shaped, edible citrus fruit with a yellow rind and a juicy, sour pulp, rich in ascorbic acid **2** the small, spiny, semitropical evergreen citrus tree (*Citrus limon*) bearing this fruit **3** pale yellow **4** [slang] something, esp. a manufactured article, that is defective or imperfect

1. Circle the *n.* in the dictionary entry. It stands for noun. Write what these other parts of speech abbreviations mean: *v.* _____, *adv.* _____, *adj.* _____ *prep.* _____.

2. Underline the origins of the word *lemon*. ME stands for Middle English, Ar stands for Arabic, and Pers. stands for Persian. What do you think MFr stands for? _____

3. Put a box around the pronunciation.

4. How many noun definitions does the entry have? _____

5. Which definition is slang? _____

6. Which definition of lemon is used in the following sentence? _____

The car that my dad bought turned out to be a lemon.

Activity: Use a dictionary to learn about the origins of these words.

1. literature _____ / _____ / _____

                pronunciation   main part of speech   original language(s)

_____ / _____

        1st meaning   other meanings

_____

_____

_____

_____

2. language _____ / _____ / _____

             pronunciation   main part of speech   original language(s)

_____ / _____

        1st meaning   other meanings

_____

_____

_____

Activity: Look up each of the following words in a dictionary. Then, write a definition of the word and a sentence using the word.

moment _____

_____

popular _____

_____

remedy _____

_____

blur _____

_____

lazy _____

_____

Use these word study cards to break big words into their parts. Write the word at the top of the card. Then, divide the word into its prefix, root, and suffix. Note that not all words have prefixes and suffixes. List the meaning of each part of the word. Next, find three words with the same root and write them on the card. Finally, write the word's part of speech and its definition. Use a dictionary to help you. One example has been done for you.

Word:	**invisible**	
Prefix	**Root**	**Suffix**
in: not	**vis:** see	**ible**-able to be
Root-related Words **1.** vision **2.** revise **3.** visibility		
Definition: invisible *adj.* not able to be seen		

Word:		
Prefix	**Root**	**Suffix**
Root-related Words **1.** **2.** **3.**		
Definition:		

WORD STUDY CARDS

Word:

Prefix	Root	Suffix

Root-related Words
1.
2.
3.

Definition:

Word:

Prefix	Root	Suffix

Root-related Words
1.
2.
3.

Definition:

Word:

Prefix	Root	Suffix

Root-related Words
1.
2.
3.

Definition:

DENOTATION AND CONNOTATION

The words you read and use have different types of meaning.
- The **denotation** [DEE noh TAY shuhn] of a word is its dictionary meaning or its exact meaning.
- The **connotation** [KAHN oh TAY shuhn] of a word is the ideas or feeling usually associated with the word. A word with *positive* connotations produces good feelings and reactions in readers and listeners. A word with *negative* connotations produces bad or unpleasant feelings and reactions. Some words are *neutral* because they do not tap our emotions at all.

The following words have a similar denotation. They all name places where people live.

house, apartment, shack, castle, home

However each word has different connotations, listed below.

house: a place where one family lives. Some connotations may be open spaces, a yard, and family. (neutral connotations)
apartment: a place where a family lives among many other families. Some connotations may be city life, crowded, and neighborhood. (neutral connotation)
shack: run-down, small (negative connotation)
castle: large, royalty, elegant (positive connotation)
home: warmth, family, security (positive connotation)

A. The words *bargain, cheap* and *inexpensive* have a similar denotation: "not costing a lot." Write a sentence for each word that makes its connotation clear.

inexpensive: low-priced (neutral connotation) _____

_____

cheap: low-priced and poor quality (negative connotation) _____

_____

bargain: something worth more than you pay for it (positive connotation)

_____

_____

B. For each word pair, explain the different connotations of each word.

1. slim/skinny _____

2. scary/horrifying _____

3. television/tv _____

4. children/kids _____

5. clever/sneaky _____

C. Use this chart to take note of word groups and the connotations they suggest. Complete the examples by supplying words with the same denotation to fill in the blanks. Over time, keep notes on words you read or hear that have strong negative or positive connotations. Complete each section for each word so that you have a list of words to choose from when you are looking for a particular connotation, or when you want a netural word that avoids emotional associations.

Neutral	Positive	Negative
ask	appeal request	demand beg insist
tell	advise	snitch
group	team	clique crowd
attempt		
laugh	guffaw chuckle	snort

D. The words in the following chart also all have a similar denotation. Fill in the missing connotation for each word. Then, use each word in a sentence that makes the connotation of the word clear.

Word	Connotation
cheerful	
glad	
joyful	
Shared Denotation: happy	

Write sentences using each of the words in the chart.

_____

_____

_____

eloquent (EL uh kwuhnt) *adj.* expressing meaning clearly, forcefully, and memorably

fluent (FLOO uhnt) *adj.* of writing or speech that is especially smooth and expressive

initial (i NISH uhl) *adj.* having to do with the beginning of something

innovative (IN uh vay tiv) *adj.* inventive; done in a new or unusual way

intuitive (in TOO i tiv) *adj.* perceived or understood immediately, without conscious thought

perceive (per SEEV) *v.* see; to understand

preliminary (pree LIM uh ner ee) *adj.* leading up to; preparing for

priority (pry OHR uh tee) *n.* something that is more important than other things

spontaneous (spahn TAY nee uhs) *adj.* seeming to occur without planning

subjective (suhb JEK tiv) *adj.* of a person's thoughts and feelings; also a grammatical term

A. True/False For each of the following, mark T or F to indicate whether the italicized vocabulary word has been used correctly in the sentence. If you have marked F, correct the sentence by changing the words that make the statement wrong.

1. _____ An interpreter must be *fluent* in at least two languages.

2. _____ Mike planned for weeks for the party to be *spontaneous*.

3. _____ The valedictorian gave an *eloquent* graduation speech.

4. _____ After the *initial* completion of the library, the mayor cut the ribbon.

5. _____ We took a *preliminary* quiz before we studied for the final exam.

6. _____ He made a list to help determine which task was the *priority*.

7. _____ The child was *intuitive* when he grabbed the toy away from the baby.

8. _____ The roller coaster was *innovative*, like nothing the crowd had ever seen.

9. _____ Jim's best friend was Jack, and because of that, he found it hard to be *subjective* while judging his performance.

10. _____ There was no way for the children to *perceive* the possible consequences.

B. Use each word pair in an original sentence that illustrates the meaning of the academic vocabulary word.

eloquent/writer _____

_____

fluent/French _____

_____

initial/reaction _____

_____

innovative/film _____

_____

intuitive/conversation _____

_____

perceive/situation _____

_____

preliminary/research _____

_____

priority/homework _____

_____

spontaneous/game _____

_____

subjective/reply _____

_____

anticipate (an TIS uh payt) *v.* give advance thought to, expect

coincide (koh in SYD) *v.* occur at the same time

comprehend (kahm pree HEND) *v.* understand; include

consequently (KAHN si kwent lee) *adv.* logically following from; as a result of

discern (di SERN) *v.* recognize clearly

formulate (FOHR myoo layt) *v.* express in a fixed or definite way

indicate (IN di KAYT) *v.* direct attention to

infer (in FER) *v.* derive by reasoning; figure out from details

perspective (per SPEK tiv) *n.* a specific point of view

predominant (pree DAHM uh nuhnt) *adj.* superior; most noticeable

A. Completions Complete each sentence that has been started for you. Your sentence completion should be logical and illustrate the meaning of the vocabulary word in italics.

1. The judges were ready to *indicate* _____
_____.

2. From my *perspective* the carnival was _____
_____.

3. Using a telescope, it was easy to *discern* _____
_____.

4. John's pool party *coincides* with _____
_____.

5. The children *comprehend* that in order to go swimming _____
_____.

6. I was able to *infer* from Jen's invitation that _____
_____.

7. Jim overslept and, *consequently,* _____
_____.

8. We were able to *anticipate* that _____
_____.

9. Scientists are able to *formulate* _____

_____.

10. The *predominant* feature of the elephant we saw _____

_____.

B. Use each word pair in an original sentence that illustrates the meaning of the academic vocabulary word.

anticipate/hurricane _____

_____

coincide/schedule _____

_____

comprehend/instructions _____

_____

consequently/change _____

_____

discern/truth _____

_____

formulate/theory _____

_____

indicate/location _____

_____

infer/meaning _____

_____

perspective/argument _____

_____

predominant/feature _____

_____

enlighten (en LYT uhn) *v.* instruct; furnish knowledge

emphasis (EM fuh sis) *n.* expression or action that gives special importance to something

emerge (ee MERJ) *v.* become visible or apparent

speculate (SPEK yuh layt) *v.* think seriously; ponder; conjecture

confront (kuhn FRUNT) *v.* face boldy or defiantly; bring face to face

differentiate (dif uhr EN shee ayt) *v.* distinguish between

disclaim (dis KLAYM) *v.* deny or give up a claim

inevitable (in EV i tuh buhl) *adj.* certain to happen; unavoidable

insight (IN syt) *n.* act or result of understanding the inner nature of things

motive (MOHT iv) *n.* reason

A. Code Name Use the code to figure out each vocabulary word. Each letter is represented by a number or symbol.

%	5	•	*	2	#	!	7	^	&	9	¶	£	$	3	¥	+	=	?	÷	4	¢	6	§	«	ç
a	b	c	d	e	f	g	h	i	j	k	l	m	n	o	p	q	r	s	t	u	v	w	x	y	z

1. ^ $ 2 ¢ ^ ÷ % 5 ¶ 2   _____

2. • 3 $ # = 3 $ ÷   _____

3. ? ¥ 2 • 4 ¶ % ÷ 2   _____

4. 2 £ ¥ 7 % ? ^ ?   _____

5. 2 $ ¶ ^ ! 7 ÷ 2 $ _____

6. ^ $? ^ ! 7 ÷   _____

7. * ^ # # 2 = 2 $ ÷ ^ % ÷ 2   _____

8. 2 £ 2 = ! 2   _____

9. * ^ ? • ¶ % ^ £   _____

10. £ 3 ÷ ^ ¢ 2   _____

B. Use each word pair in an original sentence that illustrates the meaning of the academic vocabulary word.

enlighten/students _____

_____

emphasis/speech _____

_____

emerge/runner _____

_____

speculate/future _____

_____

confront/issue _____

_____

differentiate/right and wrong _____

_____

disclaim/article _____

_____

inevitable/change _____

_____

insight/problem _____

_____

motive/act _____

_____

compensate (KAHM puhn sayt) *v.* make up for; counterbalance

distort (di STOHRT) *v.* twist or change the meaning or intent

diverse (duh VERS) *adj.* different, varied

ideology (y dee AHL uh jee) *n.* doctrines or opinions; study of one basic idea

minimize (MIN i myz) *n.* make small; reduce in size, amount, or importance

radical (RAD i kuhl) *adj.* extreme, nonconformity

recur (ri KER) *v.* come up or happen again

significance (sig NIF uh kuhns) *n.* meaning; importance

terminology (ter muh NAHL uh jee) *n.* terms or systems of terms associated with a specific science, art, and so on

visual (VIZH yoo uhl) *adj.* connected with seeing

A. Completions Complete each sentence that has been started for you. Your sentence completion should be logical and illustrate the meaning of the vocabulary word in italics.

1. The flower show had many *diverse* _____

_____ .

2. The new traffic light at the intersection should *minimize* _____

_____ .

3. It is important to read carefully and not *distort* _____

_____ .

4. To *compensate* for the long wait in the ticket line, _____

_____ .

5. The painting was considered *radical* because _____

_____ .

6. It is important to understand computer *terminology* so that _____

_____ .

7. Besides slides, other types of *visual* aids that you can use in a

presentation include _____

_____ .

8. If a nightmare *recurs*, that means it will _____

_____.

9. Students are just starting to realize the *significance* of _____

_____.

10. Each artistic group brought their own *ideology* about _____

_____.

B. Use each word pair in an original sentence that illustrates the meaning of the academic vocabulary word.

compensate/loss _____

_____

distort/facts _____

_____

diverse/cultures _____

_____

ideology/principles _____

_____

minimize/effect _____

_____

radical/idea _____

_____

recur/weekly _____

_____

significance/education _____

_____

terminology/scientific _____

_____

visual/commercial _____

_____

UNIT 5: ACADEMIC VOCABULARY WORDS

assess (uh SES) *v.* judge; measure

contradictory (kahn truh DIK tuh ree) *adj.* in opposition or conflict

credible (KRED uh buhl) *adj.* believable; reliable

deficient (dee FISH uhnt) *adj.* lacking; incomplete

document (DAHK yoo muhnt) *v.* provide with factual support

dominant (DAHM uh nuhnt) *adj.* overpowering

evaluate (ee VAL yoo ayt) *v.* find the value; judge the worth

integrity (in TEG ruh tee) *n.* honesty; sincerity

legitimate (luh JIT uh muht) *adj.* lawful; reasonable; justifiable

superficial (soo per FISH uhl) *adj.* of or being on the surface; shallow; concerned only with the obvious or apparent

A. Answer each question. Then, explain your answer.

1. Could you *assess* someone's behavior? _____

_____.

2. Could an opinion be *contradictory*? _____

_____.

3. Is someone who usually lies *credible*? _____

_____.

4. If you were to *document* an event, what would you be providing? _____

_____.

5. What does it mean if something is *dominant*? _____

_____.

6. If you were asked to *evaluate* a plan, what would you do? _____

_____.

7. How would you describe a person who has *integrity*? _____

_____.

8. If someone made a *legitimate* argument, what would they have conveyed?

_____.

_____.

9. What would it mean if the conversation were *superficial*? _____

_____.

10. If a person is *deficient* in nutrients, could an improved diet and

vitamins help? _____

_____.

B. Write new words that you come across in your reading. Define each word.

_____

_____

_____

_____

_____

coordinate (koh OHRD 'n ayt) *v.* place in the same order or system; to adjust

incorporate (in KOHR puh rayt) *v.* make part of something

initiate (i NISH ee ayt) *v.* bring into practice or use; start

intense (in TENS) *adj.* strong and focused

lucid (LOO sid) *adj.* readily apparent; clear

manipulate (muh NIP yoo layt) *v.* manage or control through clever moves

synthesize (SIN thuh syz) *v.* put together elements to form a whole

unify (YOO nuh fy) *v.* join together; unite

visual (VIZH yoo uhl) *adj.* related to seeing

A. True/False For each of the following, mark T or F to indicate whether the italicized vocabulary word has been used correctly in the sentence. If you have marked F, correct the sentence by changing the words that make the statement wrong.

1. _____ If a storm is *intense*, it is weak and will cause little damage.

2. _____ To *coordinate* a trip, make a list of things to bring.

3. _____ The slide show provided *visual* aids for the governor's speech.

4. _____ If it is possible to *unify* a community, they will not support each other.

5. _____ The musicians used several instruments to *synthesize* a rich sound.

6. _____ The information presented was *lucid* and caused all present to be confused.

7. _____ He *initiated* a new procedure that the company had been using for years.

8. _____ Sue used her research to *incorporate* facts about elephants into her essay

9. _____ A chess player who *manipulates* the pieces will most likely lose the game.

B. Use each word pair in an original sentence that illustrates the meaning of the academic vocabulary word.

coordinate/schedule _____

_____

incorporate/information _____

_____

initiate/idea _____

_____

intense/gaze _____

_____

lucid/speech _____

_____

manipulate/writing _____

_____

synthesize/music _____

_____

unify/group _____

_____

visual/performance _____

_____

C. Write new words that you come across in your reading. Define each word.

_____

_____

_____

WORDS IN OTHER SUBJECTS

Use this page to write down academic words you come across in other subjects, such as social studies or science. When you are reading your textbooks, you may find words that you need to learn. Following the example, write down the word, the part of speech, and an explanation of the word. You may want to write an example sentence to help you remember the word.

dissolve *verb* to make something solid become part of a liquid by putting it in a liquid and mixing it

The sugar *dissolved* in the hot tea.

_____

_____

_____

_____

_____

_____

_____

_____

_____

_____

_____

_____

_____

_____

_____

_____

_____

_____

_____

_____

_____

VOCABULARY FLASH CARDS

Use these flash cards to study words you want to remember. The words on this page come from Unit 1. Cut along the dotted lines on pages V27 through V34 to create your own flash cards or use index cards. Write the word on the front of the card. On the back, write the word's part of speech and definition. Then, write a sentence that shows the meaning of the word.

defiance	tentative	dingy
prolonged	equilibrium	buffer
maligned	furtively	apathy

noun
open resistance to authority

With *defiance*, the girl turned her back and walked out on her mother.

adjective
hesitant; not confident

I took a *tentative* bite of the unusual dessert.

adjective
dirty-looking; shabby

The dark walls made the room look *dingy*.

---

adjective
extended; lengthy

His *prolonged* absence is due to serious illness.

noun
a state of balance

See how well she keeps her *equilibrium* walking on the balance beam!

verb
lessen a shock; cushion

A helmet helps *buffer* the impact of a fall.

---

adjective
spoken ill of

The CD, *maligned* by critics, was still a tremendous hit.

adverb
secretively; sneakily; stealthily

She reached *furtively* for the last slice of pie.

noun
lack of interest or emotion

The bored audience looked at the speaker with *apathy*.

VOCABULARY FLASH CARDS

Use these flash cards to study words you want to remember. Cut along the dotted lines on pages V27 through V34 to create your own flash cards or use index cards. Write the word on the front of the card. On the back, write the word's part of speech and definition. Then, write a sentence that shows the meaning of the word.

VOCABULARY FLASH CARDS

Use these flash cards to study words you want to remember. Use blank flash cards
located on pages V27 through V31 to create your own flash cards or use prepared cards.
Write the word on the front of the card. On the back, write the word's part of speech
and definition. Then write a sentence that shows the meaning of the word.

VOCABULARY FLASH CARDS

Use these flash cards to study words you want to remember. Cut along the dotted lines on pages V27 through V34 to create your own flash cards or use index cards. Write the word on the front of the card. On the back, write the word's part of speech and definition. Then, write a sentence that shows the meaning of the word.

Use these flash cards to study vocabulary words to remember. Cut along the dotted lines on pages V27 through V32 to make your own flash cards for new words. Write the word on the front of the card. On the back, write the word's part of speech and definition. Then, write a sentence that shows the meaning of the word.

VOCABULARY FLASH CARDS

Use these flash cards to study words you want to remember. Cut along the dotted lines on pages V27 through V34 to create your own flash cards or use index cards. Write the word on the front of the card. On the back, write the word's part of speech and definition. Then, write a sentence that shows the meaning of the word.

VOCABULARY FOLD-A-LIST

Use a fold-a-list to study the definitions of words. The words on this page come from Unit 1. Write the definition for each word on the lines. Fold the paper along the dotted line to check your definition. Create your own fold-a-lists on pages V35 through V42.

convoluted _____

_____

deftness _____

_____

imperceptibly _____

_____

deficiency _____

_____

replenished _____

_____

incessant _____

_____

obscured _____

_____

context _____

_____

expound _____

_____

amiably _____

_____

Fold In ◄

VOCABULARY FOLD-A-LIST

Write the word that matches the definition on each line.
Fold the paper along the dotted line to check your work.

intricate; twisted _____

skillfulness _____

so slowly or slightly as
to be barely noticeable _____

lack of something essential _____

made complete or full again _____

not coming to a
stop; constant _____

made dark; blocked
from view; hid _____

environment or situation
in which something is
found, especially when
it helps explain the thing _____

explain in detail _____

in a cheerful, friendly way _____

Fold In ←

VOCABULARY FOLD-A-LIST

Write the words you want to study on this side of the page. Write the definitions on the back. Then, test yourself. Fold the paper along the dotted line to check your definition.

Word: _____

_____

Word: _____

_____

Word: _____

_____

Word: _____

_____

Word: _____

_____

Word: _____

_____

Word: _____

_____

Word: _____

_____

Word: _____

_____

Word: _____

_____

Fold In ↓

VOCABULARY FOLD-A-LIST

Write the word that matches the definition on each line.
Fold the paper along the dotted line to check your work.

Definition: ____________________

Definition: ____________________

Definition: ____________________

Definition: ____________________

Definition: ____________________

Definition: ____________________

Definition: ____________________

Definition: ____________________

Definition: ____________________

Definition: ____________________

Fold In ←

VOCABULARY FOLD-A-LIST

Write the words you want to study on this side of the page. Write the definitions on the back. Then, test yourself. Fold the paper along the dotted line to check your definition.

Word: ______________________

____

Word: ______________________

____

Word: ______________________

____

Word: ______________________

____

Word: ______________________

____

Word: ______________________

____

Word: ______________________

____

Word: ______________________

____

Word: ______________________

____

Word: ______________________

____

Fold In ←

VOCABULARY FOLD-A-LIST

Write the word that matches the definition on each line.
Fold the paper along the dotted line to check your work.

Definition: _____

Definition: _____

Definition: _____

Definition: _____

Definition: _____

Definition: _____

Definition: _____

Definition: _____

Definition: _____

Definition: _____

Fold In ↓

Write the words you want to study on this side of the page. Write the definitions on the back. Then, test yourself. Fold the paper along the dotted line to check your definition.

Word: _____

Word: _____

Word: _____

Word: _____

Word: _____

Word: _____

Word: _____

Word: _____

Word: _____

Word: _____

Fold In

VOCABULARY FOLD-A-LIST

Write the word that matches the definition on each line.
Fold the paper along the dotted line to check your work.

Definition: _____

Definition: _____

Definition: _____

Definition: _____

Definition: _____

Definition: _____

Definition: _____

Definition: _____

Definition: _____

Definition: _____

Fold In ←

COMMONLY MISSPELLED WORDS

The list on these pages presents words that cause problems for many people. Some of these words are spelled according to set rules, but others follow no specific rules. As you review this list, check to see how many of the words give you trouble in your own writing. Then, add your own commonly misspelled words on the lines that follow.

abbreviate	auxiliary	census	deficient
absence	awkward	certain	definitely
absolutely	bandage	changeable	delinquent
abundance	banquet	characteristic	dependent
accelerate	bargain	chauffeur	descendant
accidentally	barrel	chief	description
accumulate	battery	clothes	desert
accurate	beautiful	coincidence	desirable
ache	beggar	colonel	dessert
achievement	beginning	column	deteriorate
acquaintance	behavior	commercial	dining
adequate	believe	commission	disappointed
admittance	benefit	commitment	disastrous
advertisement	bicycle	committee	discipline
aerial	biscuit	competitor	dissatisfied
affect	bookkeeper	concede	distinguish
aggravate	bought	condemn	effect
aggressive	boulevard	congratulate	eighth
agreeable	brief	connoisseur	eligible
aisle	brilliant	conscience	embarrass
all right	bruise	conscientious	enthusiastic
allowance	bulletin	conscious	entrepreneur
aluminum	buoyant	contemporary	envelope
amateur	bureau	continuous	environment
analysis	bury	controversy	equipped
analyze	buses	convenience	equivalent
ancient	business	coolly	especially
anecdote	cafeteria	cooperate	exaggerate
anniversary	calendar	cordially	exceed
anonymous	campaign	correspondence	excellent
answer	canceled	counterfeit	exercise
anticipate	candidate	courageous	exhibition
anxiety	capacity	courteous	existence
apologize	capital	courtesy	experience
appall	capitol	criticism	explanation
appearance	captain	criticize	extension
appreciate	career	curiosity	extraordinary
appropriate	carriage	curious	familiar
architecture	cashier	cylinder	fascinating
argument	catastrophe	deceive	February
associate	category	decision	fiery
athletic	ceiling	deductible	financial
attendance	cemetery	defendant	fluorescent

foreign
fourth
fragile
gauge
generally
genius
genuine
government
grammar
grievance
guarantee
guard
guidance
handkerchief
harass
height
humorous
hygiene
ignorant
immediately
immigrant
independence
independent
indispensable
individual
inflammable
intelligence
interfere
irrelevant
irritable
jewelry
judgment
knowledge
lawyer
legible
legislature
leisure
liable
library
license
lieutenant
lightning
likable
liquefy
literature
loneliness
magnificent
maintenance
marriage
mathematics
maximum
meanness
mediocre
mileage
millionaire
minimum

minuscule
miscellaneous
mischievous
misspell
mortgage
naturally
necessary
neighbor
neutral
nickel
niece
ninety
noticeable
nuisance
obstacle
occasion
occasionally
occur
occurred
occurrence
omitted
opinion
opportunity
optimistic
outrageous
pamphlet
parallel
paralyze
parentheses
particularly
patience
permanent
permissible
perseverance
persistent
personally
perspiration
persuade
phenomenal
phenomenon
physician
pleasant
pneumonia
possess
possession
possibility
prairie
precede
preferable
prejudice
preparation
previous
primitive
privilege
probably
procedure

proceed
prominent
pronunciation
psychology
publicly
pursue
questionnaire
realize
really
recede
receipt
receive
recognize
recommend
reference
referred
rehearse
relevant
reminiscence
renowned
repetition
restaurant
rhythm
ridiculous
sandwich
satellite
schedule
scissors
secretary
siege
solely
sponsor
subtle
subtlety
superintendent
supersede
surveillance
susceptible
tariff
temperamental
theater
threshold
truly
unmanageable
unwieldy
usage
usually
valuable
various
vegetable
voluntary
weight
weird
whale
wield
yield

_____
_____
_____
_____
_____
_____
_____
_____
_____
_____
_____
_____

When you are reading, you will find many unfamiliar words. Here are some tools that you can use to help you read unfamiliar words.

PHONICS

Phonics is the science or study of sound. When you learn to read, you learn to associate certain sounds with certain letters or letter combinations. You know most of the sounds that letters can represent in English. When letters are combined, however, it is not always so easy to know what sound is represented. In English, there are some rules and patterns that will help you determine how to pronounce a word. This chart shows you some of the vowel digraphs, which are combinations like *ea* and *oa*. Two vowels together are called vowel digraphs. Usually, vowel digraphs represent the long sound of the first vowel.

Vowel Digraphs	Examples of Unusual Sounds	Exceptions
ee and *ea*	steep, each, treat, sea	head, sweat, dread
ai and *ay*	plain, paid, may, betray	plaid
oa, *ow*, and *oe*	soak, slow, doe	now, shoe
ie and *igh*	lie, night, delight	friend, eight

As you read, sometimes the only way to know how to pronounce a word with an ea spelling is to see if the word makes sense in the sentence. Look at this example:

The water pipes were made of *lead*.

First, try out the long sound "ee." Ask yourself if it sounds right. It does not. Then, try the short sound "e." You will find that the short sound is correct in that sentence.

Now try this example.

Where you *lead*, I will follow.

WORD PATTERNS

Recognizing different vowel-consonant patterns will help you read longer words. In the following sections, the V stands for "vowel" and the C stands for "consonant."

Single-syllable Words

CV – go: In two letter words with a consonant followed by a vowel, the vowel is usually long. For example, the word *go* is pronounced with a long *o* sound.

In a single syllable word, a vowel followed only by a single consonant is usually short.

CVC – got: If you add a consonant to the word *go*, such as the *t* in *got*, the vowel sound is a short *o*. Say the words *go* and *got* aloud and notice the difference in pronunciation.

Multi-syllable words

In words of more than one syllable, notice the letters that follow a vowel.

VCCV – robber: A single vowel followed by two consonants is usually short.

VCV — begin: A single vowel followed by a single consonant is usually long.

VCe — beside: An extension of the VCV pattern is vowel-consonant-silent *e*. In these words, the vowel is long and the *e* is not pronounced.

When you see a word with the VCV pattern, try the long vowel sound first. If the word does not make sense, try the short sound. Pronounce the words *model, camel,* and *closet*. First, try the long vowel sound. That does not sound correct, so try the short vowel sound. The short vowel sound is correct in those words.

Remember that patterns help you get started on figuring out a word. You will sometimes need to try a different sound or find the word in a dictionary.

As you read and find unfamiliar words, look the pronunciations up in a dictionary. Write the words in this chart in the correct column to help you notice patterns and remember pronunciations.

Syllables	Example	New words	Vowel
CV	go		long
CVC	got		short
VCC	robber		short
V/CV	begin open		long long
VC/V	closet		short

MNEMONICS

Mnemonics are devices, or methods, that help you remember things. The basic strategy is to link something you do not know with something that you *do* know. Here are some common mnemonic devices:

Visualizing Create a picture in your head that will help you remember the meaning of a vocabulary word. For example, the first four letters of the word *significance* spell *sign*. Picture a sign with the word *meaning* written on it to remember that significance means "meaning" or "importance."

Spelling The way a word is spelled can help you remember its meaning. For example, you might remember that *clarify* means to "make clear" if you notice that both *clarify* and *clear* start with the letters *cl*.

To help you remember how to spell certain words, look for a familiar word within the difficult word. For example:

Believe has a *lie* in it.

Separate is *a rat* of a word to spell.

Your *principal* is your *pal*.

Rhyming Here is a popular rhyme that helps people figure out how to spell *ei* and *ie* words.

i before *e* — except after *c* or when sounding like *a* as in neighbor and weigh.

List words here that you need help remembering. Work with a group to create mnemonic devices to help you remember each word.

_____   _____

_____   _____

_____   _____

_____   _____

_____   _____

List words here that you need help remembering. Work with a group to create mnemonic devices to help you remember each word.

_____   _____

_____   _____

_____   _____

_____   _____

_____   _____

_____   _____

_____   _____

_____   _____

_____   _____

_____   _____

_____   _____

_____   _____

VOCABULARY BOOKMARKS

Cut out each bookmark to use as a handy word list when you are reading. On the lines, jot down words you want to learn and remember. You can also use the bookmark as a placeholder in your book.

TITLE	
Word	**Page #**
_____	
_____	
_____	
_____	
_____	
_____	
_____	
_____	
_____	
_____	
_____	
_____	
_____	
_____	
_____	

TITLE	
Word	**Page #**
_____	
_____	
_____	
_____	
_____	
_____	
_____	
_____	
_____	
_____	
_____	
_____	
_____	
_____	
_____	

TITLE	
Word	**Page #**
_____	
_____	
_____	
_____	
_____	
_____	
_____	
_____	
_____	
_____	
_____	
_____	
_____	
_____	
_____	

VOCABULARY BOOKMARKS

Cut out each bookmark to use as a handy word list when you are reading. On the lines, jot down words you want to learn and remember. You can also use the bookmark as a placeholder in your book.

TITLE	
Word	**Page #**
_____	_____
_____	_____
_____	_____
_____	_____
_____	_____
_____	_____
_____	_____
_____	_____
_____	_____
_____	_____
_____	_____
_____	_____
_____	_____

TITLE	
Word	**Page #**
_____	_____
_____	_____
_____	_____
_____	_____
_____	_____
_____	_____
_____	_____
_____	_____
_____	_____
_____	_____
_____	_____
_____	_____
_____	_____

TITLE	
Word	**Page #**
_____	_____
_____	_____
_____	_____
_____	_____
_____	_____
_____	_____
_____	_____
_____	_____
_____	_____
_____	_____
_____	_____
_____	_____
_____	_____

VOCABULARY BOOKMARKS

Cut out each bookmark to use as a handy word list when you are reading. On the lines, jot down words you want to learn and remember. You can also use the bookmark as a placeholder in your book.

TITLE	
Word	**Page #**
_____	_____
_____	_____
_____	_____
_____	_____
_____	_____
_____	_____
_____	_____
_____	_____
_____	_____
_____	_____
_____	_____
_____	_____
_____	_____
_____	_____

TITLE	
Word	**Page #**
_____	_____
_____	_____
_____	_____
_____	_____
_____	_____
_____	_____
_____	_____
_____	_____
_____	_____
_____	_____
_____	_____
_____	_____
_____	_____
_____	_____

TITLE	
Word	**Page #**
_____	_____
_____	_____
_____	_____
_____	_____
_____	_____
_____	_____
_____	_____
_____	_____
_____	_____
_____	_____
_____	_____
_____	_____
_____	_____
_____	_____

VOCABULARY BUILDER CARDS

Use these cards to record words you want to remember. Write the word, the title of the story or article in which it appears, its part of speech, and its definition. Then, use the word in an original sentence that shows its meaning

Word: _____ Page _____

Selection: _____

Part of Speech: _____

Definition: _____

_____

My Sentence _____

_____

Word: _____ Page _____

Selection: _____

Part of Speech: _____

Definition: _____

_____

My Sentence _____

_____

Word: _____ Page _____

Selection: _____

Part of Speech: _____

Definition: _____

_____

My Sentence _____

_____

VOCABULARY BUILDER CARDS

Use these cards to record words you want to remember. Write the word, the title of the story or article in which it appears, its part of speech, and its definition. Then, use the word in an original sentence that shows its meaning

Word: _____ Page _____

Selection: _____

Part of Speech: _____

Definition: _____

_____

My Sentence _____

_____

Word: _____ Page _____

Selection: _____

Part of Speech: _____

Definition: _____

_____

My Sentence _____

_____

Word: _____ Page _____

Selection: _____

Part of Speech: _____

Definition: _____

_____

My Sentence _____

_____

VOCABULARY BUILDER CARDS

Use these cards to record words you want to remember. Write the word, the title of the story or article in which it appears, its part of speech, and its definition. Then, use the word in an original sentence that shows its meaning

Word: _____ Page _____

Selection: _____

Part of Speech: _____

Definition: _____

_____

My Sentence _____

_____

Word: _____ Page _____

Selection: _____

Part of Speech: _____

Definition: _____

_____

My Sentence _____

_____

Word: _____ Page _____

Selection: _____

Part of Speech: _____

Definition: _____

_____

My Sentence _____

_____

VOCABULARY BUILDER CARDS

Use these cards to record words you want to remember. Write the word, the title of the story or article in which it appears, its part of speech, and its definition. Then, use the word in an original sentence that shows its meaning

Word: _____ Page _____

Selection: _____

Part of Speech: _____

Definition: _____

_____

My Sentence _____

_____

_____

Word: _____ Page _____

Selection: _____

Part of Speech: _____

Definition: _____

_____

My Sentence _____

_____

_____

Word: _____ Page _____

Selection: _____

Part of Speech: _____

Definition: _____

_____

My Sentence _____

_____

_____

VOCABULARY BUILDER CARDS

Use these cards to record words you want to remember. Write the word, the title of the story or article in which it appears, its part of speech, and its definition. Then, use the word in an original sentence that shows its meaning

Word: _____ Page _____

Selection: _____

Part of Speech: _____

Definition: _____

_____

My Sentence _____

_____

Word: _____ Page _____

Selection: _____

Part of Speech: _____

Definition: _____

_____

My Sentence _____

_____

Word: _____ Page _____

Selection: _____

Part of Speech: _____

Definition: _____

_____

My Sentence _____

_____

(Acknowledgments continued from page ii)

Grove/Atlantic, Inc.
"Tanka" from *Anthology of Japanese Literature* by Minamoto no Toshiyori, translated by Donald Keene. Copyright © 1965 by Grove Atlantic, Inc. Reprinted by permission.

Harcourt, Inc.
"The Antigone of Sophocles" an English version by Dudley Fitts and Robert Fitzgerald, Copyright © 1939 by Harcourt Inc., and renewed 1967 by Dudley Fitts and Robert Fitzgerald, reprinted by permission of the publisher. **CAUTION:** Professionals and amateurs are hereby warned that *The Antigone of Sophocles*, being fully protected under the copyright Laws of the United States of America, the British Empire, including the Dominion of Canada, and all other countries of the Universal Copyright and Berne Conventions, are subject to royalty. All rights, including professional, amateur, motion picture, recitation, lecturing, public reading, radio and television broadcasting, and the rights of translation into foreign languages, are strictly reserved. Particular emphasis is laid on the question of readings, permission for which must be secured in writing. Inquiries of all rights should be addressed to Harcourt, Inc., Permissions Dept., Orlando, FL 32887. From Jazz Fantasia in *Smoke And Steel* by Carl Sandburg, Copyright © 1920 by Harcourt, Inc. and renewed by Carl Sandburg, reprinted by permission of the publisher. "The Garden of Stubborn Cats" from *Marcovaldo of the Seasons in the City* by Italo Calvino, Copyright © 1963 by Giulio Einaudi editore s.p.a., Torino, English translation by William Weaver copyright © 1983 by Harcourt, Inc. and Martin Secker & Warburg, Ltd reprinted by permission of Harcourt, Inc. This material may not be reproduced in any form or by any means without prior written permission of the publisher.

Harvard University Press
"The Wind-tapped like a tired man (#436)" by Emily Dickinson from *The Poems Of Emily Dickinson*.

Heyden White Rostow
"The American Idea" by Theodore H. White from *The New York Times Magazine, July 6, 1986.* Copyright © 1986 by The New York Times Company. Reprinted by permission. All rights reserved.

Thomas A. Hill
"The History of the Guitar" by Thomas A. Hill from *The Guitar: An Introduction of the Instrument.* Used with permission of Thomas A. Hill.

Hispanic Society of America
"The Guitar" by Federico Garcia Lorca from *Translations From Hispanic Poets.* Used with permission of the Hispanic Society of America.

Houghton Mifflin Company
"The Marginal World" from *The Edge Of The Sea* by Rachel Carson. Copyright © 1955 by Rachel L. Carson, renewed 1983 by Roger Christie. "Prometheus and the First People" (originally titled "The Creation of Man" and "The Coming of Evil") from Greek Myths by Olivia E. Coolidge. Copyright 1949 by Olivia E. Coolidge; copyright renewed © 1977 by Olivia E. Coolidge. Adapted by permission of Houghton Mifflin Company. All rights reserved.

David Henry Hwang
"Tibet Through the Red Box: from Act II" by David Henry Hwang from *Tibet Through The Red Box.* Reprinted by permission.

Johnson & Alcock Ltd.
"The Bridegroom" by Alexander Pushkin translation © by D.M. Thomas from *The Bronze Horseman and Other Poems,* London: Secker & Warburg 1982. Reprinted by permission of Johnson & Alcock Ltd., London.

Johnson Outdoors Inc.
"Compass Directions and Warranty" by Staff from *www.silvacompass.com.* Copyright © 2002 Johnson Outdoors Inc. Reprinted by permission. All rights reserved.

Alfred A. Knopf, Inc.
"The Weary Blues" by Langston Hughes. From *The Collected Poems Of Langston Hughes* by Langston Hughes, copyright © 1994 by The Estate of Langston Hughes. From Swimming to Antarctica by Lynne Cox. Copyright © 2004 by Lynne Cox.

William Morris Agency
"A Visit to Grandmother" by William Melvin Kelley from *Dances On The Shore.* Copyright © 1964, 1992 by William Melvin Kelley. Reprinted by permission of William Morris Agency, LLC on behalf of the author.

New Directions Publishing Corporation
"Do Not Go Gentle Into That Good Night" by Dylan Thomas, from *The Poems of Dylan Thomas.* Copyright © 1952 by Dylan Thomas. Reprinted by permission.

The New York Times
"Mr. Gorbachev's Role" by Staff from *The New York Times (Late Edition) November 10, 1999.* Copyright © 1999 by The New York Times Co. "Feel the City's Pulse? It's Be-bop Man!" by Ann Douglas from *The New York Times, Friday, August 28, 1998.* Copyright © 1998 by The New York Times Co. Reprinted by permission.

PHOTO AND ART CREDITS

Cover: *Cafe-terrace at Night (Place du forum in Arles)*, 1888. oil on canvas, Vincent van Gogh, Erich Lessing/Art Resource, NY; **4:** Corel Professional Photos CD-ROM™; **14:** *l.* © Dorling Kindersley; **14:** *r.* Getty Images; **14:** *background* © Dorling Kindersley; **22:** Henry Horenstein/CORBIS; **35:** Getty Images; **39:** © Kevin Schafer/Peter Arnold, Inc.; **52:** By Fred C. Stoes/Yesteryear Depot collection; **56:** Royalty-Free/CORBIS; **57:** Royalty-Free/CORBIS; **60:** Getty Images; **77:** Nancy Sheehan/PhotoEdit; **81:** The Art Archive/Bibliotéque des Arts Décoratifs Paris/Dagli Orti; **84:** Stephen J. Krasemann/DRK Photo; **94:** *t.* W. Kenneth Hamblin; **94:** *b.* W. Kenneth Hamblin; **101:** *The Sea of Time*, 1982, Susanna Schuenke/SuperStock; **111:** *Strong Steady Hands*, Alonzo Adams, Courtesy of the artist; **122:** The State Russian Museum/CORBIS; **126:** © Howard Kingsnorth/Stone; **137:** istockphoto.com; **141:** Barnabas Kindersley/© Dorling Kindersley; **141:** Corel Professional Photos CD-ROM™; **142:** Barnabas Kindersley/© Dorling Kindersley; **145:** The Toast, G.K. Totybadse, Scala/Art Resource, NY; **162:** Corel Professional Photos CD-ROM™; **166:** Corel Professional Photos CD-ROM™; **169:** Frank Siteman/Stock, Boston; **187:** Courtesy of Didrik Johnck; **200:** Brian P. Kenney/Animals Animals; **208:** Courtesy Johnson Outdoors Inc.; **212:** Connie Hayes/CORBIS; **220:** ©Images.com/CORBIS; **224:** *t.* Courtesy Johnson Outdoors Inc.; **224:** *b.l.* Courtesy Johnson Outdoors Inc.; **224:** *b.m.* Courtesy Johnson Outdoors Inc.; **224:** *b.r.* Courtesy Johnson Outdoors Inc.; **224:** Courtesy Johnson Outdoors Inc.; **224–225:** Lee Snider/CORBIS; **228:** Bettmann/CORBIS; **233:** © Lesegretain/CORBIS Sygma; **237:** *Carriage at the Races*, 1872, Edgar Degas, oil on canvas 14 3/8 x 22 in. (36.5 x 55.9 cm) 1931 Purchase Fund, Courtesy, Museum of Fine Arts, Boston. Reproduced with permission. © 2002 Museum of Fine Arts, Boston. All Rights Reserved.; **240:** Bettmann/CORBIS; **248:** Alexandra Avakian/Getty Images; **249:** David Turnley/CORBIS; **253:** Bettmann/CORBIS; **261:** Christie's Images/CORBIS; **274:** Corel Professional Photos CD-ROM™; **279:** Esbin/Anderson/Omni-Photo Communications, Inc.; **284:** © Damir Frkovic/Masterfile; **289:** Dave King/© Dorling Kindersley; **292:** Robrt W. Ginn/PhotoEdit; **298:** Bettmann/CORBIS; **302:** Lorette Moureau; **308:** *The Veteren of a New Field*, Winslow Homer/SuperStock; **312:** Joseph Nettis/Stock, Boston; **313:** Maps.com; **313:** *background* Esbin/Anderson/Omni-Photo Communications, Inc.; **317:** © Chris Bennion/Seattle Children's Theater; **328:** Liz McAulay/© Dorling Kindersley; **339:** Robbie Jack/CORBIS; **347:** Pearson Education/PH School Division; **351:** Pearson Education/PH School Division; **355:** Pearson Education/PH School Division; **372:** Pearson Education/PH School Division; **376:** Pearson Education/PH School Division; **380:** The Folger Shakespeare Library; **380:** *background* Nathan Benn/CORBIS; **381:** The Folger Shakespeare Library; **385:** David Muench/CORBIS; **395:** Prometheus Carrying Fire, Jan Cossiers, Art Resource, NY; **403:** Courtesy of the Library of Congress; **407:** Papilio/CORBIS; **418:** Courtesy of the Trustees of British Library, www.bl.uk/imagesonline.; **422:** Getty Images; **423:** Getty Images; **426:** Department of Printing and Graphic Arts, The Houghton Library, Harvard College Library; **429:** Scala/Art Resource, NY; **445:** The Eclipse of the Sun Predicted by Hank Morgan, illustration for 'A Connecticut Yankee in King Arthur's Court', by Mark Twain (1835–1910), published 1988 (engraving) (see 193780), Belomlinsky, Mikhail (Contemporary Artist)/Private Collection/www.bridgeman.co.uk; **458:** Giraudon/Art Resource, NY; **462:** Getty Images; **463:** AP/Wide World Photos; **464:** Getty Images; **465:** © Jochen Tack/Das Fotoarchivl/Peter Arnold, Inc.